MATILDA AND THE CHICKENS

Books by Mrs. Robert Henrey

The Farm Books

A FARM IN NORMANDY
THE RETURN TO THE FARM (*Peter Davies*)
MATILDA AND THE CHICKENS

The London Trilogy

A VILLAGE IN PICCADILLY
THE INCREDIBLE CITY
THE SIEGE OF LONDON

History

LONDON

Autobiography

THE LITTLE MADELEINE (*In preparation*)
A JOURNEY TO GIBRALTAR
THE FOOLISH DECADE
THE KING OF BRENTFORD (*Peter Davies*)
A FILM STAR IN BELGRAVE SQUARE (*Peter Davies*)

Fiction

DELPHINE (*Peter Davies*)
AN ATTIC IN JERMYN STREET
PHILIPPA

MATILDA
AND THE CHICKENS

by

MRS. ROBERT HENREY

Illustrated with line drawings
by
DIANA STANLEY

LONDON
J. M. DENT & SONS LTD

J. M. Dent & Sons Ltd.
Aldine House · Bedford St. · London

Made in Great Britain
by
The Temple Press · Letchworth · Herts
First published 1950

My dear Jean Lorimer,

This book tells of a winter on my farm in Normandy, the farm where my son, Bobby, was born ten years ago. I shall, during the course of these pages, take you into the homes of my neighbours, into their farms, down to the shops in the village where, during the winter gales, the sea comes up and sprays my shopping basket with salty foam, and introduce you to people, without any humbug, by their real names.

Many of the characters have already appeared in my two early books, 'A Farm in Normandy' and 'The Return to the Farm,' which I wrote under a male pseudonym, but the people in *those books were not disguised, so that on occasion when readers have come to look over the ground for themselves, they have been delighted to find that everybody knew the Poulains and the Déliquaires.*

You and I are both women who earn our living by the pen, I by writing, you on the executive side of our great magazines. I have long promised you a book. May this one give you a few happy hours of relaxation in our Norman orchards.

MRS. ROBERT HENREY.

2 CARRINGTON HOUSE,
HERTFORD STREET,
PICCADILLY, W.1.

I

AT PRECISELY 11.20 hours, as it was supposed to, the heavy French train—curved steel coaches and a smell of roast chicken from the restaurant car—screeched itself to a standstill beside one of the unroofed cement quays of the rebuilt station of Lisieux. Because there were never any porters at this busy junction I had whispered to the ticket-collector, when he had put his head into our compartment soon after leaving Paris, that I would give him a hundred francs if he would deposit my three suit-cases and my typewriter on the quay. He arrived, smiling, as soon as we were in view of the shining basilica of Ste. Thérèse. The express, bound for Caen, had four minutes wait at Lisieux, and prided itself on keeping to schedule. Rioux, the carrier's handyman whose little boy has only one eye, appearing from the opposite direction from which I was looking for him, said in a homely voice:

'M. Fournier sent me to fetch you in the truck, madam. The taxi never was any good.'

Briskly, his hands and arms encumbered with luggage, he led the way to the station yard. The locomotive let out a long-drawn-out whistle, and the ground shuddered as the wheels started to turn.

The town, except for the cathedral, like so many Norman towns, had completely lost its recognizable points, all the centre having been flattened by allied bombing, but on market days, of which this was one, people, emerging from encampments, swarmed round the stalls, determined not to stint themselves on food. While Rioux parked his truck in a side street no longer bordered with houses, but merely rubble and chipped stone, though it was four years since the bombs had fallen, I elbowed my way into the crowd flowing slowly along alleys between stalls. On the outer ring of the market there were cyclamen in pots, the colour of lipstick, and branches of golden mimosa from the Riviera. In the centre were the fowls—turkeys, ducks, geese, and hens, squatting, their legs tied, on hay-stuffed baskets. My mother had three ducks each laying an egg a day on our farm but no drake, and I wanted to buy one here and bring it back in the truck. The one that suited me best was for sale with its female, and though the farmer, eager to do business, might have given me the drake alone, I hated to separate it from its companion, and so bought the two for just under a pound. I chose a sprig of mimosa, some horse-radish from a man who, in spite of two wars, still clung to a peasant blue blouse, and a flat osier basket in which to keep my knitting wool. Thus laden I returned to the truck.

The truck, entirely of steel, shook on a high-pitched note, but the front, being all window, gave a sweeping view. The two ducks, warm on my skirt, loudly quacking, smelling very strongly, looked about with the lively interest that ducks show in everything. Rioux said:

'We read about the little boy, madam.'

'Thanks,' I answered, flattered. 'Mother said there was something in the local papers.'

'In *all* the papers,' Rioux corrected. 'About his making a film in English, dubbing it in French in Paris and then going back to London to present a bouquet to the Queen. Of course, what got us were the thirty million francs.'

'It sounds a lot of francs,' I answered. 'And anyway they do so exaggerate.'

'I don't know,' said Rioux doggedly. 'That 's what they wrote in the papers.'

He gripped the driving wheel to accelerate round a corner, and asked:

'Not afraid of going fast?'

'I try not to show it. How 's your little boy?'

Four years earlier Rioux's baby, left by himself while his parents had gone to a funeral, gouged out an eye by falling on some faggots. The parents, on their return, while tying up the pony at the door of the shack, heard him cry. 'Will you be quiet?' Mme Rioux called out affectionately before even she caught sight of her little son in the half-light. Then suddenly she yelled: 'But he 's covered in blood!' She knelt on the floor, gulping, sobbing, trying to understand what had happened, praying that what she feared might not be.

Rioux, having negotiated the sharp corner with the heavy lorry, went on with a cheerful warmth in his voice:

'You can't imagine what a happy boy he has become, madam!'

I knew how pretty he was, as pretty as mine. I asked hesitatingly:

'Does he wear a glass eye?'

'He could do,' answered Rioux, 'but what with him growing every six months we would always be having to change it—going to Caen or to Paris to buy new ones. It 's not worth the expense till he 's finished growing, at about eighteen or twenty, I should say.'

'All the same,' I said, thinking of Bobby, 'it 's sad.'

'In a way,' he answered, 'but on the other hand, he won't be called up. He 'll have a chance to do something useful while the others are wasting their time. Isn't it a wicked shame to have our kids taken away from us at the very moment they need to learn a job?'

'Perhaps it 's necessary,' I said dubiously, but feeling I ought to set an example.

'For what?' he asked. 'I reckon a little country like ours simply wouldn't matter if there was another war. We would have to watch the Americans and the Russians tossing atom bombs at each other.'

'I know,' I conceded, 'but the trouble is their bombs might fall on us.' I was going to add: 'That 's why I want my son to have a good time while he can,' but I felt ashamed because Rioux's little boy only had one eye and mine was, for the moment, so lovely. Changing the subject, I pleaded: 'I wish you wouldn't go so fast, Rioux, and, by the way, when we reach the village you might stop at the baker's; I 'd like to pick up the bread.'

This was the first time since the year of Bobby's birth that we were to spend Christmas on the farm in Normandy—the previous time was the strange, terrifying winter of the 'phoney' war with our thoughts turned to the Maginot Line and, over our heads, the drone of German reconnaissance planes. The collapse of France, our flight from the farm, leaving Matilda, my mother, pennyless at the quayside at Saint-Malo, the Battle of London, bombs, rockets, and V2s, and the return to Normandy to find the farm pillaged but my mother safe, though in distress, had left lines cruelly under my eyes. The restocking of the house, painfully, one necessary thing at a time, had required four years to complete. Now, in some ways, it was more comfortable than before the war. I had electricity everywhere, but we were not dependent on it for cooking, having a further choice of gas, the Aga stove, or, if all else failed, the ancient fire of burning logs in the low-raftered room. Our four-hundred-year-old house had become commodious, but that did not prevent us from

having to do everything ourselves. Various circumstances made it impracticable to have a maid. My mother and I were called upon to put out increasing energy at a moment when, growing more tired, we had less. The baker, for instance, no longer delivering our bread, nor the butcher the meat, I was obliged to walk to the village every evening, two steep miles down from the plateau to the sea.

Bobby, born on the farm during the twilight of what now seemed a very far-off period, had grown tall and strong during the dangerous years of war. He was suddenly almost uncomfortably famous, and in London I could not buy a ribbon or a pair of stockings without the sales girls crowding eagerly round us. Concurrently with his growing up, I had joined the ever-widening number of women writers, so nervously at first that for several books I had hidden myself behind my husband's name. This secret was now out. Bobby and I, in our different spheres, had emerged simultaneously into the sunshine. There were moments when I was seized with a panicky fright, as if warned that for each spasm of happiness there is an eternity of weeping.

Bobby returned to the farm with such enthusiasm that I could only think the place flowed in his blood. He embraced his grandmother, who smiled imperceptibly, for she was not demonstrative, even a little bitter, being full of rheumatic pains. She lived in the thatched cottage all by herself, except for her cats and my pekinese.

The weather was mild, almost warm, with high winds, the sort that make a Channel crossing to be feared, but now, with the sea just a view in the distance, the orchards looked tenderly green, and the earth had a sweet smell as if winter had not seriously begun. As soon as I arrived at the top of the orchard, having quite forgotten what the country looked like a fortnight before Christmas, charmed by the mossy banks, the mistletoe, and the apple-trees, and the redness of the holly berries, and even more, perhaps, by the distant vistas of browns and greens, I felt curiously as if I were rediscovering a secret of the past. I have always considered these orchards, these lanes, as specially remote from the things which spoil most stretches of the countryside. The peasant pursues his existence, as he did centuries ago, in a vacuum, as it were, from the rest of the world. He makes cider, scratches his apple-trees, saws wood, and barricades himself indoors at five o'clock with his family and dogs. The wireless seldom enters his home where the black cauldron hangs over elm logs. His speech is his own, gaining strength and colourfulness by the absence of strangers. The earth round him is tyrannic and earthy. He remains cunning and primitive.

My mother's ability to live so much of the year quite alone under her thatched roof was in part hereditary. My maternal grandmother was a strange woman who lived in equal solitude on the banks of the Loire. As a little girl I used to accompany her to the forest of Roussy, where she searched for sticks and buried treasure. Her food was mostly walnuts and dried apples, and she earned her living by washing linen on a raft in the shallow river. My mother had, I am sure, a desire for solitude in her blood. She was brave to the sounds of the night. The barn owl could not frighten her, and she would have walked unperturbed through a churchyard by moonlight.

My sixteenth-century house was at right angles to Matilda's thatched cottage. The electric oven was in her kitchen, and we lunched in her low room. At dusk, after she had put the chickens to bed, she retired to her own house, locking the door. In the morning Bobby and I would wait to hear the ducks jabbering as they waddled round the fence of our flower garden

towards the orchard. Matilda liked to feed her farmyard before she made our breakfast.

The drake and its female seemed delighted with their new home. They ate hungrily, bathed under the running water of the trough, and were led by our own fat ducks into the tall grass. Matilda's farmyard was at this moment unusually fine. In most farms this feathery world—by tradition, the care of the farmer's wife—was being cut down because of the high price of grain. Our eggs cost more than we could sell them for at market.

Cows were our farmers' business. They were magnificent and oozed prosperity. When they ambled to us, interested in all we did, they smelt of cream and butter. The last ten years had mightily enriched our farmers. They had never known such a boom. They might have banked their paper francs if inflation had not haunted their ever-worrying minds. Wisely they used their profits to beautify their livestock.

I offered to give Matilda a cow of her very own, but her hands were not strong enough to milk it. The major portion of our land was farmed by René Déliquaire, a strange and lovable peasant with high Mongol cheek-bones, a magnificent Norman accent, a great master at talking to the accompaniment of his hands, and, for the rest, a disconcerting mixture of what was modern and medieval.

With no cow to milk, Matilda looked after her farmyard with the care of a collector for his rarest pieces. It was also a matter of personal pride, for until she had taken to it after the war she had scarcely known how a chicken lays an egg. Three years earlier, in the spring, Mme Déliquaire had given her four black hens and a cock of variegated feathers. With these she began her poultry yard.

Nothing ran smoothly at first. The cock had no use for the hens. He liked his women to be white. Every morning, secretly, he crossed the kitchen garden, squeezed through the hedge, and ran across the neighbouring orchard to the Poulains' farmyard where, chasing off the males, he made love to a bevy of white Sussex hens. Unnoticed by Mme Poulain he would feed with her pretty females, bolt back to Matilda for a second lunch, and then return to his harem. In the evening, on his way home, he would narrowly escape being eaten by the fox.

Matilda, trusting, inexperienced, did not notice anything except, of course, that the black hens' eggs were always clear. Mme Poulain eventually discovered the stranger in her yard, but as he was so good-looking and so amorous she saw no reason to send him away, even though he beat her cocks. Then this curious thing happened, that as a result of his courting the white hens these pretty females refused to sit. It was now to Mme Poulain's advantage to tell Matilda that her cock was unfaithful to his wives. She added: 'He 's a useless male—useless to your hens and useless to mine.'

Matilda imprisoned him in a rabbit hutch, where he became so tempestuous that she cut his throat. The women on our farms never wring a chicken's neck. Mme Poulain, now that her cocks were free to court their own women, brought Matilda twelve germinated eggs which the black hens sat on, and she soon had a picturesque medley of types and colours.

The next spring Mme Déliquaire gave Matilda two ducks and a baby turkey-hen which looked like an overgrown blackbird. We suddenly became enthusiastic about rearing turkeys. In Normandy a female turkey is called a *picote*, and the male, which when fully grown becomes that magnificent fellow with the proud strut, the immense fan tail, and the scarlet head and throat, a *berlou*. Their offspring are *picots*. I think it was for picturesqueness that we wanted the turkeys. None of us realized what an immense amount of work it would mean for Matilda.

Our baby *picote* nearly died of home sickness. She dragged her loneliness round the farm, crying sadly, 'Wee-wee, wee-wee, wee-wee,' and Mme Beaudry, whose husband tidied the lanes in the parish, said: 'You had better give her back to Ma'am Déliquaire.' Happily Matilda tenderly looked after her 'wee-wee' whose feathers became a shiny black, shot with the shimmering colours of the rainbow.

The next February the *picote*, grown up, suddenly laid two eggs, unmistakably large and spotted, which Matilda took round to Mme Déliquaire, asking her urgently for advice. Mme Déliquaire explained that whereas a hen must be 'cocked,' as they say in Normandy, by the male before she lays each egg, if that egg is to be given life, a turkey hen can have her entire cluster of fifteen or so eggs germinated by a single visit from the male. Mme Déliquaire accordingly sent round her magnificent *berlou* for a two-night stay on our farm. When Bobby and I arrived for Easter the *picote*, who had been duly married, was sitting on seventeen eggs, thirteen of her own, and four which she had stolen from a hen.

She had built a nest with hay inside a roll of wire netting. It was above some rabbit hutches in a cart shed. From this moment I loved her. She was an adorable mother and would have starved rather than leave her eggs. Each day, after breakfast, I climbed a rickety ladder to extricate her from the netting. She spat and ranted, and showed open beak and claw in such a frightening way that nobody else would approach her. I learnt to clutch her firmly under the wings and throw her off till, with an enormous noise and a darkening of the heavens, she flew into the yard where she would swallow ten grains of golden Indian corn, drink a little water, beat her wings, do her business, and fly straight back to the nest. Every day she became lighter to handle. On the thirtieth day she was almost a skeleton.

She lost two of her eggs: one was clear, the other got mixed up with her claws and broke as I 'shooed' her off the nest one day. A week before her own babies were due, four yellow chicks appeared under her black wings. She seemed to know they were not what she had been waiting for and I had no trouble to take them away. At that time we had two hens sitting on half a dozen eggs each. We gave all twelve to one of them and presented the four chicks to the other. This stratagem worked fairly well and allowed us to turn all our attention to the *picote*.

The *picote's* husband, the beautiful *berlou* who was being fattened up for the wedding of our farmers' eldest son, Roger, which was to take place on 10th April, died before our *picote's* children were born. He swallowed his potato mash too hot and burnt his throat, with the result that he starved to death. Mme Déliquaire piously buried her *berlou* at the foot of an apple-tree, but Mme Beaudry, who was not sentimental, dug him up the same evening and cooked him for her dogs who were hungry.

My pekinese, who was in London with us through the Battle of London and whom I afterwards brought to France to end his days on the farm, was seen one afternoon to be sniffing at something under a rabbit hutch. The first of the *picote's* children had fallen from the nest, all black and slimy, freshly hatched, and the pekinese was giving it a bath like a nursery maid. We took it, with two or three others that were just breaking their shells, and put them in a wooden box with hay and flannel behind the stove in the cottage. When Mme Beaudry came to weed the kitchen garden she told us that we had probably killed them, because newly born *picots* must never be touched. As nobody knew what to do, Matilda crossed the stream at the bottom of our orchard to ask Mme Déliquaire. The next day, on her advice, we put the mother bird and her eleven babies under a bell-shaped metal chicken coop, and Matilda began a regime of intense feeding.

When I was a very little girl at Blois my grandmother used to take me to look for strange herbs.

I was reminded of this seeing Matilda, a scarf over her still golden hair, an open mesh basket under the arm, a knife in the hand, setting forth twice a day in search of the pearly green flowers of the great stinging-nettle for her *picot* feed. At the same time she would gather dandelion leaves, clover, and plantain for the rabbits. I would watch her zigzagging across the orchard, looking expertly on every side. She knew every tree, almost every blade of grass and where the squirrels stored their nuts.

But none of us quite realized at the time how hard my mother worked for her *picots*. Their feed—creamy milk, hard-boiled eggs cut up very fine, the flowers of the nettles, young parsley and barley flour—was renewed five times a day, and oftener if the mother bird ate, with a few hungry beakfuls, what we hoped would be enough for all her children. The other members of the farmyard were also jealous of these delectable feeds, especially the ducks, who, if they could get anywhere near them, passed their greedy bills across the plate with the action of a carpet sweeper.

On the first fine day the *picote*, much fatter now, was allowed to take her children from the stables where we kept them into the yard. Soon they explored fringes of the orchard, but when rain threatened we all had to run after them, for a drop of water under these babies' wings gives them pneumonia, and they die.

They were the strangest-looking things, lugubriously dark, with triangular faces. They stalked about like eighteenth-century revellers with masks. The farm was full of their 'wee-wee' cries. All our neighbours told us they would die before growing their pimples.

How eagerly we looked for these pimples! We counted the days. We debated our chances. Only then, apparently, would our eleven babies be safe. Nothing more could happen to them. They could go out in the rain without catching pneumonia. They would no longer require hard-boiled eggs and nettle flowers.

As they approached the age of two months the first manifestations appeared. They looked like young ladies with earphones. We redoubled our care, but one afternoon I noticed that the smallest of the family started to lag behind, his head sunk into his shoulders, vulture-like. As he advanced painfully one had, looking at him, the impression that he was about to announce something catastrophic like the plague. Mme Beaudry, who was at her best when giving bad news, said in her huge voice: 'This one is going to die!'

Even Mme Déliquaire could give us little hope. 'What will you, Mme Henrey—they come from Egypt?' I felt overwhelmingly sorry for my baby 'wee-wee' and I took him up to my bedroom, where I put him on some straw near the central heating. In the evening I gave him a drop of milk and administered M. and B.

The next morning when I took my patient out of his blanket, he looked at me with gratitude, as if he thought I really had done him some good. He had such a wise expression that I would not have been surprised if he had dictated me his will. Suddenly he seemed to say: 'It 's too late now!' His beak opened, revealing a tiny parched tongue. Then he flopped down, breathing out two or three times without taking in any air. I thought, in watching him, I understood what people meant by a person 'expiring.' With a last effort, he died.

I was absurdly upset and I wept. I prepared a grave for him in the front garden under the greengage-tree, but Matilda said my sensitivity was theatrical. She wanted the corpse for the cats. Mme Beaudry must have told her how she had dug up Mme Déliquaire's *berlou*.

The death of the little *picot* reminds me that by this time Roger Déliquaire was already married. The rejoicings took the form of a banquet lasting two days. As the Déliquaires farmed so much of my land, I was the guest of honour.

Jeannine, the bride, the daughter of a market gardener whose little shop overlooked the church, persuaded Roger that life in a village was more fun than on a farm. She was accustomed to peeping over the cauliflowers at the weddings and funerals drawn up on the parvis, and she argued, not incorrectly, that our orchards were very muddy. Déliquaire, though he did not say anything, must have been sad to see this boy, whom he had brought up in the love of the land, suddenly want to leave it. I was sorry too, having expected that in time he would become Bobby's tenant farmer.

I chose a present, and on the appointed morning went down to the village for the wedding breakfast. Matilda, the previous evening, had brushed her black costume and invented a hat. My son wore a bright red pullover I had made him, and dark blue shorts. The weather was springlike with mayflower and laburnum in the hedges, lilac in the gardens, and white and pink candles on the chestnut-trees.

The wedding breakfast was in a garden where Jeannine's parents had their hothouses. The bride, tall, speaking in nervous laughs, was in her satin gown; Roger, a joy to watch on the farm when wielding an axe, looked anxiously uncomfortable in his black tail coat, tugging at unfamiliar cuffs as if he hoped they would suddenly come off. The white carnation in his button-hole tickled his closely shaven skin.

The luxuries of the table, which six months later were to fill the shops, were then only obtainable by much scheming. There was no coffee, or white flour, for instance. Even our rather nasty black bread was rationed. The Norman peasant had ways of overcoming these difficulties, for food is barterable against food. A christening or a wedding is his chief means of displaying his hidden wealth. It becomes a matter of honour that nothing should be missing. My farmer, Déliquaire, was very sensitive about what others said of him, and I was not surprised to find the odour of real coffee agreeably filling my nostrils.

He took me aside at the first opportunity. To begin with I was to be partnered during the festivities by the successful son of a mole-catcher, a M. Cauvin, with whom Déliquaire had grown up and who was now 'fabulously' rich, a farmer in a big way. I gathered that this M. Cauvin had several times lent my tenant money on a friendly basis, practically putting him on his feet. It was a great honour for me to be partnered by M. Cauvin. Clearly I was the most important female. He was the most important male. It was a pretty way of bringing us together.

There was something else on my friend Déliquaire's mind. He wanted me to realize that the coffee was real coffee and that the *brioches* (they are airy and golden and made in the form of a figure of eight) were made with white flour and real butter. Had I not taken good note of these two facts, the expense incurred in the obtaining of such rare commodities would have been less worth while. He brought me a cup of coffee, and I said that I had seldom tasted better, which was strictly true. As for the cake, it was the first of the kind I had seen for ten years.

He was now satisfied that I was aware of the quality of the goods. The next thing was to make me ask, 'How did you do it?' He beamed with satisfaction and cunning, and whispered rather loudly that the coffee came from Belgium (I could have guessed it) and had been bartered against butter, and that the flour for the *brioches*—well, that was quite a story of its own. He had bought a truck of wheat, which he had sent to a miller who had made the flour. There would be enough of it to last until the festivities ended the following night.

On the lawn Roger and Jeannine were being photographed. Bobby was with them. M. Cauvin, stockily good-looking, introduced himself. He seemed just the sort of man one hopes for on such an occasion. We took our places in the confusedly forming procession, linking arms with not yet very confident laughter. The bridal couple led the way, and we followed jerkily into the village street, where small groups of expectant people stood suddenly still, mouths open, eyes taking in every detail.

The mayor was waiting on the first floor of the squat town hall on the opposite side of the road, and on the way up the men, feeling it was expected of them, made loud asides inspired by an official notice on the wall about bulls for breeding, but the ribaldry was not infectious, it being yet too early in the day. Our mayor, who had the reputation of carousing with the farmers, sleeping little, knowing the price of an acre of land, a first edition of Jean Jacques Rousseau, or a keg of cider, looked overcome by the importance of his office, slim, prim, and spectacled. The ceremony lasted only a few minutes, after which two little girls made a collection, whilst the mayor kissed Jeannine and gave her a beribboned box containing his private wedding present. He said he was sorry he could not come to the church, so we went without him down highly polished stairs, not bothering this time to form a procession.

In the centre of the high, draughty, end of last century church, I found myself contentedly reunited with my own family—Bobby interested but shivering, Matilda over-conscious in her new hat, my husband vague. None of us, so far, had the impression of having properly married Roger and Jeannine. The civil ceremony seemed empty of religion, the religious service dismal and affected. The beadle in dusty magnificence looked like something out of a play. The only person apparently sincere was a widow who, quite unconcerned with the wedding, came in a moment to drop on her knees, mumbling fervently before leaving like a gust of spring wind.

I think honestly most of us were thinking of the lunch. It would, of course, have been better up on their farm as, when a little girl, I saw weddings in the Loire with the food served on trestles in tents or even on the grass, with guests staying for three or four days and sleeping on hay in the lofts.

The chief objection in this case was that Jeannine was not a farmer's daughter. She was taking Roger away from the land, not uniting two farms. All this was a pity, because Déliquaire was as earthy as earth. Outside the hotel, typically French with long chintz-curtained windows and geraniums, he was talking to a cousin from Dieppe, enumerating a list on his fingers with delightful gestures. 'And all from my farm, eh? Everything we shall be eating during the next two days—a two-month-old calf, a sheep, eight turkeys, fifteen chickens, three rabbits. . . .' He winked as he saw me, and in a swift aside: 'Don't forget you will be sitting on M. Cauvin's right hand!'

This M. Cauvin—Déliquaire's history was inextricably mixed up with his. Often since, Déliquaire, sitting at the corner of my immense sixteenth-century fire-place at the farm, unhurriedly lifting and putting back into place a mesh of hair which, in falling, had covered an eye and half a cheek, spoke about his friend Cauvin, 'so rich'—his hands showed their palms to heaven eloquently—'so rich that his father . . .'

Well, Cauvin's father was, as I have already said, a mole-catcher, but chiefly he had a gift for selling things. Déliquaire claimed he could have sold a man a stone, and to show he was not exaggerating he rubbed his index against his thumb, dancing slightly on the edge of his chair. Cauvin senior (sixty years ago) had a horse and cart and on Wednesdays went to the horse market at Trouville, returning home with five or six animals tied head to tail behind the cart. Before the next Wednesday he would have sold them all at a good profit.

At this point, listening intently, I asked:

'I suppose he knew a lot about horses?'

'Perhaps, yes,' conceded Déliquaire, 'but it was mostly that he knew how to sell.'

At the beginning of the century Vanderbilt bought a castle in the region, and Cauvin's father, while the place was being altered, obtained a contract for hauling the timber. In those days they charged by the horse collar, and 'who was to know,' asked Déliquaire, whose eyes glistened with sympathetic cupidity, 'if he put three horses to draw a load which only required two?' Déliquaire added that Cauvin senior was able, for some reason, to escape the war of 1914. 'The important thing,' reflected my farmer, 'is to keep out of wars.'

Déliquaire and the Cauvin I was introduced to went to school together. At seventeen they would slip off to dances on Saturday night, but when Cauvin senior saw his son leaving the house he would say: 'That 's all right, my boy, but dance or no dance you will be up at four!'

'I 'm not sure,' added Déliquaire thoughtfully, 'that we are not too gentle with our sons.'

At Roger's wedding I knew vaguely that Cauvin had helped Déliquaire to set up on a farm. The Cauvins had themselves been fortunate in finding men who trusted them, lending them money as it should be lent, in a helpful way. I liked Cauvin. I liked the sensible way he talked. He knew so many things from the art of felling trees to the money aspect of a farm. We had about two hours between the end of lunch and the beginning of the next meal which would then go on till the bride and bridegroom left us, amidst ironic laughter, to spend the night in a place shrouded in secrecy, a place which the more adventurous guests would hunt for, by custom, until they found it, in the hope of playing a practical joke on the unfortunate couple. Cauvin offered to drive us to one of his rented farms, an enormous place upon which stood a château so old that underneath it there were trap-dungeons—men hurled their enemies most horribly into oblivion. There were drawbridges, pepper-box towers, and the most adorable baby donkey which I wanted to buy and take back to Matilda, who, modestly, had refused to accompany us.

M. Cauvin, like a Spanish grandee, said: 'You shall have it as soon as it can leave its mother.'

'When? Next week? Next month?'

'No,' answered Cauvin. 'In September or October.'

I declined in the end. Matilda had quite enough animals to look after.

This wealthy farm was administered by Déliquaire's young brother, which fact I had not immediately realized. He came to us as we were admiring the donkey, short and knotty, clean-shaven, brick-red cheeks, sparing with his words but friendly, obtaining his effects by knowing what he spoke about, and by little sarcasms which at first intimidated me, afraid not to catch sufficiently their meaning. But he said:

'Wait till later in the year, Mme Henrey. If you change your mind about the donkey, I 'll bring him over to you one day when I go to visit my brother.'

'I did not know Déliquaire had a brother,' I said.

I was trying to discover a likeness, but if there was one it was not facial. Our Déliquaire was too picturesque for anybody to be quite like him. Though his high cheek-bones gave him that curious Mongol look, his face was flat and elongated so that he resembled the figure in the moon. He was pale and his ears stuck out. He spoke plaintively and softly. Whenever I used to see him working round my house, inspecting one of his cows about to calve, or scratching the apple-trees, I would send Bobby to invite him to have a cup of tea by the fire. He neither spat into the red embers like my previous farmer, nor smelt of *calvados*. He drank rarely, liked China tea, and did not smoke. His manners were strange but delicate. He would look at me suddenly with a candid expression in his blue eyes which melted me, but I had to be careful—he was craftiness itself. He and his wife, who was a Madeleine like myself (we sent ourselves reciprocally gifts of grapes or peaches on our name day!), fitted into each other's plans like clasped fingers. Whatever she wanted, he agreed to. Whatever he did was, in her view, admirable. He was the head of the house, the incapable-of-doing-wrong, the husband. She was always good-tempered, generous, kind to her animals. He liked to go dancing with the young girls, to drive his motor van, to attend the race meetings, to watch football, and to shoot. She hated to leave her house in the evening. They agreed about that too.

One evening, when we were talking about Roger's wedding, I asked:

'Is Jacques also thinking of getting married?'

Jacques was the younger son. I had known him first when he was Bobby's age.

Déliquaire filled his lungs deeply, the question giving him anxiety, and placing the index of his right hand against the flat of his nose, this being his most characteristic movement when deliberating, answered jerkily:

'Sons are unpredictable. Who would have guessed about Roger? Jacques is a fine child—his mother's boy. It would be nice to see him on a place of his own.'

'Have you somebody in mind?'

'What good is it me having somebody in mind? I know a girl with some acres in her dowry. The parents own a couple of orchards this side of the Touques river.'

'That sounds interesting.'

'No, not so interesting. Jacques won't look at her.'

'It *is* infuriating,' I agreed, 'but one can't force these things.'

'I 'm not for forcing anybody,' he said. 'Myself, for instance, I married for love.'

'Oh, tell me!' I exclaimed. 'I 'm so glad!'

He looked at me queryingly.

'Yes, love,' he repeated. 'My father was dead, but my mother would not come to the wedding. She would not even have us at home.'

'But it 's a success,' I put in. 'I don't know a happier couple.'

'My mother was wrong to object,' he mused, more for his own satisfaction than on my account. 'If parents object it 's up to them to suggest another girl. That 's fair, isn't it? But my mother had nobody else to offer. She couldn't have. She was so poor that her only acquaintances were labourers, and it would have been no good my turning down the girl I loved to marry an even poorer one.'

'That 's well argued,' I admitted.

'Madeleine had no money but she was comely,' he said, drawing her remembered figure with his palms through the air. She was a cook. I became a valet so that we could be employed together. We served an Irish gentleman, a veterinary surgeon, who looked after a millionaire's race-horses.'

'An American millionaire?'

'Yes, a man called Macomber.'

'Good heavens! Bobby and I had the apartment next to his at the Ritz the other day. I can see him quite clearly, a gentleman in a velvet smoking jacket, who used to peep out into the passage to ask for news about my little film star.'

'That would be the man.'

'Now I know,' I said, 'where you got your love for English cigarettes and horse-racing.'

'He cut down his race-horses, and his veterinary surgeon returned to Ireland,' Déliquaire continued. 'Cauvin said to me: "You 're wasting your time in service. I 'll help you to go on the land."' He smiled. 'I hadn't quite wasted my time. I learnt a lot about racing form.'

There were things like this that made Déliquaire very English; they gave him a happy-go-lucky side, interests beyond his immediate surroundings. He probably spent rather more generously than he should have done. Lately the money had been coming in too easily. Cauvin had found him a little farm near Tourgeville. Soon it proved too small. It was Cauvin again who heard of the one next to mine. He had now been on it sixteen years, difficult years at first, owing Cauvin money, never quite certain whether he would be able to repay it. There were no trips to the races or dancing on Sunday nights. The only week-end outing was to fetch pig-food in a tub on his cart on Sunday mornings. This last war had been Déliquaire's great opportunity, not going to it, just staying on the land, selling everything at mounting prices. When I arrived after the Liberation, I found his farm so stocked with cows that he did not know where to turn for more grass.

It was to enlarge his farm that he became my tenant, renting some twenty acres. The money had long ago been repaid to Cauvin. If Roger had married the daughter of some equally wealthy farmer almost anything might have happened.

The other Déliquaire, slapping the baby donkey on the neck gently, said:

'You'll tell me in August, Mme Henrey. No, it doesn't matter a bit, but I'm afraid it's a male. They are pretty useless. When I have a female, my brother wants it.'

Cauvin said: 'The wedding guests are dancing in a cabaret on the seashore. Shall we go?'

'Let's!' I answered, thinking it might be fun.

II

'I WAITED to make the cider till M. Bobby was here,' said Déliquaire. 'It might amuse him, seeing it's his first Christmas on the farm since the year he was born.'

Jacques was already in the vat room washing out a 2,000-litre barrel, which would store our household requirements for the

next twelve months. The vat room was the compartment nearest the stream in what was commonly known as 'the Cider Press,' a long, half-timbered, thatched building almost exactly four hundred years old. This magnificent period piece had for centuries been the subject of litigation between adjoining farms whose owners each had a half-share in it. This indeed had been the case until my return to Normandy after the Battle of Caen when the owner of the other half, appalled by its dilapidated state, sold me his share for the equivalent of ten English pounds. Some months later he had brought me the legal papers concerning its long history, for being a notary he had preserved them with care.

Before becoming the sole owner of the cider press I had not dared touch the fabric, fearing that any attempt to strengthen it might bring down the other half for which I would be held legally responsible. Immense oak-trees fashioned out with the axe supported the long roof. A superb exterior staircase led to the hay-lofts. No building I have yet seen is so much like something out of a fairy story. I sent for builders, carpenters, and thatchers to estimate the cost of the more urgent repairs and then abandoned everything, not even daring to ask the Treasury for permission to export so large a sum.

The vat room contained three major barrels—the one Jacques was cleaning, another about half as large again, and a giant which when full contained about six thousand litres. Very cool in

summer, with sawdust on the ground and ivy leaves peeping through the oak-beamed windows, generations of farmers had come here to quench thirsts and to gossip. The apple crop is the profit to the Norman farmer. It is also his dangerous pleasure. As soon as the apples are knocked off the trees a number of exciting alternatives keep him craftily scheming. He can make just enough cider for his personal needs and sell the remainder of his apples to a cider factory or to the English, who come to fetch them at Honfleur. But the price of apples in August, before the crop is gathered, is not the same as in September or November. Prices fluctuate like gold shares on the Stock Exchange. If he misses the top of the market, or for some reason decides he can make more money by selling cider instead of fruit, he may turn the whole of his crop into the presses towards Christmas. That perhaps is the biggest of all gambles.

The cider we drink on the farms has water added in the manufacture. When it is destined for that fiery drink known as *calvados*, or apple-jack, the cider is made with the juice alone and is then known as 'pure juice.' Fifteen litres of pure juice are needed to make one litre of *calvados*.

When first my husband bought me the farm in Normandy the field, or perhaps one should call it the orchard, in which my house and gardens stand, had not only the required apple-tree planted every ten yards but occasionally some immense pear-tree of great age. The farmers made *poiret* with the tiny hard pears in the same way as they made cider with the apples. More or less undrinkable in this form, it was all turned into pear-jack. Lately the demand has been less, and it was my intention this Christmas to have most of the pear-trees uprooted to replace them with cider apple-trees to make even more valuable the already rich harvest of this exceptional piece of land.

Nobody quite knew why the orchard on which our house is built gave such magical apple crops. All the rest of my land hired out to Déliquaire gave him a right to the apples as well as the grass. But I kept the home orchard for myself. I allowed Déliquaire's cows to graze on it in return for which he supplied my household with dairy produce, but I had the joy of disposing of my apples in any way I pleased.

The trees round my house had given me about five tons of apples, of which I had sold four to meet the current expenses of the farm. The remaining ton now lay in a heap in the press room, waiting to be turned into cider.

Déliquaire had sent his agile son through the trap-door into the barrel, the aperture at the bottom shaped like the entrance to a dog kennel. There was just enough room for a man, not too fat, to squeeze in on his stomach. They had tried to send Bobby in, Déliquaire reminding me of a benevolent Bill Sykes pushing young Twist through the open window at Shepperton, but Bobby, unusually timorous, fled, peeping in again through the door when Jacques had taken his place. The door of the vat room was so massive that the key was a foot long.

Déliquaire handed his son a birch broom, like the ones witches flew through the night on, clamped a piece of sacking against the lower part of the aperture, then hurled a bucket of water into the dark interior. We heard the birch broom, in Jacques's arms, sweeping above his head, this way and that, the water dripping—this swirling and dripping echoing horribly. After the first wash Déliquaire removed the sacking so that his son could sweep the

dirty water out. Later he replaced the sacking and clean water from the stream was thrown in.

During the long spells of brooming, Déliquaire sat on a small keg by the open door with his French spaniel Mireille. He looked happy to be doing nothing, and I said:

'Mother tells me you sold your apples for less than you sold ours. Can that be true?'

He laughed. 'We went on a hunting trip,' he explained, pointing vaguely in the direction of the forest of Saint-Gassien. 'When we came back the price had dropped.'

'One can't do two things at a time,' I said. 'You should sit in an office like a city broker.'

He grinned knowingly. I thought he looked more picturesque here in the frame of the open door, the giant barrels and massive oak beams on one side, the orchard and the stream on the other, than I had ever seen him. He wore a dark green sweater with a roll-top neck, and over this another woollen garment of a different shade of green with buttons on one shoulder. His felt hat was as strange as it was old, and his trousers were of chocolate corduroy. His dog Mireille also had patches of chocolate in her markings. She would occasionally dart off on some circular tour on the grass, quickly returning to sit, with tender expression, at heel. He stroked her floppy ears and said:

'I hoped by waiting a little longer, a day or two, I might get a better price for mine than for those I sold for you. I thought, "A day's shooting with those cattle dealer boys will do me good." We drove over in the new van. I took my gun and Mireille and some provisions for lunch. A fine, brisk, autumn day with the wind just right and the earth smelling good. The boys shot some rabbits and hares and I a fox, but what with one thing and another, night fell and we decided to spend the evening at the inn.'

From the tenebrous cavity of the nearby barrel came a voice, deformed by a muffled echo, saying:

'Let 's have some more water, dad.'

'Water? Ah, yes, water,' answered Déliquaire who, with thoughts roving distantly, had forgotten the existence of his son, invisible in the barrel. He rose slowly, lifted the empty pitcher, and said: 'I forgot to get any. I 'll go to the stream.'

He returned in a short time, squeezed the sacking at the orifice of the barrel, threw away the dirty water, and pitched in the clean. He then returned to his seat and, confident that he would not be disturbed for another ten minutes, went on:

'It 's good to come across one of those inns where they still roast you a chicken on the spit. Those places with sawdust on the floor and a long table at which you can stretch your legs and have a drink, watching the fire, the dogs at your feet. We talked about the things we 'd done during the day. Two or three other fellows had been out in the woods. We all got talking together. After supper we came over drowsy. It was too late to drive home. We thought we 'd spend the night at the inn and do a bit more shooting in the morning. I followed the hostess to my room. Clean and comfortable it struck me. "But the dog," she said; "you must leave it in the kennels like the other gentlemen." "Ah, madam," I answered, "this dog has never slept in a kennel."' He looked down appreciatingly at Mireille and fondled her. '"If my dog didn't sleep with me," I said to the hostess, "she 'd be miserable. At home she 's the first into bed—certainly, madam, between the sheets—and when it 's cold she nestles up against us, snug as anything. When she dreams she wakes us up, but that 's the way we like it, my wife and I. We 've a soft spot for animals. I 'll pay the price, but my dog sleeps with me."' He turned to me for a sign of approval. 'That 's true,' he said. 'You ask my wife. Besides, what 's a little mud in the bed? By morning it 's dry and shakes off as easy as anything. People in strange inns may grumble, ma'am, but what I want I can pay for.' He tapped the wallet in his hip pocket. 'That 's fair, isn't it?'

I admit I liked the story mightily. It seemed so much of another age.

'Meanwhile,' he mused, 'those damnable apples had dropped in price. I tried two merchants, one here and one at Dives. I sell to the one who pays most.' He raised his hands beseechingly, as if admitting a great sin and asking divine forgiveness. 'One has to, hasn't one?'

'It 's common practice,' I said. 'But tell me. How is Roger?'

All sorts of adventures had befallen Roger since his marriage. Indeed they began the very night of the dinner. He and Jeannine had slipped out from the banquet after midnight. One cannot blame them for being impatient for each other, but all the wits had been waiting for this moment. Their departure gave rise to murmurings and winkings, heads placed close together in palaver. Only half a dozen of us knew where they were going to spend their nuptial night. Actually it was to be an attic facing the belfry. They were no sooner in the street than shadows followed them. Roger was for running. He took his wife's hand and they fled along the dark, sea-swept street. They feared the catcalls that would greet the switching on of a light in their bedroom. Roger slipped on the asphalt and hurt his thigh. He was some time recovering from this accident. M. Trémois, his father-in-law, had tried to make a market gardener of him, but Trémois, a most excellent man, was finicky. He and Roger had quite different conceptions about how a job of work should be done. Roger was very fast. His father-in-law accused him of always forgetting to put his tools away. The Déliquaires were like that. They were happy-go-lucky.

Déliquaire was always saying that his eldest son would come back to the farm, but he never emitted a word of criticism. On the contrary, he would excuse him by saying: 'Odd jobs are well paid in the village. I dare say he can make more by being a jack-of-all-trades than working regular with me.' Roger was tasting freedom and thoroughly enjoying it. He would hire himself out for short spells to anybody. He had joined a road-building gang, and even broken stones for the municipality, all of which was excellently paid.

Déliquaire filled his lungs and answered:

'He wants to be a truck driver now. They 've offered him the job at a cider factory.'

He said this with pride, knowing a thing or two about driving a truck. Indeed my crafty peasant had the same sort of hobbies as any of your town lads. Any excuse was good enough to jump into the driving seat of his beautiful new van. He drove for the fun of driving. His machinations for obtaining petrol coupons were devious and complicated. For a long time he had delivered the milk for a co-operative for no other reason than it allowed him to rattle along the roads. On Saturday he drove almost any distance to see a football match or a horrible game called 'moto-ball' which the men were mad about. Meanwhile, of course, Mme Déliquaire carried on with the farm. Her work never stopped. One needs to live in the country to see that, just as in the towns, the women do all the work. I am not sure whether we should be proud of this or start getting angry with the men. Déliquaire could have left the farm for a whole week without anybody really noticing it. His wife was the whole machinery. If she had been kidnapped for an hour, the life would have gone out of it. At all events, Roger's desire to drive a truck for a living could not help but tickle his father's imagination. I said, rather unkindly:

'That isn't a profession.'

My womanly instinct rebelled against what I considered an idle occupation. Déliquaire countered:

'He 'll make more money than at home.'

I suspect that if Déliquaire had owned some land instead of having all his capital in livestock, the sons might have been more anxious to collaborate. I thought it unwise for the moment to pursue the conversation. He rose rhythmically and removed the sackcloth from the barrel. Jacques emerged on all fours, pink and smiling.

On my way back to the house I found Bobby, disguised as Don Quixote, mounted on a broomstick, a lance in his hand, charging the apple-trees. He used to run off after breakfast with a canvas bag slung over his shoulder and then sit with his back to a cherry-tree, pretending he was feasting in a Spanish inn. During the last few days in London he had positively pined for his farm. To sniff the salty orchards and rub his back against the cows gave him greater joy than the magical events in London and Paris. Success had flowed past him, his thoughts being so much here. In spite of the nearness to Christmas, the problem of his education kept on disturbing my thoughts and I was for ever on the point of declaring that come what may, he must have a proper teacher in the house, but then the onerous, unforgiving household duties showed me the utter impracticability of lodging a stranger—a stranger to saddle us with more washing, more cooking, new vexations, and perhaps unreasonable demands. A French teacher would be unacceptable to his future English masters; an English one would raise Treasury difficulties. I therefore continued to give him a two-language education of my own.

His character was becoming visible. Qualities and defects took shape like important lines in a photograph will come up in the developing bath. I noticed with surprise bursts of individuality that I could trace back to tiny beginnings in his pram in the rose garden whilst the Germans were sweeping towards the mouth of the Seine—his dreaminess, his sudden irascible moods. These were traits of myself. I had the feeling of a mirror being held up to my own soul, laying it uncomfortably bare. We clashed on occasion, both being of violent temperament, sensitive in the extreme. I blamed him often; I could feel in his eyes equal blame for me. We began for the first time to measure one another. I knew then he was no longer quite a child.

Our farmhouse was marvellously pretty with four-foot logs burning in the stone-pillared fire-place. Our own cut-down trees matured against the west wall of the stables under the thatch on which the turkeys, now tall and strong, free to wander (we never fattened our fowls), liked to perch. I had learnt to choose the wood according to my mood—poplar to explode and to crackle dangerously, sending up hot, rapid flames; apple and pear to smell good; elm to last long and burn faithfully. With elm on the fire I could leave the house confidently, knowing there would be no spark, no danger. I treated this wood with the sort of affection one shows to the nanny in whose arms one's baby is safe.

Mme Beaudry arrived as we were finishing lunch and asked what she was to do. This Brittany woman, wide bosomed, muscular, with greying dark hair tied up neatly in a bun, an apron round her enormous waist, a triple chin like that of a Roman emperor, a man's deep voice which at times amounted to a bark, had such high blood pressure that she worked every moment of the day. Her vitality had a grimness about it which made her look like a steam engine moving inexorably forward under pressure. Her husband, the parish road-mender, was pallid and thin, and now that he was old his low blood pressure had sapped out of his wiry frame the last drops of energy. Mme Beaudry liked draughts and fresh air. M. Beaudry was lately for huddling by the fire. You would have imagined she could have taken him under her arm and given him a spanking. On the contrary, it was she who got beaten. Her husband, soft spoken and amiable when he was sober, turned surly and suspicious under the joint effect of a hot day and too many libations at friendly cider presses, of which there were many dotted along the lanes which it was his business to keep trim. He returned at night and beat Anastasia, or at least that is what she often told us the next day.

I had engaged Mme Beaudry first about eighteen months earlier because my faithful Mme Bayard, who could polish a parquet floor better than any woman I know, had less time to do charring. Her son was passing his examinations to become a school teacher, and the family was going up in the world. Mme Beaudry was no good at polishing floors. The more delicate branches of house work in which Mme Bayard excelled would have been much too finicky for Mme Beaudry. Sawing logs, killing fowls and plucking them, rinsing the wash and hanging it on the line, throwing bucketfuls of water over the tiled floors, lifting a weight that would have staggered any normal man—those were the sort of things that Mme Beaudry did to perfection. Just to look at her tying on the piece of sackcloth which she used as an apron was a foretaste of her abrupt efficiency.

'And what shall I do to-day, madam?'

The first thing was to do the washing-up in the cottage. My mother preferred Mme Beaudry to Mme Bayard. Mme Bayard rubbed her up the wrong way, whereas Mme Beaudry was knowledgeable about the farmyard and an expert vegetable gardener. Mme Beaudry had no great opinion of our capacities and her words of advice rang with gloom. To hear her she was the only person who could do anything right. We were inclined to the idea that this was true. At all events she knew a great deal more than we did about everything, and we accepted her criticism as the price of her guidance. She came to us two or three times a week, always in the afternoon. The rest of the time she worked for Mme Déliquaire. This arrangement kept us amazingly well informed about the little pieces of gossip and scandal on the opposite side of the stream, though her tongue was so sharp that I always feared she might provoke an incident. She could not cure herself of giving her stories an unkind slant. She was drawn to the Déliquaires because they had an abundance of cream, milk, and butter, and were immensely generous. She could not fail to admire Mme Déliquaire, who was almost a saint. We all hurried to Mme Déliquaire when we were in trouble—Mme Beaudry, Mme Gilles, myself—and we were never disappointed. When I ran out of anything, I flew to her kitchen. When I wanted to know why my hens were not laying, off I went again.

The very importance of Mme Déliquaire was what made Mme Beaudry bitter. If M. Beaudry had bestirred himself in life, Mme Beaudry would have the milk and cream and butter and all the other wealth on my tenants' farm. *He* was a timorous man. *He* was lazy. *He* would go off drinking with other men. *He* wasted his money on liquor and tobacco. *He* prevented his wife from turning that limitless energy of hers into success. *He* idled all day and then came home and plagued her.

The Beaudrys had a little house with green shutters on the road to Saint-Vaast, which they owned. So in a way they had been successful. But when Mme Beaudry went to Mme Déliquaire's to wash up after Sunday lunch, or scrub the floor, she got mad that it was not the other way round. She argued that if she had been properly backed up by Beaudry she could have risen higher than any of us.

The previous spring she had brought Beaudry to work in our kitchen garden. It was a pleasure to watch them. Their tools shone, and everything they did had the beauty of perfection. If she could have kept him up to scratch for any length of time, they might have been millionaires.

She came from the inland, potato-growing moors of Brittany, one of a numerous family sent out by her mother to earn a living because there was not enough to eat at home. She was fourteen when she came to Normandy, and wore a white lace head-dress and the wide peasant velvet dress, tight at the waist, beneath which one wore nothing but a petticoat.

The farmer's wife with whom she had been placed as a servant said to her one day:

'My girl, when you climb up the apple-trees or stand on a ladder to store hay in the loft, you put temptation in the way of the men. I shall take you to the village and buy you some linen knickers.'

She had to keep on the first pair till she could save up enough to buy another, for her employer had said: 'You will appreciate them all the more if you have to wait.' After the knickers were paid for, she sent the remainder of her wages home. Her mother thought that this sum, earned in a month, represented the wages of a year, so great was the difference in remuneration between Normandy and Brittany.

Beaudry seduced her in spite of the knickers, and when she was expecting a child decided to marry her, not without strong maternal opposition, for Beaudry's mother had a young woman in mind for her son, a young woman with expectations of a few acres of land. On this occasion, at least, Beaudry showed strength of character, announcing to his family:

'It 's the boys who have to sleep with the future wives, not the parents. So I shall marry whom I please.'

Mme Beaudry, as the Brittany girl thus became, after suffering atrocious labour pains and being cruelly torn, had a son. The next day she was at work in the hayfields. Her organs fell disastrously and I think, from what she said, that in consequence her conjugal life gave her little satisfaction, which accounted for their separate bedrooms—she keeping the window at night wide open, he having his tightly closed.

She ate and drank like a man, though never getting drunk, but as she did not smoke she disliked her husband wasting his money on cigarettes. If she was hard with him, hard with others—I am certain she thought me the most futile of women—I was obliged to admit that she was desperately hard with herself.

She had lately been obliged to have a serious operation for the irreparable damage done at the time of the accouchement. She was waiting in her little house for the ambulance to arrive and was in considerable pain, having for many days urinated blood. Carefully dressed, as neat about her person as ever, seated on a kitchen chair, she said to her husband in a sharp, matter-of-fact way:

'Maybe I won't come back. Maybe I shall die.'

He thought about this for a moment and queried:

'What will happen to me?'

'You 'll get up a little earlier in the morning and light the fire.'

'I can't bear thinking about that. It would be too dreadful. Do you really think you might not come back?'

'I don't care a straw if I come back or not. But if I do die, you 'll find my best night-dress put out on my bed. One never has so many visitors as when one is dead. I would like you to lay me out in my new night-dress.'

Beaudry spat violently, looking terrible.

'You make me belch,' he said, 'with your new night-dress. Who will look after *me* if you die?'

At eight the next morning Jacques arrived at the cider press with the chestnut horse Miquette. Though they were right at the bottom of the orchard, the commotion, as they crossed the stream, woke me up. It was still dark. Matilda did not let the fowls out till day broke. She had their morning feed to prepare as well as our breakfast, and because of her rheumatism she took a long time to dress.

My first task in the big house was to stoke up the 'donkey' for the central heating. Sometimes the coke was still burning. A good shake and a handful of charcoal were then sufficient to set it off, giving us warm rooms and steaming hot water. At other times I had to start from the beginning, with shavings and all the uncomfortable preliminaries. The great fire in the living-room was just as unpredictable. If, on going up at night, I had left one of the larger elm logs on it, there was a good chance of finding the embers red. Déliquaire had bought us some bellows at the fair at Dozulé. Within a minute the fire would roar again.

Bobby was not easy to wake. He had a room of his own, a museum piece, half timbered, with the same stone fire-place, but in reverse, as the one in my bedroom round which (it was exactly above the big one in the living-room) the house was built. An opening in the half-timbering, without a door, communicated in a Hampton Court sort of way, so that when lying in bed I could see him in his. I had often tried to send him to his room at night at a reasonable children's hour, but as I was not sufficiently severe, it ended by his refusing to go up before me.

We breakfasted in the cottage in the central room round which all the other rooms were built, warmed day and night by the stove whose wide black pipe radiated heat serpentwise, as in a Canadian log hut. The coffee brought over from England and the milk already boiling would be standing on the stove with long pieces of French bread toasted by the almost red-hot surface. The cats were three this Christmas, the mother Miquette, who had the same name as Déliquaire's chestnut mare, and two of her sons by different marriages, Tilly, black as an Ethiopian, and Baba, the younger one, spotted like a leopard who preferred heat to food. All three were turned out of the cottage remorselessly by Matilda each evening, but in the morning, when she opened the door, they would be sitting on their haunches, waiting to rush in. At breakfast, hungry, they purred for milk and toast.

The first thing to do, after breakfast, was to start up the motor in the well, kneeling under the pointed thatched roof to jerk the starting handle. The tanks above the houses took some twenty minutes to fill. Now that the farm was fitted with electric power it was stupid not to have an automatic water supply, but this, like the repairs to the cider press, was made impracticable by controls and foreign exchange.

From the cider press came the monotonous chanting of Jacques's voice calling to the mare, 'Miquette! Miquette!' as the animal turned round and round the sixteenth-century press, harnessed to the four-foot solid oak wheels which travelled along the circular trough crushing the apples. 'Miquette! Miquette! Go on with you, Miquette!' The mare gave a mighty heave, and the two big wheels creaked with the same high-pitched noise as breaks through a still Spanish evening when the oxen drag home their prehistoric carts.

Everything here was of oak, fashioned generations and generations ago. I had the curious sensation sometimes of visualizing the great heaps of bones of all the farmers, succeeding each other, now dead, since first those beams were hewn out of living trees. Shades of drunkenness and cupidity, hard work, and tortuous, cunning minds! How many imprecations, loud-mouthed quarrels, and fights had taken place in these high-raftered chambers! How many desperate men, rendered crazy by the deadly fumes of apple- or pear-jack, had hanged themselves by a bull halter from these beams! Facets on these grim stories were to be found on the parchments handed me by Maître Bompain when the building became all my own. But the writing was old and difficult to decipher.

'Miquette! Miquette! What do you suppose you 're doing? See, Ma'am Henrey,' he added for my benefit as I entered the building, 'she likes the taste of the bruised apple. She stops to lick the juice off the wheels.'

The mare, having turned round completely in her harness of wood and rope, was passing her tongue thirstily over the smooth curved tread of the oak wheel nearest her.

'Hey, Miquette! Hey, Miquette!'

She started off again, but a moment later stopped to look at the green orchard and the rippling stream through the open door.

'She has an eye for the countryside,' commented Jacques affectionately. 'It 's in the blood, Ma'am Henrey; even the animals like the apples and fields.'

His cheeks were pink and his voice gentle, this younger Déliquaire son. He was half child and half man.

All alone, before his father's arrival, meticulously, because he had been brought up seeing it done as it always had been done since before Elizabethan times, he was starting the various operations. The apples (you will remember there was just over a ton) had been stacked overnight in the central well round which ran the trough. A sufficient quantity was taken from time to time to cover the trough lightly. Then for twenty minutes the two heavy wheels crushed them into pulp.

Miquette stopped and Jacques picked up a giant spoon made of shiny wood. Spooning out the crushed apples, he laid them in heaps (first at the corners, then at the sides) on a reddish-brown square of sacking stretched out on a platform under the cider press. The sides of the sacking were then turned in over the squashed apples, making a square envelope. Another piece of sacking was stretched above, ready to receive the next consignment from the trough.

In short, imagine two prehistoric machines. One with a bowl

in the centre and a high trough all round it—the horse dragging the oak wheels over the apples. In another part of the vault a platform being raised higher every twenty minutes by fresh red-brown envelopes containing what came from the trough. Above these layers hung the trunk of an entire oak-tree, the tallest you can imagine, which later would swing down and press great slabs of elm against the apple-filled envelopes, driving the juice

into a pit from which it would be siphoned into the cider barrel in the adjoining vault.

All this with much talking to the mare, a heady vapour of apples, the barking of Déliquaire's chocolate daubed spaniel, Mireille, and the deep voice of the farmer himself who had come in on the heels of his dog.

'There 'll be cold weather before Christmas, Ma'am Henrey,' he announced, looking up into the boisterous sky. 'I 'll just have time to dig round your apple-trees.'

The wheels were crushing fresh apples in the trough, preparing them for a third envelope. Behind the wheels two blades passed through the bruised mess, keeping it in the centre. A heavy stone was crazily tied above this contraption to keep it in place. I had never seen anything quite so archaic.

Déliquaire was amused by my exclamations, and the modern in him started to argue with that part of him which was old-fashioned. He began thus:

'Ma'am Henrey, there are very few of these four-hundred-years-old presses left, and I 'm not saying that they don't make better cider than the modern hydraulic presses which some farmers have put in. I 'm even saying that those same farmers have said to me: "The cider we make now isn't what it used to be—not for people like us who know what it should taste like." But then what business have people to be fussy these days? Money has to be taken into account. That 's what I say.

'Just look at this old method—the method of our great-great-grandfathers. It 's the wood and the slowness of pressing that keeps the cider sweet. This afternoon there will be ten envelopes of crushed apples waiting for the oak bar to come down. A turn of the screw every half-hour and by nightfall those red-brown squares will be as flat as pancakes. Your ton of apples will have yielded, to my way of thinking, five hundred and sixty litres of pure juice, which Jacques will pump into the barrel next door.

'To-morrow when you 're still in bed, Jacques will come back with the mare to unscrew the bar and empty the envelopes into the centre well round the trough. He will add to this five hundred litres of stream water, which will be immediately absorbed into the pulp. We shall then go through the process all over again—a second crush with the oak wheels and the mare slowly turning, the envelopes filled again. After lunch the bar will come down. A turn of the screw every half-hour, and by evening we shall have five hundred litres of diluted apple juice which we shall pump into the barrel next door. By Christmas Day the thousand and sixty litres will have fermented and be ready to drink. You shall try some with your turkey.

'There it is, Ma'am Henrey. I know, being a writer, you like old customs, and this lot of woodwork is pretty enough to go into a museum. No, I 'm not joking. The trunks of oak above and below the platform and the hand-fashioned screw thick as a man's body which passes through them—no living man could make, or even imagine how it was made. 'Twould be like making the pyramids again.

'The difference between cider made this way and the modern way is the difference between bread made by hand and by machinery. If you 'd never tasted the old-fashioned farm loaf, you wouldn't know what you were missing. Is that right?'

He put a clogged foot, small and very neat, on the mouth of a pitcher, leaning forward on his knee, and, rubbing the side of his nose, continued:

'So it is two days' work to turn your ton of apples into cider. We began this morning; we shall finish to-morrow night. From dawn to dusk—call it eight hours each day, making sixteen all told. Sixteen hours and the labour of a man and his horse, without counting me to supervise. Now supposing that instead of these oak contraptions we had one of those modern hydraulic presses? Instead of sixteen hours, we would take scarcely more than two. By lunchtime to-day, hop! We would have finished. And another thing. Instead of five hundred and sixty litres of pure juice from the first pressing, we would have fourteen litres more for each *razière*, making a hundred and sixty litres extra for each ton. Now even though your cider was not quite so good, wouldn't you be glad to have a hundred and sixty more litres in your barrel?'

Somewhat exhausted by this long *exposé*, he drew himself up and lent a hand to Jacques, folding in the edges of the sacking. I could see he was proud of the way his boy worked. It was really a pleasure to see. Talk about machines! The envelopes were as neat, as even, as pretty a picture as any painter could wish for.

This burst of parental pride made him suddenly swing all the other way.

'It 's like milking by electricity,' he began. 'I 've heard that some farmers, impressed by what they saw in Germany when they were working forced labour on the farms, want to try it here. Well, there 'll be no milking my cows electrically. I like to tell how they are keeping by the feel of their udders. Besides, it draws off too much, I 've heard say.'

'Not the newest machines,' interposed Jacques.

'That may be,' conceded his father, 'but in Normandy with the cows never sleeping in, except in the depth of winter, but going quietly from orchard to orchard often a long way from the farm, it would be harder work bringing them in night and morning to put them under the machines, than to go out with the milk pails and draw them by hand.'

'There 's equipment you can take along with you,' said Jacques. 'That 's the sort the Poulains are talking about.'

'Well, I 'll tell you,' said his father. 'These modern inventions —hydraulic cider presses, electrical saws, electrical milkers—they

land you in queer street when the first slump comes along. There 's only one way of working the land—all the family together, with no overheads and no wage bills. That 's why the fellows who cut down these oak-trees and fashioned that giant screw by hand made a better business out of farming than many of these high-falutin experts. It 's wrong, I say, to draw more out of the earth than nature meant us to. Where else is the grass so sweet as ours?'

The church bell having tolled, I wondered, on my way down to the village, who was dead. The tolling of the bell, coming upwards from the seashore to our rich orchards on the undulating plateau, often sent a chill down my spine, catching me suddenly whilst happy, not thinking there were any cares in the world but mine. In the cities the grim battles to make good leave one less aware of the private lives of one's neighbours. One fights for money or success, with nails out, desperately. In these pretty villages, where life is smoother, people fight exclusively against death. Cancer is the enemy that terrifies, the octopus that stretches its tentacles, seemingly, into every home.

This time, as I had rather expected, it had just killed Louis Baudon, who owned the grocer's shop opposite the post office. Louis Baudon had come to our village from Burgundy at the age of ten—a dark-haired little boy wearing a wide straw hat, a basket on his back, and corduroy trousers fastened round the waist with a red flannel belt. He had come to hire himself out as a plasterer.

In my girlhood in Paris, when a house was being pulled down, the apprentice plasterers used to form a living chain to remove the bricks, which they carried on their backs in baskets. The red flannel round their waists was to prevent them from catching a sudden cold after the heat of their labours. The men were dressed in the same way. When the husband was ready to leave the house, his wife would hold the flannel at one end while the man spun round, like a bullfighter winding on his silk sash. The thighs are where a man most easily catches a chill, and red flannel stores heat. Did not our grandmothers wear red flannel petticoats?

The young southerner quickly saved enough money to start a building firm of his own, and amongst many other contracts he put up this grocer's shop which fell into his hands, the customer who had ordered it becoming bankrupt before it was finished. Louis Baudon thought it would be good business to have a grocer's shop, and he knew just the girl to put in as cashier; a clever young person called Lucienne from the road to Saint-Vaast, who had been brought up in a shack on the edge of an orchard just above Déliquaire's farm. Many of our orchards have stone and half-timbered buildings in varying stages of disrepair, very old, older than anybody can remember, and when people were less difficult, not minding hewing their wood and fetching their water, nearer to nature, they were glad to live in these picturesque, fairy-tale structures in which farmers now store their hay or keep their pigs, when, as often happens, they are not left to be blown down by winter hurricanes.

These buildings give the Norman countryside its strong personality, so that when you are sitting in a railway carriage you are aware every minute through which province you are passing. They form the distinguishing mark upon its green, cow-studded features. There is such a building at the corner of my kitchen garden, where farmers' wives who preceded me baked their bread. The ovens of Caen stone are said to be the finest outside the Louis XIII château which dominates our distant view.

On the road to Saint-Vaast two of these pretty but very dilapidated structures faced each other in opposing orchards. In the smallest and poorest lived Lucienne with her brother and their parents. In the other Mme Beaudry and her husband were waiting to buy the piece of land on which they were later to build their present home. And in those days Lucienne and her brother so often went supperless to bed that Mme Beaudry used to pour some soup into a pan and leave it all steaming in a secret opening in the hedge. Then silently, swiftly, as in some story from Grimm, the hungry children would dart out of their cabin to seize the soup.

This Lucienne had become Mme Baudon, and a pretty and clever wife she made, running the grocer's shop with a good word for everybody, but attentive to the money. I imagined well how broken-hearted she must be at the loss of her husband, 'Though mark you, my dear lady,' said a woman to me in the market-place, 'he suffered such agony these last three months that he cried aloud for somebody to finish him off, like an animal in the slaughter-house. Morphine had ceased to kill the pain.' She added, breathing deeply, with relief: 'It 's a scourge peculiar to moist, damp regions. Everybody knows that. Thank goodness I 'm not from here.'

I looked up, surprised.

'No,' she went on, 'I 'm from quite a different part of France. The Jura, between ourselves, where it 's dry and cold. Now, cancer is a mushroom, isn't it? At least, in a manner of speaking. So what will you, with these orchards, always under water, that 's what makes the grass grow. Your place, for instance, is no better than a bog in winter. How can you expect——I mean, not you in particular, but so many Normans?'

'As long as you 're happy about yourself,' I said.

She went on: 'The funeral will be the day after to-morrow. There was to be a wedding. The church was already booked—a couple from Saint-Vaast, but, you understand, *it* had to be done in a hurry. They 'll send a young abbé to Saint-Vaast. The couple can be married there, though they have to open the church specially. Everybody will be at the funeral.'

There was a new butcher called Vannier. He had a shop-in-a-wall, a chicken-run, and a cottage which was almost under the belfry. When the bells rang one had to rise on one's toes and shout: 'M. Vannier, please, I would like four fillets of beef and some lamb cutlets!'

He had opened his establishment with a grant because he had been a prisoner in Germany, and many of us went to him for a change. His wife sat at a kitchen table with a copy-book, keeping the accounts, between the refrigerators and the open door through which the wind blew from the Channel, cold and salty. Mme Vannier liked cats. There had been a little old woman who lived in a room above the public wash-house. One day she said to Mme Vannier: 'They are taking me to hospital and I don't think I shall come back. You might look after my black cat.' She died, but her cat went wild looking for her, and towards the end of the summer it had a sore on its back as large as a saucer. The villagers used to throw stones at it. In the autumn, when I was back in London, Mme Vannier succeeded in enticing the cat to her home. It was now sleek and magnificent, and while Vannier was cutting the meat it would look up knowingly at the knife, waiting for the butcher to flick a morsel off the counter. By the weighing machine sat another cat who knew what each knife was used for. Vannier's movements were swift and graceful, like those of his feline companions. 'In England,' he used to say for my benefit, 'ours is a trade. Here it 's an art.'

The people in our village were as fussy about their food as they were before the war. Those who could afford it bought the tenderest pieces, and the *tournedos* and fillets were prepared, I might say, with affection, unhurriedly, to the accompaniment of important data as to whether the animal was male or female, in whose orchards it had grazed, and on what day it had been killed. Sometimes the cattle dealers looked in, adding spice to our housewifely talk, though I must admit we were not squeamish ourselves. There was still a Rabelaisian streak in our farming population. After great rejoicings, for instance, like a wedding lasting three or four days, not in the village as in Roger's case, but on the farms, especially those a few miles inland, old customs remained. On the last evening, towards midnight, a surprise packet would be auctioned in favour of the cook. Dear soul, she deserved the money. The young fellows, not to appear mean, bid furiously against each other, egged on by those in the know. When a large enough sum was reached, the winner undid the parcel, yards of string, layers and layers of paper, and when at last everybody was bending over, excited in the highest degree, there appeared horribly, the most outrageous part of some male animal's anatomy! These things one saw occasionally in the butcher's shop. Then somebody would ask: 'Is there a wedding up on the plateau, Vannier?'

Vannier's shop, which did not look like a shop at all—it merely had a rickety wooden door and four panes of glass too high to look through—was at the top of the village between the corner place where Roger's parents-in-law sold the produce of their market garden, and Émile Duclos, our horticulturist, whose roses bloomed over half an acre of hillside.

I sold my eggs to Roger's mother-in-law, Mme Trémois. Just now we had up to ten a day, not counting ducks' eggs, and Mme Trémois paid me twenty-six francs each for them, selling them for thirty. That she continued to take our output at this price was a kindness, for, the government having placed on the market a great number of Dutch eggs, the price in Paris was falling. Everywhere in the village there were more goods than purchasers. Gingerbread and candied fruit were coming back in succulent mountains; at the new baker's, next to the golden-crusted bread, I had seen *croissants* oozing with butter, rich apple flans, and a peacetime Norman speciality called *sablés*, a delectable biscuit. At the pastry-cook's, opposite, were cakes made with cream and butter, so airy that a gust of wind would have blown them away. For Christmas there were chocolate images of St. Nicholas, yule-tide logs, clogs with pralines inside, and the sort of footgear one associates with Puss-in-Boots. Wherever one looked the attractive luxury had replaced the merely necessary.

On my way back with the morning's shopping, I looked over the fence to see if there was anybody in Émile Duclos's cottage. To be honest, when I heard the tolling of the bell, I had expected to be told that it was for him. I liked him for his colourfulness. It was he who laid out my garden when we first had the farm. He wore a green baize apron, and long, turned-up moustaches like the red-tunicked soldiers of the South African war. A few tufts of hair floated in the breeze. He held his cap respectfully in one hand and a geranium in the other. He said: 'If madam would do me the honour to accept this small plant as a mark of my obedient esteem.' My heart melted immediately. We discussed what flowers to plant. He declaimed a string of learned Latin names, and seeing that I understood not one, added quickly: 'If madam will leave it to me, I shall do as I did last week for Mme la Baronne de ——.'

He was touchingly 1910—the time our mothers wore tight waists and parasols, and Russian princes hired villas at Deauville. Already running respectfully from one geranium to another, cap in hand, he had met and married Mme Duclos, whom anybody, even meeting her as late in life as I did, must have recognised as a perfect Toulouse-Lautrec type, the sort of woman who sat regally behind the cash desk in a French baker's shop or restaurant.

Their daughter was married to a gardener called Besnard, who would step into Émile Duclos's shoes at his death. Mme Besnard, though you may not believe me, was equally 1910. She had the most beautiful eyes you can imagine—an artist might have drawn them by making bold lines in charcoal. For men who like a woman to be a woman, Mme Besnard was just the one, honest-to-goodness curves, thighs, a bust, and so much hair that one had the impression she hardly knew what to do with it.

The Besnards in turn had a son, Clément, a pale face with his mother's eyes. One felt he had no business, being a young man, to have such eyes, and that our sex would have better employed them.

All the summer Mme Duclos had sat at the window of her little cottage, looking out on the powdery road. She suffered greatly from her kidneys, but most of all it was the heart. She sat on the very edge of her chair, being tightly corseted. This tight lacing pushed her bosom upwards, within a few inches of her chin, but what I used to notice were her hands, plump and white and pretty, and the gold bracelet which was closed so curiously over her wrist that she used to say: 'Oh, madam, there is no fear I shall lose it. It will have to be sawn off, and that won't be before I 'm dead.'

And the gold bracelet, which at the time of her marriage could not have cost much, was now each year, because of so many devaluations, becoming quite a thing to own.

Émile Duclos had cancer. When last he had come to my farm, painfully, telling me he must now count the days, his cheeks were already slipping in. I understood suddenly what had always intrigued me, his acute fear of dogs, even of my pekinese. He was terrified that a dog would jump up and bite him from behind.

This summer, when his wife was so very ill, he would say to me when I met him in his courtyard: 'I 'm not too bad, not too bad, madam, but my wife, you know, she is lost.' One hardly dared say, as one would have wished to: 'Take heart, M. Duclos, I 'm sure your wife will pull through.' One felt he was so grateful that she was nearer death than he.

She died in the autumn when we were in London. I wondered about the gold bracelet, I wondered about him. All the roses on the hillside had been cut. They were grown for funerals. It was one of their chief sources of revenue. But now they had all been cut for her. If there were any left, in an unseen corner, I supposed they would be put on M. Baudon's grave.

Mme Besnard met me at the gate. She still had splashes of beauty. Her eyes were magnificent. I said to her:

'How is the father?'

'He 's inside, madam,' she answered. 'Come in.'

'No, no,' I answered. 'Not to-day. Another time. I 've all these things to carry, and they will be waiting for me at the farm.'

She had opened the door, and a little man wizened like a dried fig came tottering across the newly washed linoleum, one carpeted slipper half an inch in front of the other, his poor moustaches unwaxed and drooping, but his cap respectfully in a trembling hand.

He knew now he was the next to go, but he said bravely:

'The morale is good, madam.'

'It 's true,' said his daughter, standing just behind me. 'His morale is excellent. That 's the important thing. This morning he drank a teaspoonful of milk, and is so proud he wants to take a walk round the hothouses. He would like to look at his geraniums.'

I think he had seen so many miracles in garden and orchard—the seemingly dead apple-tree which bears fruit on a hollow bough. The rose-tree which looked sure to die, yet lives. . . .

I turned my eyes away, unable to sustain his pathetic glance.

'I thought perhaps,' I said to Mme Besnard, 'that your husband might come up to the farm some time. I 'd like him to plant some young trees.'

III

THOUGH we had two woods on our land, besides innumerable thickets and hedges, there was not a single Christmas-tree. I took Bobby one morning to our neighbours, the Poulains, rich tenant farmers with over forty acres of land, which in our part of the world is impressive, but Mme Castel, the granny, a tiny little woman bustling with life, exclaimed:

'Alas! my poor Ma'am Henrey, neither have we. Ernest may even have to buy one.'

Her young son-in-law, who had been made prisoner in the Maginot Line, had come back after five years on a German farm to find his own, thanks to his mother-in-law and his wife, in magnificent trim. The little boy André, whom I had helped to bring into the world before fleeing with my own to England, was now as agile at climbing trees as a squirrel. He was so wide awake about country things, so crafty in a peasant way, that Bobby, though nearly a year his elder, was rather unwilling just now to match himself against such an adversary.

'There 's the château,' I said pensively, my mind still occupied with the Christmas-tree.

The Louis XIII château, a perfect gem on the hill facing my bedroom window from which rose the sun each morning, was surrounded by a magnificent wood, the sort that provides a romantic setting for the second act of a pantomime. Though the Germans had pillaged the already impoverished château and cut down many trees, the three pepper-pot slate towers, the russet and grey façade, the noble weed-covered courtyard, the magnificent crumbling fruit walls, the wood still dense enough to lose oneself in and, below all this, the rich farms all depending on it, had changed pictorially not at all since the days of the French kings. Two hundred years ago I would not be surprised if all our farms, the Déliquaires', the Gilles', the Poulains', and my own had not formed part of this seigneurial domain, though I hasten to add that my house was more than a century older than the château. Each spring the villagers went to the wood to pick lilies of the valley. We went there ourselves, though we did not meet anybody all day, and I had wonderfully the impression of a walk into the past. This country of republicanism is more monarchical than England. It treasures the luxuries in life.

The wood was full of young fir-trees growing from moss-covered earth, the warm wind jingling through their needles.

Above them the sky was hidden by the foliage of mighty oak and elms.

Mme Castel answered quickly: 'Oh, Ma'am Henrey, it 's safer not to go. The Germans did so much damage that the Admiral de Carpentier'—the present owner—'has put up a notice in the village, saying that he will prosecute anybody who tries to steal his fir-trees.' She added: 'If, on the way home, you were to meet two *gendarmes* they might ask you where you had cut down your tree.'

'You are right,' I answered. 'We must not go to the château.'

We were in the big room of the farm, stone floor, immense Norman cupboard with silver bars, the kitchen stove, a bright window, a large deal table, and a bowl of Christmas roses. Mme Castel was dressed in black, with steel-rimmed spectacles, real grandmother's spectacles which from time to time she jerked on to her forehead. Against her was Yvette (Vevette, we called her), nearly three, tugging her skirt with one hand whilst she shook a rattle with the other. In the fold of Mme Castel's arm was Annick, not quite two, bald and pink. Upstairs, at the foot of the parents' bed, five-month-old Marie-Madeleine would be sleeping in her pale blue cot. André was at school.

Yvonne, Ernest's wife, pretty eyes and soft features, was turning with a large wooden spoon a sweet-smelling mixture of apples and *calvados*, thick and brown, in a flaming copper pan.

'Oh,' I exclaimed, 'the beautiful copper pan! How I envy you!'

'The men like something sweet to finish off their meals,' she said. 'It 's jam, really, but more crystallized. I like to let it simmer eighteen hours.'

I had sometimes come in upon them at their midday meal, the family grouped at one end of the long table, the farm hands continuing in order of importance, each man with his own jack-knife, curiously uncouth in their manner of eating. Ernest sat at the head of the table. As the master, he served himself first with a large spoonful of jam, then sent the pot round. Émile, their chief farm hand now that the German prisoner had gone, slept on a bed of his own making, mostly hay and horse-rugs, above the stables. The Normans, still curiously medieval—the cowherds and labourers, I mean—have queer habits and are apt to foul their bedding like animals. The Poulains' farm hand used to say churlishly: 'I don't want anybody to go looking at my bed.' The Déliquaires once slept a servant above the big room till Déliquaire exclaimed one day: 'There must be a hole in the roof. Yellow water keeps dripping through!'

If these things were not so our province would not have any longer its peasant aloofness from the rest of the world. That is why so many of us, though frantically interested in the Poulains' experiment to milk by electricity, felt suspicious about it, fearing that we were seeing the end of what we loved. Victor Duprez, our erudite and peasant-understanding mayor, the Poulains, and I had electricity on our farms, but on the other side of the road to Saint-Vaast there was none. Thus Déliquaire and the Gilles, not to mention the Beaudrys, were obliged to go to bed by candlelight or oil lamp, exactly as a century ago.

Having made so little progress towards finding a Christmas-tree for Bobby, and knowing I would have no peace till I found one, we decided to go to our own small wood which grew in the form of a wedge, narrow at one end, wide at the other, between a hayfield called the Burgundy, and a large orchard sloping down to the same stream which, later in its leisurely course, watered the orchard in which my house was built.

The orchard, known as the Valettes, had bracken in the centre, hiding foxes' lairs, and in spring was highly coloured with wild flowers growing right down to the water.

We squeezed into the wood, searching carefully, but only at one end was there a tree of the fir family, and that very old, with branches too high for us to reach. The undergrowth was everywhere dark and thick. Though the hayfield and the orchard were let, amongst others to Déliquaire for grazing and apples, my woods I kept to myself. I loved them wild and mysterious; here nothing had been touched by the axe for a good half-century. Twice since my return after the war I had been offered high prices for the timber. The rugged owner of a saw-mill, when there had been no coal in the village, spoke of half a million francs for the right to cut both woods to the ground. I answered I would as soon have all my hair shorn as women in czarist days did to pay their husbands' debts. We burned great quantities of wood, of course, at the farm, but trees were always falling in the winter gales, and I planned to have Besnard, Duclos's son-in-law, pull up nine or ten large pear-trees round the house, trees between eighty and a hundred years old, which in summer stultified with their thick foliage their more valuable neighbours. In their place I would ask him to plant cider apple-trees, planning ahead for when Bobby was of age.

Disappointed at not finding a Christmas-tree, we went down to the river. One could wade it, but there was also a little bridge made of young hazel branches, over which Victor Duprez's farmer led his donkey when he went milking in the orchard that our mayor had lately bought from old M. Louis Gravé, a fine orchard, rich in trees, with a walnut and two medlars overhanging the water.

This Louis Gravé had a brother we called 'deaf Joseph' who, when I was modernizing my house and building the cottage, was one of the three carpenters. The woodwork of the cottage roof, preparatory to thatching, was put up by them when an overhanging pear-tree was heavy with small, luscious fruit, and the three carpenters liked to take their midday meal on the scaffolding. The bricklayers and plasterers had theirs underneath. When I used to pass that way I could hear, but not see, these jolly carpenters munching their sandwiches, swallowing their cider, and talking. They talked very loud, the two who were not deaf, for the benefit of deaf Joseph, and deaf Joseph because it never struck him that he was speaking louder than was necessary. Their conversation was very gay, and the workmen underneath used to stop eating to enjoy the fun. I did not understand at first why the bricklayers laughed when I came on the scene. Suddenly from above a loud voice would break out:

'A fine wench she was. Do you remember, Joseph?'

'A fine wench!' shouted deaf Joseph. 'That she certainly was, and if you ask my opinion, we'd have had time to up with her skirts!'

'You bet we would.'

'She wore a pink kemise,' said Joseph, who meant a 'chemise,' but the Normans pronounce their *ch*'s hard.

'No, Joseph, you forget. She didn't have a kemise!'

'But she had a lovely bosom and a fine round behind.'

'Oh, that she did!'

'Have another swill of cider, Joseph.'

'Thanks, I will, but I remember now, she *did* have a kemise!'

'No, she had *not* a kemise.'

Deaf Joseph had a few acres of land on the road to Saint-Vaast, and he lived all alone in a funny little house at the top of one of his orchards. All the rest of his land he had given to his daughter who had married Gilles, the locksmith. This Gilles was a remarkable young man. Born in Rouen, he had first taken his pretty wife to a suburb of Paris called Arcueil, where they had a son, André. The child so nearly died from malnutrition that they came to live in a shack in one of Joseph's orchards, and Joseph gave them a lean cow which they afterwards almost worshipped, for she saved little André and provided drink and food for the family during its difficult years.

There had been in the orchard where they came to live one of those strange buildings I have already mentioned. Gilles was not rich enough to do it up as it should have been. He was accustomed to those houses on the outskirts of Paris where the roofs are mended with biscuit tins beaten out flat with a hammer. The Paris workman tinkers with his house for three hours every Sunday and spends the remainder of the day at the cabaret. Gilles, I am sorry to say, mended the roof of his home with biscuit tins and corrugated iron. In winter, when the trees were bare, it looked a little strange.

But I had much true admiration for this spectacled workman. He remained a workman, sometimes in a factory at Dives, more latterly making keys with a locksmith. His pretty-eyed wife, Joseph's daughter, presented him with two more sons, Robert and Michel, sold nearly all the milk and dairy produce, saving money franc by franc, until they could rent extra land and own a sleek herd. André was grown up and made keys and locks with his father in the village, Robert would soon find a similar occupation, Michel, not quite twelve, was Bobby's occasional henchman.

The morning after our unsuccessful expedition to the small wood, just as I had lit the fire in the big room, it still being quite dark, there was a scratching at the door. I looked out, wondering.

Michel Gilles was peeping up from the branches of a fir. His mother had tied a red muffler round his head because he suffered from earache and his nose was dripping.

'Please, Ma'am Henrey,' he started, nervous and smiling, 'I 've brought Bobby's Christmas-tree.'

'How very kind of you. I didn't know——'

I was on the point of asking him where he had found it when he made another polite smile and fled. The green branches lurched against the window, smelling resinous and sweet in the morning freshness. I remembered that Jacques Déliquaire had left a wooden horse box in the stables. I filled it with earth and planted the fir in the centre. Then I dragged it just inside the living-room, where the highest branches of the tree nearly touched the ceiling.

After breakfast Bobby decorated it with tinsel and glittering balls we had brought from London. In spite of an instinctive antagonism for anything which makes extra work, I was obliged to admit that the tree looked magnificent in this nearly medieval room with its beams, its stonework, and great fire. There was a cast-iron pot which we had once used for cooking pig food over the logs, as in Welsh picture books, and this, filled with holly and painted white, we placed on the table. Suddenly the cold set in, and the next morning the countryside was as white as if it had snowed and the earth was crinkly underfoot. Déliquaire said: 'I was right to get that digging round the apple-trees finished.' Everything froze, and the beauty of the scene was marred by a continual fear that next time I turned a tap nothing would flow out. Giles Matthieu, our good-looking young plumber who had married one of Dr. Lehérissey's daughters, declared that the weather would soon become warmer and that it was not enough to drain the tanks—the curves under the wash-basins would have to be opened up. He gave me to understand that this was not within my competence and I would do better to wait until we were certain the cold would last. The next morning the enormous cement reservoir filled with rain water in the kitchen garden had three inches of ice on it. The garden taps were frozen. For the first time I had been obliged to sleep with the windows closed. We increased the central heating, made enormous log fires and poured boiling water into the duck pond to keep the members of the poultry yard happy. In the afternoon I panicked and asked Matthieu to come up and empty the reservoirs.

Giles Matthieu went to the attics and hay-lofts, inspected Bobby's photographs on the wall of the writing-room, had a cup of tea, and declared that he would stake his reputation our pipes would not freeze. The previous year he had made everything snug with felt and straw. I was anxious to be reassured, and he added that if anything, contrary to his expectations, did go wrong, I need only telephone and he would send me a workman within an hour. I had an uncomfortable feeling, whenever young Matthieu came up to the farm, that I had never sufficiently thanked him for saving our lives in the summer of the French collapse. The night Le Havre burned we wandered pitifully through the sleepy village in search of somebody who would drive us a few miles farther towards the Brittany coast. In this moment of panic Dr. Lehérissey said: 'I own a house not far from Saint-Malo.

It 's yours if you can reach it.' Matthieu's father, who was standing with his son in front of the shop, said in the most ordinary voice: 'Madam, my boy will be happy to drive you there.' 'When shall we start?' asked young Giles. Consider that these fine people must have been as terrified as we were and that the place we were bound for was eight hours' driving distance, so that what the Matthieus were really offering to do was to break up their family in a moment of extreme danger. They might have needed to flee themselves within the next few hours —in that case they would have been without their son and without the car. There was something biblical in Giles's fine act. After he had brought us safely to our destination and I was looking at Saint-Malo, the blue sea shimmering, the blond baby crying in my arms, I said to him: 'How shall I ever be able to repay you?' In London, during the whole of the war, I thought about this, my gratitude overflowing, but as soon as I arrived back in the village wicked people said: 'You ought to be careful. The Matthieus were always saying unkind things about the English during the occupation!' Now, even supposing they had (which was not true), would that have diminished my debt to them? And once again here was this good-looking young man saying to me: 'Don't worry, Mme Henrey, if you get into trouble with the pipes, I 'll be there!'

The next morning it was so cold that, getting up, I felt too miserable to care how I looked. I ran to the taps. There was still a normal flow. I thought the engine above the pump might be frozen, but a few violent turns of the starting handle were sufficient to give the thing life. The rain water reservoirs in both gardens had more ice than I had dreamt was possible—so much that later a man had to break it with a sledge-hammer. The central heating was cold, and the coffee lost its heat as soon as one poured it out. The ducks searched miserably for water.

The orchards were picturesque and crackled underfoot. The village, full of good things to eat, looked pleased with itself. Mme Baudon's customers composed their expressions for a few words of unfelt sympathy before buying fairy lights and marzipan. Looking at her behind her cash desk I saw she had real tears. She said to us almost angrily:

'You don't know what I 've lost. I don't myself—not yet. Why did it have to happen so soon?'

Maître Vincent, the notary, said circumspectly:

'Two or three small boxes of chocolate as seasonal gifts, if you please, my dear Mme Baudon, and how would it be if we fixed next Wednesday for the family council, to talk about the will, I mean. Would three o'clock be convenient?'

'Three o'clock would be convenient, Maître Vincent. Would you care for a bottle of Grand Marnier with your chocolates? The price goes up after this week.'

'So it does, Mme Baudon. I remember. It might be wise to take two bottles. That would make a worthwhile saving. Now, let me write in my little book: "Wednesday at three o'clock." A very sad Christmas it will be for you, my poor Mme Baudon. You must try to be brave.'

'He was too good to me, Maître Vincent. That 's the whole trouble. When one is too lucky, it doesn't last. I 'll make you a slight reduction on the chocolates because of Christmas. Are you quite sure there 's nothing else I can get for you, Maître Vincent?'

'Nothing else, thank you, Mme Baudon. Good day.'

The Christmas-tree looked beautiful that evening. At the last moment we had bought a great many more decorations. M. Schwartz of the bazaar had just received some novelties from Paris, which, gaily displayed in the window, had tempted us. M. Schwartz had a big round face with pink cheeks, highly coloured like the dolls he sold. His first reaction was to scold violently. His second was to follow his prospective customer step by step, being suspicious by experience, for he was almost blind. He could lift up his eyelids as one lifts the lid of a kettle, and the first time he did this I turned white and nearly fainted. He totted up the bill by throwing his body over the counter and bringing the paper right against his poor eyes, which during the First World War received the full force of a rifle discharge. In the recent war he had lost his wife and his son. There stood by his desk a very antiquated sewing machine which I once asked him to sell me. 'Sell that?' he barked. 'Not likely! It belonged to my wife!' I remembered her—portly, extremely kind, with what must in youth have been a very pretty face. She died in a concentration camp.

Our Christmas-tree, accordingly, was glistening and gently swaying in the big room. A large elm log, split in half, was burning gently, safely, bark uppermost, with other logs leaning against the stone pillars of the fire-place, waiting to be laid across the hot embers. We had been reading *Treasure Island* aloud.

Supper had been cooked on the logs, bread toasted, tangerines dreamily peeled. Now my husband had laid down the book and Bobby had gone up to bed. We heard his footsteps on the ill-fitting parquet above our heads, dust occasionally falling. The hot-water bottles were waiting for the kettle to boil. The presents had been placed at the foot of the tree on the summit of which a star glowed. The elm was burning over a furnace of red embers in which strange worlds were drawn. Centipedes, driven from the middle of the wood by the increasing heat, appeared suddenly, madly rushing round in circles, uselessly seeking escape from the still unburnt bark. One could follow from the cushions of a deep arm-chair their long-drawn-out realization of death by burning. Seized by panic, smoke choked them. Some dropped over the side of the log into the furnace, where their minute bodies made, for a fraction of a second, a black spot in the glowing red. Over the cold, white-covered orchards came the sound of church bells for midnight mass. Looking at the star on the Christmas-tree, I thought of Mme Schwartz in her concentration camp, wondering if she too had been faced with the furnace of the extermination chamber. In London, not burning logs, my Christmas night would not have been troubled by tortured centipedes. I rose, feeling sick, opened a cupboard where I had hidden a box containing a mechanical toy I had bought for Bobby, and wrote his name lovingly across the paper. He had just turned the wireless on in my bedroom, and the sound of carols came floating down. A fox barked outside as it hungrily prowled round the poultry yard.

The fire was still smouldering when we came down in the morning; a few twigs, a log, and it was flaring up warmly. We had bought three ready-filled stockings at a toyshop in town, and these we hung up across the chimney. Bobby came down full of excitement. We all felt it was his Christmas.

We had killed a turkey for lunch, and I had brought over an English plum pudding which we would decorate with a sprig of holly and set light to with *calvados*. After breakfast I went down to the village for the bread. This daily descent was the hardest thing about life in the country. On the other hand it kept one in touch with what was going on.

Half-way down the lane I met Solange with André Poulain. André's overcoat was open and his hands were thrust into his trouser pockets. His eyes, fixed downwards, seemed to examine the pebbles of the lane, and his heavy boots echoed against the tall trees. He looked like a precocious man, the too-early double of his father, and one pictured him more easily with a gun under his arm than with any childish toy. Yet he was a year younger than Bobby. Solange was holding a prayer book, by which I took it that they had been to mass. I had immense pity and affection for this girl whose family name I do not recall. Solange rang sufficiently sweetly in my ear, for was it not the name of George Sand's sad daughter, and everything to do with the great writer is close to my heart.

I first met this girl in a curious way.

It was in late summer, just after the birth of Annick, Yvonne Poulain's third child—a Thursday to be exact, and the family was making ready for the baptism and the rejoicings which always follow. Exceptionally I had to go to the village immediately after lunch. I was to have a permanent wave. Yvonne was fetching Annick's godmother, who was due to arrive at two o'clock by the coach from Le Havre. My appointment with the hairdresser being for the same hour, she offered to drive me down in the pony trap.

The godmother proved to be Solange. She was sitting on a stone bench by the sea, a rather pretty young person of twenty-six or twenty-seven, with a worn coat and a cheap travelling bag from which knitting-needles and a begun jumper were sticking out from an aperture next to the zip.

As soon as she saw us she rose. Her right leg was clamped in a steel apparatus, and now she looked pathetic as if she was accustomed to subserviency. On the way down Yvonne had given me to understand that she was some poor relation being made godmother out of pity rather than choice.

I thought no more about the matter till the following day. On Friday we all went down to the village early, especially the young wives, because it was market day and we liked to see the cheap but fascinating wares displayed in front of the town hall on the open-air stalls. I was half-way down the lane when from behind me a pony and trap came clattering along. I heard Yvonne calling to the pony to stop, and as I looked round I almost brushed the animal's shaggy head.

Yvonne was in a gay mood and, introducing me a second time to Solange who was sitting next to her, asked me to jump up and make a third. Then she touched the pony and we went off at a quick pace.

Looking back on this drive, I am not quite sure how much Solange told me then or later. Remembering that she was lame, my first question was about her long journey by coach and whether it had tired her. I am talkative by nature and have an intense sympathy for anybody who is unhappy, to the extent that I do not rest till I have discovered the reason of their unhappiness.

Solange was spontaneous in her confidences. She had been starved of the companionship of women, and my questions, put gently and with obvious sincerity, immediately touched her. She was an only girl brought up with six brothers in a working-class home, and instead of liking boys and men she had a horror of the sex. She said: 'There is nothing pleasant or amiable in a boy. He makes a noise, he breaks things, one is continually obliged to serve him. When he is not at work, he just lolls about the house.'

I asked her how long she had been lame, but she was not certain. She thought it had been from birth because she never remembered anybody playing with her as a child. When she went to school the doctors examined her and made her wear the apparatus. She thought it had been infantile paralysis.

All these men who got on her nerves—she seemed to consider her father as little better than the boys—would normally, like a great percentage of the male population of Le Havre, have gone to sea. They would have manned the great liners that I used to watch from my bedroom window slipping out on their way to New York. Some would have been deck-hands, others stokers, cooks, stewards, and the very youngest, cabin boys. They would have done the things that it amuses men to do. She would have been left in relative peace at home. The German occupation had upset all this, putting an end to shipping. The older men lost their jobs and idleness made them a nuisance in the house. The younger ones grew up without any profession at all, and they were almost worse. Now old and young, a pathetic collection of human wreckage, were employed fitfully to clean up the débris in the town and waterfront, for our bombers laid the city almost flat. Casual labourers are what they had become. When they were laid off or when they went on strike they were all over the uncommodious dwelling. On Sundays there was a chance they would go fishing or disappear with a gun. They were a universe, these men, to themselves. She did not understand them, and one can hardly blame her for thinking them a useless, idle lot. I think the very youngest was of school age—the silliest of all periods for a boy.

All these details Yvonne, knowing better than I, had dismissed briefly the day before, when I was less interested, by saying:

'Yes, I 'm sorry for her. You know what it is. The parents have made a mess of things.'

It must have been in the pony trap that Solange suddenly said:

'Most people think one gets inured to pain, to being miserable. My apparatus crucifies me, but when I take it off to go to bed it's worse. My nights are black and sleepless, but occasionally, because my senses are not as dead as my limbs, I toss feverishly between the sheets wanting love, never getting it. I never played at school. No man has ever looked at me. I 've never been kissed. The only children I shall ever nurse will be other people's. Women of our world, after enough time cooking for others, serving others, sewing for others, turn into stone. I shall turn that way too, but it hasn't come yet.'

'Perhaps you could go to the cinema?'

'No,' she answered. 'What good would it do me to see women being made love to? I 've a hard enough time as it is trying to forget I 'm human.'

This conversation rushed back into my mind as I saw Solange with her prayer book coming back from mass with André Poulain, fists in pockets, heavy boots echoing against the trees. She had ended her remarks in the pony trap by saying that at the end of a dark night she rose two hours before it was necessary, for the joy of going to church. Seeing her now with André walking slowly up the hill, I knew that each step was agony but that she had obtained her satisfaction, kneeling in front of the altar, religion replacing beauty, a husband, children, and two active legs. She was just as great a saint as Thérèse of Lisieux in whose honour a basilica had of recent years been built. We had exchanged greetings. I was going on my way when I turned back and called:

'Solange, ask Mme Yvonne, if you can bring Yvette round this afternoon to see the Christmas-tree. André can come too. He may like to play with Bobby.'

They arrived just after three. I took Yvette on my lap and Solange sat politely on the edge of a chair. She accepted a cup of tea, and after a good deal of persuasion brought her chair nearer the fire.

'It seems impertinent to wish you a happy Christmas,' I said.

'There are worse off than me,' she answered. 'There 's a girl in my street who is strapped to a plank.'

'Do you still knit?' I asked, remembering the needles in her bag the day I saw her sitting by the sea.

'Yes,' she answered. 'I try to knit for money, but I don't make much.'

'Do you knit for the Poulains?'

'No, Mme Castel knits for all of them.'

'However does she find the time?' I queried.

Solange explained that Mme Castel no longer slept. Her mouse-like activity practically made no difference between day and night. She remained as a sort of guard in the children's room all night, knitting and reading. Occasionally she would doze for an hour before daybreak.

Yvette's eyes roamed with great interest round the strange room. I bent down and whispered:

'Who knitted your polo, Yvette?'

'Mémé.'

She had been dressed in my honour, a beige coat which soon would do for Annick. Underneath I caught a glimpse of the knitted dress.

'Can I see the pretty dress?'

Dimpled fingers opened the coat and large inquiring eyes looked for a sign of appreciation.

'Is your petticoat just as fine?'

She was enjoying herself immensely and showed me with pride what she wore underneath, waiting for the hem to appear with as much interest as if she had never seen it before. She then inspected the Christmas cards on the sofa, especially one from England, depicting a Father Christmas smoking a pipe, and she began to laugh knowingly. I thought her fancy had been taken by the white beard or the scarlet cloak, but it was neither. Her parents had apparently slipped a chocolate pipe in her stocking, and her father had even tried to put it in her mouth but she would have no such thing, realizing that young women do not smoke pipes, even of chocolate. The pipe on the Christmas-tree reminded her of the chocolate one. Her womanly instincts were amusingly apparent. Bobby, searching in his Christmas stocking, had discovered a broom which he had tossed aside. Yvette now seized it, and clambering down from my knees was soon sweeping the carpet. She then toddled to the tree, discovering a painted wooden figurine, one of several, which she fell in love with. We had been given them during the Battle of Britain and they had decorated successive trees. I told Yvette she might have the figurine and that we should call him Tommy. I could see she was not quite satisfied.

'One for Annick?' she begged cajolingly.

'You must promise to give it her,' I said, impressed by her generous spirit.

'Yes,' she said. 'Promise.'

I gave her Tommy's companion, christening this second figurine Paul. This name she remembered more easily than the first. She tried a dozen times before she could get it pat. I suppose it was her first English lesson. I was later to learn that she had, according to her undertaking, presented Paul to her sister Annick, but I believe it was more due to cunning than to generosity. Though she was scarcely eighteen months she was already sufficiently awake to realize that by giving this bribe to Annick, Annick would leave her in peace to play with Tommy!

The weather remained so cold that the next morning my washing, hung up scarcely an hour earlier between a pear-tree and the garden gate, stood out stiff and studded with diamonds like lamé. The tiny mechanical tractor, magnificently to scale and fitted with rubber tyres, which at his own request I had given to Bobby for Christmas, lay unlooked at in a corner. I could have fed my household for nearly a week on the money this toy had cost, and I was disappointed.

André Poulain and Michel Gilles had each been given toy guns which shot out rubber-blunted arrows. On Christmas afternoon, whilst I had been talking to Solange, André and Bobby had rounded up Michel, and the three boys had gone off to 'shoot' rabbits. Michel Gilles, though his gun was new that morning, had lent it to Bobby for most of the expedition and my son had been appointed chieftain of the band. He now came to me confidentially and asked: 'Is it not a sorry thing for the chieftain not to have a gun?'

I have a natural horror of guns, but I supposed that my son's desire to own one was instinctive, just as Yvette had immediately seized the broom. This reason, more than any other, made me accede to his request.

The next three days saw little of Bobby at the farm. As the weather became warmer he went off immediately after breakfast with his two young friends. Towards the end of the short holidays the chieftain quarrelled with André, and Michel was not allowed to leave home because he had burned his coat while lighting a fire at the mouth of a rabbit burrow. I then discovered that the boys had removed the rubber from their arrows. Yvonne Poulain made the same discovery and André's gun was destroyed. She gave as an added reason the fact that he kept 'mémé' Castel in a trance all night by his horrible nightmares. She used to find him under the bed shooting imaginary arrows at Yvette and Annick. Bobby was told that in future if he wanted to play with his gun he must do so alone. I hoped this attack of folly would vaccinate him against a too early love of firearms.

On my way down to the village somebody cried: 'Madame! Madame! Madame!' and turning to look over the hedge I saw the postman.

My letters used to be forwarded to me every day from London by registered mail, and the postman, having caught my attention, exclaimed as he handed me the package over the hedge: 'It will be at least three o'clock before I can come up to you, madam, so I thought you wouldn't mind taking this now?'

I sensed something dramatic, and while signing his book asked what was wrong. Our new postman was followed by bad luck. He was untidily dark—wisps of hair tumbled out from his red-lined cap, and he never appeared without a smouldering and humid cigarette stub miraculously attached to his upper lip. His voice, soft and pathetic, retailed the most appalling tales of unhappiness. Whilst a prisoner of war his wife had sold their little business and run off with another man. Returning thus from the wars to poverty, he married a widow as miserable as himself, and there were children.

He lived in the chauffeur's quarters of an empty villa just above the village. Actually at the moment he hailed me I was petting a white goat tied to a peg at the side of the road. Having taken the packet he was pressing on me, I waited for the explanation.

'I must go home,' he said.

'Is there something wrong?'

'Yes, dreadfully wrong. My three-year-old son has upset the coffee-pot on his baby brother. The doctor thinks he may lose an eye. It suppurates! It suppurates! Oh, madam, the pity of it! My wife is in bed with a nervous shock. I must go home for a while. I'll deliver the rest of the letters later.'

The white goat was nibbling my glove. The postman doffed his cap and was gone.

IV

A DOZEN steps in the form of a narrow banistered staircase led up to the baker's shop under which, through area windows, one could see the flour-powdered bakers, stripped to the waist, thrusting their long peels into the fiery oven.

Our new bakeress, small, slim, and light on her toes, took two crisp French loaves from the burnished brass rack, and cutting them in half placed the four ends in my shopping bag. On the counter the golden *croissants* and the brown, buttery *brioches* resembling Humpty Dumpty figures of eight sent up rich, warm vapours that tickled the nostrils.

A door, kicked strongly open, revealed a little boy wearing a beret and a black school apron. Tightly pressed against his stomach were two paper bags filled with flour. One of them had bespattered his clothes.

'How clumsy you are!' exclaimed his mother, irritated. She would have said more had it not been for my presence in the shop. Her fingers itched to box his ears, but like a good shopkeeper she controlled her feelings.

'One of the bags is burst,' said the little boy.

'No, it isn't burst,' answered his mother. 'It 's as it always is. You just don't take the slightest trouble. I can't ask you to do anything!' She threw up her hands and continued, addressing me: 'Oh, these boys! What on earth can one do with a boy, madam? There 's no doubt about it, I would rather have a daughter. It must be charming to have a girl. At least we would understand each other.'

'Is this your only child?'

'No, there are two—two boys. That 's the point. That 's why I tell you I would rather have a girl. Imagine, madam, two boys about the house!'

'I have a feeling girls are nearly as bad,' I answered. 'When I was a little girl I must have been quite troublesome.'

The long walk down from the farm had quite exhausted me.

Something about this shop and its talkative owner made me wish to rest a moment amongst the sweet-smelling loaves. If I had gone into business I might have chosen a bakery. I remember a baker's shop in the wine-growing country near Bordeaux. The villagers used to bring their Sunday joints to be cooked in the oven. The onions were red, nearly as red as tomatoes.

'Your *croissants* are delicious,' I said. 'We took some up to the farm for Christmas and warmed them in front of the fire. We could smell the butter.'

'They are the same as they were before the war,' she answered, 'but business is bad.'

'Probably the other people let the place go down?'

'I don't know about that. I expect I was spoilt in my last shop. We sold grocery as well as bread, but the ration returns were too much for me. Once a week I had to stay up all night counting the points and filling in the forms. In the end I was tired, so tired I could stand it no longer. Then the school was too far from the hamlet, nearly three miles away across country. That was all very well for the lad you 've just seen, but the little one couldn't make it.'

'How old is the little one?'

'Nine and a half.'

'Exactly the same age as my own!'

'You have a little boy?'

'Yes, just the one.'

We both hesitated, I wondering whether I should say anything about Bobby, she on the point of going on about hers, and during this almost imperceptible moment, anxious to discover how fortune might have treated another little boy of nine and a half, I asked:

'You said the school was three miles across country and that he couldn't make it. You mean he was too young?'

'No, on account of his wound.'

'Is he wounded? How terrible. What was it? A sporting gun?'

'A revolver.'

I hesitated, taken aback. Then cautiously:

'A German?'

'No, worse than that, in a way. The war was all over, or at

least the most dangerous part of it. He was shot by an American sergeant at a cross-roads.'

She put her hand to her brow. The shop was empty except for us. Her breathing was a little faster, and I said softly:

'Don't be afraid. Tell me.'

'Our first place had been destroyed during the invasion, a bakery like this but larger, at Saint-Lô. The Americans had made their headquarters in the town, and after four months, seeing them every day, we got used to their presence, just as we had got used to the Germans. Early in October I heard that my parents who had fled during the battle had turned up in a village not far away, and I felt I just had to see them. We had a car, but it was out of order, and a friend offered to drive us over. We were given a permit. Everything was quite in order as far as the authorities were concerned, but driving in the dark we should have taken more care. At Saint-Lô, where they knew us, we did pretty well what we liked. The driver forgot it was different on the road. He didn't stop when he was told to. I remember saying to him several times: "I'm sure they are whistling at us." Honestly I don't know what was the matter with him. He went straight on towards an American sergeant on patrol duty at a cross-roads.

'It was about seven, and I suppose we were taken for spies. The sergeant fired point-blank at our driver, and the bullet must have gone right through him and grazed my thigh. I was sitting at the back, clutching my little René who was frightened and calling out: "Mama! Mama!" The driver sunk down in his seat. It was horrible to see him suddenly inert. I remember thinking: "He's dead, and it's all my fault." Something warm fell on my hand. I looked down instinctively at my child and saw the blood gushing out of him, and . . . oh! . . . his arm was hanging from his body by a piece of flesh no wider than a string. The American sergeant who had fired the shot had run up and was looking through the window. He cried out: "My God! My God! What have I done?" I didn't dare move because of René's arm, and I could feel myself fainting. But I didn't faint. They put us tenderly in a jeep, I holding the little one, expecting his arm to come off at each jerk, sick with anxiety. Ah, madam, I hope you never know what it is to see your child in that state!

We were taken to the military hospital at Saint-Lô. Madam, the way those American doctors battled for the boy! They who had nearly killed him swore they would save his life. The doctors all got round him. Some were for amputating the arm right away. I heard others say: "With kids it isn't the same as with grown-ups. Kids produce miracles. Let 's try." They gave him so much blood, madam, that, between ourselves, he 's more American than French. Knowing he might die at any moment, I kept on remembering the way he had cuddled up to me in the car, saying: "I 'm afraid, mama," and I answering: "There 's no need to be frightened with mama, darling. Cuddle up close." Madam, I was there watching, when we all thought he was dead. They were pumping blood into him. What do you think happened? The top of an ear twitched, and from white, death white, the lobe turned pink. He was not dead. I remember looking up and seeing on a shelf bottles of blood in a row like jam pots. My mind was so full of fear, of sickly torment of unavowable hope, that unable to contain so many violent emotions it was obliged at this moment to seek an outlet. The jam pots full of blood stand out sharply in my memory. I shall see them always. The doctors were bending over my child and I knew that there was a chance—slender, but a chance; he would be given back to me in some form, but, in whatever form, mine. They pumped more blood in him and put the arm in plaster of Paris. The man who had been driving us died towards morning. There was no saving him. He had lost too much blood. I suppose it was because he was a grown-up, not a child like René. René—let me see—he was six and four months. A child of six, madam; can you imagine?'

'Oh, yes,' I answered, 'I can imagine.'

'People who talk about penicillin,' she went on, 'when they have an earache or a cold should be taught better. I know what penicillin can do; what it did to him. Penicillin and three blood transfusions. When a mother has lived through a night like that, she begins to know what it is to put a child into the world and suffer for him. But with me it was only the beginning. If you have the stomach for it, I 'll tell you the rest.'

She looked up at me and saw I was crying.

'He was in plaster of Paris. The Americans left our town, and whether it was that they had done the job too quickly or that it was beyond the possibility of man to do better, the circulation was on one side of the arm only, not underneath, and suddenly his poor hand began to turn blue. It was one evening, madam; he touched one of the fingers of his stricken hand, idly, without thinking, and suddenly—it came off! Stupefied, for he felt no pain, saw no blood, he looked up at me, showing me the finger, trying to make out in his own poor mind whether he was dreaming. I opened my mouth to shriek, but no sound came. I remained for an instant fixed to my chair. I saw him catch hold of another finger and, madam, it came off like the first. I was near going mad, for whereas he was too young to understand the full horror of what was happening—what it portended, I mean—I felt myself losing consciousness. All this time—it may have been no time at all—he was looking first at me, then at his fingers, and four had come off, clean, real, and natural, except that inside they were hollow where the bone was turned to powder, like thimbles. I bit my lips and clenched my hands so as not to go mad, and taking him in my arms rushed him to the doctor. Gangrene had set in. They removed the plaster and placed his arm in a sling with a piece of wood under it. If it had not been for the nightmare of the fingers, he might have lost all his arm; indeed he would have done. When we came home in the night, madam, I took them up and examined them one by one. I couldn't throw them in the fire, could I? They were my flesh. I placed them in a little box. I shall never part with them. They will be buried with me.

'Soon, because of all that had happened, the leg, yes, the leg, refused to function. The torture of plaster of Paris started all over again. It 's scarcely two months since he has been out of it. That 's why three miles to school and three miles back was not to be thought of. There he is in the passage. Hi, René! Come here!'

He arrived in his black overall, a face pale but intelligent, finely chiselled like his mother's, and slim like her. Shamefully, because I did not want to look at him like a strange thing in a circus, I asked:

'You don't mind if I see your hand, do you, René?'

'Oh, no, madam.'

Bending over him, my eyes full of tears, I felt a great desire to kiss him, not on the face which was so pleasing, but on the poor little stump. I felt at that moment as if I had been allowed to peer into the wounds on Christ's hands. Gulps of thankfulness welled up inside me that it had not happened to my son. I felt undeservedly lucky, anxious to prevent any such thing from happening in the future by act of contrition, like placing one's lips on the leper's sores.

V

THE cold spell was followed by a day of warm, spring-like weather. I was so relieved that my pipes had not frozen, to feel the grass again soft under rubber boots, to smell the pent-up odours of the countryside, that I could have clapped my hands like a voyager brought safely through an ice-covered sea into a harbour surmounted by green fields. Sheltered too long in the heart of a city I had despised the elements, considering them unimportant in a modern world. Now that the cold was finished, I could dress more attractively, and at night undress without shivering. I had a bath and washed my hair. We had been invited to lunch on New Year's Day by our friend Victor Duprez, the mayor.

Towards evening the wind suddenly rose and within a matter of hours our buildings, thatch and slate, became the centre of a whirlwind. Lying in bed, terrified, I felt the house, old by four centuries, riding the storm. Towards five in the morning, after I had dozed off, the child's lattice window blew open and the gale entered the house like a living thing, rushing over the floor boards, opening the cupboards, shaking the bedclothes, rummaging the chest of drawers, blowing into flames the smouldering logs in the downstairs hearth. Wakened by the noise, it was some time before I realized how the enemy had entered the house. Having closed the window, and covered up the child, I went back to bed and slumbered again till eight, which, being seven British time, was the hour to put an arm bravely out of warm sheets and turn on the radio for a happy New Year from London and news of the storm at sea. From the Orkneys to the English Channel, by way of the Irish Sea, it was one long gale warning. I thought: 'Thank goodness the electricity is still working. I wonder what has happened to the telephone? How many apple-trees have been blown down at £40 value apiece? How many slates have crashed into the garden? How much thatch has been wrenched off the cottage roof?'

Though it was still quite dark, soon the first shafts of pale day would appear from behind the Louis XIII castle. I dressed hurriedly to inspect the fires and try to save the furnace for the central heating before it went out. If there was still a glimmer at the bottom, I could quickly revive it with a handful of charcoal and a good draught. Otherwise it meant half an hour's infuriating work emptying, cleaning, rekindling.

Matilda had released the farmyard. The ducks were cackling, the turkeys screeching, our two cocks crowing joyously. I switched on the electricity. There was no light. I presumed the bulb was broken, and tried the one on my dressing-table. That also was unsuccessful. I then hurried to the radio which twenty minutes earlier had worked so well, but when no friendly light appeared on its visage, no sound from its interior, hearing from outside the wind redoubling in force, shaking the trees, hurling itself against the half-timbering, howling in the attic, pulling out the slates, throwing them savagely on the gravel paths, I ran downstairs, trying every light on my way, the passage, the big room, the old kitchen. In the courtyard, Matilda, with a scarf over her head, looking more and more like a Russian peasant out of *Crime and Punishment*, was throwing golden corn picturesquely at the chickens.

'A happy New Year,' I said quickly. 'Have you any current in the cottage?'

She looked at me with sullen compassion, not even deigning to reciprocate by new year wishes.

'Didn't you hear the crash half an hour ago?' she asked. 'I should have thought anybody would have heard it. I should have thought anybody a mile away would have heard it. You 'd better go and look in the orchard. Go and look at the branch that held the high voltage, and your cottage roof sliced in half as if a giant had taken an axe, and the brick at the corner of your house where the electric light cable was fixed. Everything is in a lovely mess. Fancy not hearing that!'

'*My* cottage roof, *my* electric cable,' thought I. 'It 's always *mine* when anything goes wrong.'

I rushed round the stables, sinking into deep mud with each

step. The warm blasts of angry winds screeched and bellowed, fell for an instant, regathered force and came back with howling fury. It had become light without my noticing the change. The sky was grey and sullen but the atmosphere was tepid.

Four thick cables, two bearing high tension, two electric light, were fixed to the gable of the cottage roof by a steel arm jutting out about five feet from the thatch. The two electric light

cables then continued to the old house, being fixed to it by another, less powerful arm. The first of these arms, the one to the cottage, had been wrenched from the master beam as if some giant, farther up the line, had pulled with all his strength upon the wires. One side of the roof had been lifted from its right position and placed askew, as might happen with a toy house fitted with a detachable top. The cables lay, some on the grass, others across the cottage. The arm on our house, the old house, had also been wrenched away, bringing with it a large boulder of sixteenth-century stone.

I ran into the big room and seized the telephone. I was sufficiently naïve to think that the high-tension wires might still be alive, and I imagined the child electrocuted and the houses going up into flames. The telephone gave no amicable buzz. Rain fell suddenly in torrents. The fires were not made. I had brought cakes of mud into the house. My hair was dishevelled. I did not feel like wishing anybody a happy New Year.

I dispatched my husband to the mayor's farm over whose property, adjacent to ours, the high-tension cables ran from the transformer station a mile away on the high road to Caen. I also told him to try to discover where the telephone line was broken. He came back half an hour later in such a curious accoutrement because of the torrential rain, with Bobby's transparent mackintosh tied round his head like a bonnet, that, to his intense confusion, I broke out laughing. The male mind likes to take its disasters seriously and my levity seemed to him out of place. He reported with gravity, shaking off the water, that M. Duprez's kitchen staff, who had been frying steaks for breakfast, informed him that they also were without light or power but that their telephone was working and that he had taken advantage of it to call up M. Louette of the company. He added that the current had been cut automatically at the time of the accident, which reminded me that during his absence I had brushed up against the wires, found myself still alive, and therefore rolled them up tidily in a corner of the garden. Our telephone lines had apparently been snapped by a falling branch in the lane, opposite the entrance to Ernest Poulain's farm.

By now I had lit the fires and stoked up the central heating, and my mind was cheered by anticipation of an amusing lunch. I made myself look as nice as possible, put on an American blouse, and asked my son how he found me. He said the blouse looked stupid (it had a zip running down the middle), and though I thought he was wrong, I instantly changed it in favour of a green jumper of my own making. This pleased both him and me, and we went down to the village to take part in the excitement of New Year's morning.

The local fire brigade, which is also the municipal band, was ranged up the stairs in the town hall serenading the mayor who was trying to look impressed and serious. He had his back to the collection of fossils and bits of rock discovered on the seashore and carefully preserved in a glass case at the end of the room where the councillors meet and the civil weddings take place. The councillors were all here to wish the mayor a happy New Year, including Mlle Lefranc, the smiling nurse who had helped Dr. Lehérissey bring my son into the world and with whom I gossiped so agreeably for many days afterwards. Déliquaire, another councillor (we used to call him the Councillor 'Because' owing to his habit of beginning each sentence with

this word, at the same time bringing his forefinger affectionately and smoothly to the side of his nose), was also amongst those present. He, together with the others, were thinking that as soon as the company had listened to the *Marseillaise*, dropping a few tears of circumstance, the mayor, by custom, would offer them all a drink in each of the cafés in the village, and for once they would not have to say 'What 's yours?' because this was his New Year gift to them.

Recognizing us in the crowd, as he descended in great dignity the steps of the town hall under a triumphal arch of musical instruments, the mayor kindly invited us to join the councillors, the fire brigade, and the police force in the series of traditional free drinks, which invitation, because he was to be our host at lunch, we could not decently refuse.

It must have been nearly half-past one when we drove up to his farm in his car. The wind was much less strong and the rain had ceased, but from the top of the hill the sea appeared broken by angry white-crested waves. Twenty yards beyond the Poulains, instead of forking left to our place, we took the lane to the right. Two minutes later we were driving under the thatched arch leading into his property.

I have often tried to analyse the reasons that made me invariably cross his threshold with pleasure. Aggressive, cajoling, erudite, gentle, and blasphemous in turn, bespectacled, almost ugly and yet extraordinarily attractive, he was a man of a dozen conflicting personalities. I remember one evening in April going with my husband to dine with him. He arrived so late that we made ourselves comfortable by the fire in his study and read half a volume of Chateaubriand before his arrival. He arrived finally like a tempest, opened a bottle of champagne and, looking at my husband, exclaimed:

'I have always hated you for buying that farm.'

'But then why did you sell it to me?' asked my husband.

'My father forced my hand,' answered the mayor. 'Now he 's dead, I wanted you to know.'

'I knew,' said my husband.

They were facing each other over a tray of liqueurs and a first edition of *Adolphe*. When we left it was a dark and gloomy night.

I said: 'The mayor looked so angry I thought perhaps he might follow us out and——'

'Let off a gun over the hedge?' queried my husband, laughing. 'I love him for saying what he said.'

Victor Duprez was like that. His profession was to buy and sell land, but though he loved to buy it he hated to sell it, not out of cupidity, for it was not possible to find a more generous soul, or one for whom money, as such, meant so little, but out of a deep affection for the Norman soil. Not to understand this trait was not to understand our mayor. His close dealings with the peasants, his drinking with them of the produce of their orchards, his exchanging with them of peasant talk all through a night sometimes, had given him a key to all their thoughts and reactions, tortuous and curious. Often he spoke like them, at other times quite differently. His wife was of a family who like her husband's traded in land, but her father being dead, her mother, alone, I fancy, carried on the business, or at least she must have taken an interest in it, for at this New Year's lunch she said something to her son-in-law about a piece of business on which it would be necessary to take his advice, and he most courteously acquiesced.

In the study, before lunch, we took stock of ourselves—the mayor and his mother, the mayor's wife and her mother, a Duprez aunt who was over seventy and blind, and ourselves, making eight in all.

The house dated from the 'nineties, when Trouville and Cabourg figured in the musical comedies of Caillavet and Willemetz, and famous painters, their works not then costly, splashed their canvases with blue sea, striped parasols, and women with large hats and narrow waists. When first I came to Villers the house belonged to a M. Allard from Paris, who had a bailiff and a few cows. A few months before the war, Victor Duprez's patriarchal, dark bearded father having just died, he bought the Allard property, quickly stamping the house with his personality and building round it a model farm. Though he regretted having been obliged by his father to sell our domain, the Allard house was probably better suited to his needs. More spacious, it allowed him to entertain as befitted his station. Our house was sunk in the middle of a picturesque bog, quite inaccessible to polite society, whereas fine cars easily rolled up to the Duprez villa and every day there were people to lunch or dinner. His study was the sort of room a painter would have liked as background to a portrait. The book-cases were filled with seventeenth-, eighteenth-, and nineteenth-century bindings, mostly first editions discovered during expeditions to buy or sell châteaux and manor houses up and down the confines of our ancient province. Though he was not bellicose, except verbally, he had a cult for Napoleon which influenced the furniture and pictures, and when after lunch his guests talked animatedly, he had a habit of sinking back in his *bergère* and snatching five minutes' deep sleep as the conqueror of Austerlitz is depicted as doing. Often Victor Duprez snored, which brought him a sharp reproof from his wife, but I must say to his credit that he looked intelligent even whilst asleep.

Mme Duprez's menus retained an elegance untarnished by the war, three wines as well as cider, fish from the market at Trouville and caught fresh the same morning, a chicken or a young turkey, with perhaps a sirloin of beef and a sweet made with fresh cream. Though it was pleasant to sit at another's table, feeling clean and decently dressed, it was the hour or two afterwards, conversing in front of the fire, that made the house hospitable. We talked, I think, about Christmas displays in the Paris stores, elms, linen sheets, theatres, first editions, how much one should pay for a new dress and where one should buy it, Colette, the distinguished authoress and how she went to sign her books at the Bon Marché, kitchen gardens, whether anybody would repair the electric cables on New Year's Day or the morrow, which was a Sunday.

The Duprez aunt, though she was blind, stopped us short on the matter of bed linen, almost as soon as we had broached it. She sat thin and prim on the edge of a hard-backed chair, with a cup of coffee in her narrow, veined hands.

'Linen sheets!' she declared. 'Ah! Don't let us even talk about them! When I was a young woman I used to buy a pair for a golden Louis.' She added forcefully: 'I do wish the Bon Marché would start mailing me their catalogues again. It 's very tiresome, not having them.'

'My dear aunt,' said Victor Duprez, who was not yet asleep, 'what would you do with their catalogues?'

'Get somebody to read them out to me,' answered the old lady, 'just to compare the prices. I remember what everything used to cost.'

'My house by the sea wants reslating,' said Mme Duprez, *mère*, an angelic woman with baby curls over a young, plump face. 'This storm will have finished it. But at my age does one spend three-quarters of a million francs on reslating one's roof? I shall live in the pavilion and close the big house.'

'I have already told you,' said her son, 'it will cost a million and a quarter to make the pavilion comfortable.'

'Then I shall stay where I am.'

Of course we all knew that she would never leave the patriarchal home where her husband, dark-eyed, black-bearded, violent, had laid down the law, presiding at meals wearing a bowler hat, even at night when there were important guests, because, as he would say aggressively, his bald head was sensitive to draughts. He was a mixture of gentleness and vituperation, compliments and insults, peasant oaths and deep, massive learning, all of which he had handed down to his son.

Four had struck when we exchanged our light shoes for gum-boots to wade to the farm. Bobby had rushed ahead of us, and now returned with grave tidings, delivered in a panting voice.

A *picote* has just fought a duck, and the duck has lost an eye, and granny, who was beating the *picote*, has slipped on the floor of the stables.'

Matilda, her brightest kerchief round her head, a broom in upraised hand, her blue apron solidly tied, her feet in clogs, appeared in front of us, chasing the turkeys with horrible imprecations.

'Pests! Murderers!'

The broom cracked down on the nearest bird, who uttered a surprised bark.

'Careful!' I cried. 'You 'll kill it.'

'A good job too,' she answered sullenly. 'You *would* pity them. You always pity the wrong ones. Eight months I nursed the beasts, the pests. I 'll slit their necks and never rear any more, no, not in all my life!'

She threw her arms impotently into the air, flinging the broom into the hydrangeas, and, diving into the wash-house, plunged her hands into soaking linen. She was obviously in no mood for conversation.

The unfortunate duck, her eyes besmirched with blood, not knowing where she went, tried to follow her terror-stricken companions. Night was falling, and unwilling to take a decision, either to put her out of pain or to take measures against the turkeys, I left them to their own devices and went about my affairs. Early the next morning my husband was going back to London with Bobby.

I had caught a cold during the night of the storm, and the house, being full of draughts, too-hot fires, and spluttering candles, filled me with unaccountable depression. My enthusiasm during lunch had gone and I was miserable at the thought of being left alone in chaos whilst the male members of the household went off to enjoy themselves.

In winter no trains run along the branch line which meanders through the orchards. I had therefore instructed Fournier to send his lorry to drive us at 8 a.m. to Trouville. The journey was cold and bumpy. At the station my son was in high spirits. Whether this in itself vexed me, or whether something I could not explain urged me to return to the farm, I do not know, but I bade the travellers farewell, without even going as far as the platform to see the train leave.

I had more or less decided to take the injured duck to Mme Déliquaire and ask her to kill it. Seeing the broken telephone wire, the electric cables sprawling over my broken roof, realizing that nothing in the big house would be tidy, that the fires would be out, the beds not made, the rooms cold and muddy, my depression increased. A wave of Italian influenza was spreading so quickly through the village that most of the tradesmen were down with it. On my way up I had asked M. Jollivet, the carpenter, to mend the cottage beam. He at least gave me a little hope, promising to come up on his bicycle within half an hour. He was one of the old craftsmen who would have worked night and day to complete minutely the smallest contract.

As I reached the farmyard the sun came out.

Matilda, who had an attack of nerves because the electric oven was useless, and upset by this January madness sweeping over her poultry-yard, was for killing the injured duck immediately. She said that the turkeys, smelling blood, were ceaselessly attacking not only the wounded duck but all the others, and that their cruelty was driving her miserable. She felt, I believe, quite unjustly, that I was not pleased with her because she had gone for the turkeys the previous afternoon with a broomstick. She thought I was siding with the aggressors, and she would have liked to work me up into the same state of indignation as herself. I stood for a moment at the foot of the old pear-tree, waiting. I soon found myself preoccupied with the wounded bird. She seemed blind in both eyes, and she only moved when the others led the way. She was obviously thirsty, and anxious for her companions to take her to the pool, but they went off in the opposite direction. At this the *canette*, as we called her, seemed no longer to think life worth living. I decided it was the moment to take her to Mme Déliquaire.

Catching sight of Bobby's oilskin, I tried to throw it over her, for a duck even blind is not easy to catch. She rushed off in spite of all her sapped vitality, but hurled herself against all sorts of objects, even against the pekinese who, anxious to play the part of nurse to every animal smaller than itself, had arrived to sniff her.

This encounter helped me to capture the *canette*. She trembled violently, as if she knew that these hands were to lead her to the executioner. I bent over her poor head. Her eyes were hidden by clots of dried blood. I was so filled with a desire to save her life that, wrapping her in the oilskin, I took her to the big room where a handful of apple sticks were burning brightly.

I had made breakfast here for my husband and Bobby, tea instead of coffee, and toasted French bread. A pot of tea remained on the stool. I dipped some cotton wool into the amber liquid (it was pre-war China tea), and placed the swab gently over the *canette's* eye. She drew back, afraid. I felt her skull throbbing. I repeated this operation with infinite patience; first one eye and then the other. As I worked I threw the swabs into the fire. The pekinese lay at my feet.

One eye, I thought, had been quite gouged out, but the other, after I had worked on it for nearly half an hour, made a glorious reappearance. The *canette*, as surprised as I was, started to blink. I also noticed she was hungry, and I supposed she had found nothing to eat since the previous afternoon. I soaked some bread in warm milk and placed the cup in front of the fire. She drove her bill gluttonously, clumsily, into the sop, splashing the tiles, scattering a milky snowstorm, which, out of greediness, the pekinese quickly lapped up. Then, faintly at first, louder in a moment, the other ducks could be heard quacking in the courtyard, as presumably they were going to the water to drink, and hearing this the *canette* suddenly raised her head and answered: 'Quack! Quack!'

'Well,' thought I, 'here are two good reasons for not killing her—she has an appetite and an interest in her friends!' So I gently carried her back to the foot of the pear-tree.

M. Jollivet, wearing an American army blouse and a beret, had arrived with several beams strapped to his bicycle. He carried his wood very solemnly to the carpenter's table in front of which, plane in hand, he made the strangest contortions, bringing his spectacled eyes level with the wood, then dancing back on his toes to get a more distant view. His presence on the farm reminded me that I desperately wanted a new parquet floor in my bedroom. The dust from the attic fell between the worn boards. I showed him exactly what I had in mind, asking him to draw up an estimate.

Meanwhile several electricity experts and two *gendarmes* came marching down the orchard. They told me with some excitement how the accident had happened. A tall oak between two of the mayor's orchards, uprooted by the hurricane, had fallen majestically across the high-tension cables. Four cement pylons had been broken or twisted and wreckage was strewn over a quarter of a mile. The legal problem was to ascertain if the oak was dead, for if this was the case, the mayor might be held responsible for the damage. This was indeed a fine subject of contention, for the damage was estimated at over £300 and nobody expected that the mayor would cheerfully pay so large a sum. When was a tree quite dead? Who was to judge this delicate question? What experience had these two *gendarmes* in forestry? They took some notes about the condition of my two houses and went into animated details with M. Jollivet.

'How soon shall we have the current back?' I asked my friend M. Louette.

'Soon! Soon!' he answered. 'Luckily it's an important accident, affecting a main cable to Caen. In three days all should be mended.'

At lunch Matilda was still suffering from nerves, and the meal was not a success. I was vaguely concerned about Bobby, fearing he might catch cold in Paris. Suddenly M. Jollivet looked in to say that the turkeys were again attacking the ducks. We sprang up and rushed into the courtyard. The ducks, driven mad with fear, were huddled in a corner; the turkeys were barking raucously. We put them to flight and I went to the big house to make the beds.

My bedroom has two windows. One dominates the country to the east, the bar of Le Havre, the estuary of the Seine, and Deauville; the other faces south across my flower garden. A woodpecker with a crimson head as large as a parrot was slowly climbing up a pear-tree. It looked like some tropical bird in an enchanted forest. I watched it with a feeling of exhilaration,

computing it to be about a foot long. As the light caught its plumage, new colours appeared, chrome yellow and dark green. Suddenly a great noise arose from the courtyard, and when I rushed to the corridor window I saw one of my grown-up *wee-wees* on top of the injured *canette*, trying with her talons to gouge out her remaining eye. The *wee-wee* was thus indulging in the savagery of her Egyptian ancestors, and soon my poor little duck would be killed. I raced downstairs, and as I emerged breathless from the boiler-room, I saw the *berlou*, magnificent, his fan full out, his side wings gracefully curved, his features crimson with pride, watching his cruel sister with manly approval. This colour photograph was thrown at me as I passed. The *wee-wee*, her black feathers sinister in the now darkening afternoon, had the spread of an eagle. She was treading her victim, whose head flowed with blood. She did not move at my approach from her poised position. On the contrary, her talons sank deeper in. I threw her off her balance, and, grasping the talons in one hand and the bird's neck in the other, I twisted her with all my force.

'If you go on like that you 'll kill her!' shouted Matilda from her cottage door.

'What do you think I 'm trying to do?'

'If that 's the case,' she answered without pity, 'I 'll get a pair of scissors.'

Had I really intended to kill the bird? Anger blinded me. The *picote's* head suddenly drooped, and her claws, which only a few moments ago had been rigid and battle-drawn, now relaxed and gently pushed away the unfortunate duck as if in death the murderess was saying: 'Go now, I can't do you any more harm!'

Matilda had arrived with the scissors and the blood flowed warm on my bare arm. The turkey cock had watched the killing of his sister, fan out, throat gurgling, with the impassibility of the cowardly male. I hated him for it. I hated him as I would have hated an apache who might have watched a woman of the streets murdered in front of his eyes. I hated all the *picotes*. I hung this one by its talons to a branch of the pear-tree. Its head flopped down and its wings suddenly unfolded themselves in all their glory. A beam of light, shooting over the thatch, lit them up till they shimmered with unguessed colouring.

'Pluck it while it 's still warm,' advised Matilda. 'You 'll find that the feathers will come out easier.'

What surprised me most was that I had killed my *picote* so easily, I who each time there was a bird to be eaten asked Mme Beaudry to bleed it or took it to Mme Déliquaire. I was surprised and horrified. I remembered crying over the baby *picote* which had died in my bedroom that spring. I had killed this one in a fit of rage. I took the *canette* and looked at her poor head streaked with blood, and carrying her to the fire repeated my treatment of cotton wool and cold tea. Then I put her back in the courtyard and unhooked the dead *picote* from the pear-tree.

I plucked her in the big room. Before I had finished Matilda came to tell me she had made me something hot to drink. My cold, with the approach of night, was heavier.

On my return the first thing I noticed was the turkey's long neck which, hanging over the side of a folding stool, had taken the shape of a question mark. In the failing light she seemed to be reproaching me for having killed her. My sentimental nature was nearly getting the better of me, when I recalled her talons scooping out blood and flesh from the poor little *canette's* head. 'Oh, no!' said I. 'She was too cruel!' I sat down and started to throw more feathers into the fire. What with the milk, the cotton wool, the tea-leaves, the mud from my boots, the little feathers that flew in eddies round my hair, the chimney full of twigs and white ash, the big room was a sorry sight, and in less than half an hour I would have to put candles by the hearth. I delivered the dead bird to Matilda and gave my *canette* a last meal of bread and milk.

Night came down suddenly. No housework done, no telephone. The storm had abated and everything was calm round the house. The evil deeds of the day were finished. I went to bed with Baba, the white and brown kitten, who slept angelically in my arms. There was no radio, only a dripping candle.

The next morning the *canette's* eyes were covered by a horrible froth. I caught hold of her and placed her in the fold of my left arm as Mlle Lefranc, the nurse, used to do with Bobby when he was newly born, and with my right hand I dabbed it clean.

Her head did not throb any more. The fever was gone. Her webbed feet were cool. Her long neck rubbed against my cardigan as her head bobbed up and down intelligently. She understood that the cotton wool was good for her. She could hear water dripping from the tap in the kitchen and was intrigued. Then she abandoned herself to the warmth of my body and the crackle of the fire and slept like the mayor after lunch, dreaming, I expect, of puddles and ducklings. I gave her some bread dipped in warm milk and took her into the courtyard where I changed the water in the pool. She waddled in and had a thorough bath. I had not dreamed of such a miraculous recovery.

That evening I gave my *canette* her last poultice, but as the weather had turned cool and I thought she might catch cold I brought her very close to the fire. Steam rose from her head and neck. She looked like a powder-puff after it has been washed in warm water and hung up in front of the fire to dry. And like the powder-puff, the down began to fluff up, delightfully pink and soft. She was happy to be looked after, to be fussed over. The pekinese was at my feet. The kitten was curled up on the stool. The telephone was mended and the electricity people had just called to say we would have the lights on again before the end of the week.

VI

THE next morning, even before I had gone across to the cottage for breakfast, three men walking abreast, their persons encumbered with saws, sledgehammers, steel wedges, pulleys, and a rope, appeared at the top of the orchard. When they reached the first of the tall pear-trees they laid down their gear and, straightening their backs, lit cigarettes that glowed in the soft light of breaking dawn.

Being gloved, to save my hands, and booted because of the soaking grass, having just bravely started the motor under the thatched well roof, I went inquisitively towards them. Gradually I recognized M. Besnard with his spectacles, dark moustaches, and blue gardener's apron, his son Clément, blond, tall but pale since the Germans thrashed him, and a third gardener, their employee, burlier, wearing a woodman's axe in a leather belt.

We had finally marked a dozen pear-trees for cutting down. Most of them, of delightful forms, were about eighty years old, giving the orchard a Red Riding Hood appearance—thick trees and pretty cottage, haunted if not by a wolf, at least by many foxes. These trees, though every year laden with tiny fruit, were no longer of much use to us. Pear-jack had gone out of fashion. Most farmers were replacing their pear-trees with young apple-trees.

The one under which the gardeners had arranged their tools was dangerously near the high-tension wires, and I feared that one day it might do the same sort of damage as the mayor's oak.

I might, of course, have asked Déliquaire to uproot these trees, but though he would certainly have done so to oblige me, he had reached that philosophical frame of mind when he disliked doing anything which he did not consider absolutely necessary. I had therefore sent for Besnard and offered him the equivalent of two pounds for each tree, this price to include the sawing and the splitting of the trunks and branches into logs three feet long, and the binding of the twigs into bundles to light the fire in the big chimney.

There was little profit for him at that figure, but he was anxious for work, there being fewer villas to look after than in pre-war days. Most of the Edwardian houses with their once beautifully kept lawns and fine flower beds were now holiday camps for Parisian children. Whilst Besnard and I had been discussing the matter, Déliquaire came along with the milk, and I told him about our arrangement. Déliquaire drew in his breath noisily, and answered: 'I 'm not pitying you, ma'am.' By which he meant that, in his opinion, I was getting the better of the deal.

M. Besnard was not the sort of man to break his word. He commented:

'Ma'am Henrey has always dealt with us. There must be give and take. My father-in-law and I have always planted the apple-trees on the estate.'

'Have you uprooted big trees like these before?' asked my farmer.

'Not up here. Once or twice in the marshes.'

'Funny things,' he said. 'Roots as large as their trunks. Have you a pulley and tackle?'

'Yes, I 've all that.'

'Be careful how they fall,' said Déliquaire, rubbing his cheek. 'Take care of the apple-trees. There 's apple-trees everywhere. These here are worth, maybe, fifty or sixty pounds apiece. Tricky work, bringing down pear-trees.'

He shook us both by the hand, this rite being most important in meeting and parting, and departed with his milk.

'By the way,' M. Besnard called after him, 'we shall need a horse and cart for the logs?'

His voice remained on a pitch of interrogation.

Déliquaire turned round, and answered deeply:

'Of course!'

His reply was accompanied by a wide sweep of his free arm. Just as Mme Déliquaire never sent a beggar away, herself growing plump and rosy on her unruffled disposition, so her husband was always doing me little kindnesses he liked to perform out of satisfaction to his sense of grandeur. He made a good deal of money with his horse and cart, hiring it out by the half-day or the day, but Jacques always had to go with it. Déliquaire refused to let a stranger drive his horses.

Summer is lovely, but winter is the time to work. I was determined this year to supervise the cutting of wood and the planting of trees.

The gardener's mate, whose name I discovered to be Marcel, was at the top of the pear-tree sawing off branches, when three other men carrying ladders and cables, preceded by M. Louette, arrived at the gate. I greeted them with joy, and M. Louette promised that the era of candles would soon be over.

Matilda, having emerged in clogs and kerchief from the cottage, was waving to me, by which I surmised that breakfast was ready. I went back to the well, switched off the engine, and hurried indoors.

On my return to the orchard about an hour later Marcel, having sawn off all the branches, was perched on the summit of the pear-tree like a bear on the top of a pole, fastening a rope round the trunk. An electrician, wearing inwardly curved skis with spikes, had climbed to the summit of a wooden power pylon, and whilst tightening the cables was shouting to M. Louette, who was in a similarly exalted position nearer the house. All these men between earth and heaven portended an exciting day. Clément and his father were fixing pulleys and passing their end of the rope round two stout apple-trees. They explained that when they began to tug the device would magnify their efforts.

Marcel slid down the trunk and all three began to tug at the end of the rope. I ran back expecting the gaunt tree to crash, but we were disappointed. The electrician, having finished tightening his cables, climbed down the pole, and, with his legs wide apart because of the steel skis, came clumsily across the grass. He helped to tug. M. Besnard said:

'We shall have to dig deeper round the roots.'

I went up to make the beds, sweep the floors, polish the furniture, and do my hair. The big downstairs room, magnificently clean, smelt of burning apple logs. The farmyard was happy. I was able to do some writing until it was time for Matilda and me to lunch frugally. The gardeners, not allowed to leave anything underground, were digging very deep. They had uncovered four enormous roots, each nearly as fat as the trunk, and were sawing and hammering and splitting the knotty wood with iron wedges.

'If the work goes no faster than this,' thought I, 'M. Besnard will regret his bargain.'

Déliquaire had come along to finish scratching the apple-trees in my private orchard. I fancy he wanted to have a look at what was going on. Mme Louette, who could never resist following her husband, appeared at the garden gate in time for a cup of coffee. Not for a long time had my boggy home been so full of life. Mme Louette and I were sitting by the fire when George, the woodcutter, knocked at the door.

In appearance George was neither young nor strong. Short, clean-shaven, he had expressive eyes and a fine gift of persuasion. He and several other youths would go from farm to farm, hiring themselves out by the job. He had a new partner hiding modestly behind the gate. After a moment he beckoned this boy to meet me. I judged him to be nineteen or twenty, and I thought him extremely good-looking. They asked me if I had any trees to cut down, their eyes turning reprovingly in the direction of M. Besnard, who with an axe in his hand was walking slowly across the orchard, but though jealous, they remained polite and gallant.

These young woodcutters were considered sharp lads. Nobody denied their efficiency but all agreed they must be carefully watched. I had employed George and his brother to make my kitchen garden and fence it round. They had even cut down some oak-trees to make the gates. The speed of their work was unbelievable. They liked to agree to a price beforehand and then work every hour of the day till it was finished. Possibly I paid them more than I should have done. They may have boasted of it. They were most engaging and I, after all, was a woman. A woman is always apt to be lenient with a band of polite young men.

George said: 'We hoped, ma'am, you might give us one of your woods to tidy up. What with the Germans during the war and the farmers afterwards cutting down their timber because of the shortage of coal in the towns, M. le Carpentier at the château and yourself are almost the only people left with any wood.'

'I 've nothing to offer you this year,' I answered. 'Nothing, except——'

They smiled encouragingly.

'Except what, ma'am?'

'On the other side of the lane by the entrance gate there 's a piece of hilly pasturage called The Point. As you know, that belongs to me. There are tall elms all round it in the hedge. Two over there, the ones with the ivy growing right up to the summit, face a pretty half-timbered building in one of Ernest Poulain's fields. I have been wondering what would happen if they fell down.'

'It 's a nice day without any wind, ma'am, and you 're quite right to have them down. The elms in Normandy are in a bad way. Most of them are hollow at the base.'

'I know, but I hate the idea of cutting down trees.'

'These are a century old. They 'll fall of their own accord, and then they might cost you dear, ma'am. A building like the Poulains' is worth a million francs.'

'I suppose it is,' I admitted.

'There 's no firewood like elm, ma'am.'

'I know, but the truth is I don't want to spend any money.'

'And why should you, ma'am? The dealer will come along, measure up the trunk, and pay you cash. With that cash, ma'am, you would have enough, more than enough, to pay us to cut the head and branches into logs, lots of logs, so many they would stretch the whole length of your stable wall.'

'You mean I would have the logs for nothing?'

'Yes, ma'am, and a little money besides.'

'Very well, but you must only cut down the two trees in front of M. Poulain's half-timbered building. None of the others.'

'May we start right away, ma'am?'

'This evening?'

'Yes, ma'am, this evening.'

The two elms proved to be seventy feet tall. When later I arrived with the pekinese to examine them, the hilly part of the field on which they lay smelt delightfully of sap, the weather being mild as spring.

George and his good-looking partner had brought two men to help them, strange characters, dark-haired and sinister, wearing seamen's caps and crimson kerchieves round their necks. The trees had always been hidden by a wide-leaved ivy, most popular with goats, which had now been hacked off, revealing the trunks, dark and impressive, ready for the chains. The head and boughs were already cut and split into eighteen-inch logs neatly stacked on the grass. As a general rule in Normandy logs are cut a yard long, but elm, being knotty and hard, is the exception. They would be a little small for the hearth, but Matilda would be glad of them for the stove in the cottage.

Woodcutters charge more for elm logs than those of other trees. George asked for the equivalent of six shillings and eightpence a *stère*, which is a cubic yard—in other words, three feet in all directions. It is the simplest thing, therefore, to discover the number of *stères* by measuring the length of the stack.

Victor Rabu, a merchant from Trouville, offered me thirty shillings a cubic yard for the trunks, and as he estimated there were five cubic yards, I would receive from him the equivalent of seven pounds ten shillings. The head and branches, according to George, would produce twenty-four *stères* of logs which in labour would cost me eight pounds.

Though one of the elms was quite healthy, the other, most directly over the Poulains' half-timbered building, was hollow at the base. I had therefore been wise to take warning by the mayor's misadventure.

Three other elms in the hedge of equal age and height appeared upon examination hollow, and under persuasion from George and Victor Rabu I ordered these to come down as well. I hoped thus to have fifty *stères* of wood at no expense whatever.

This curious accountancy was one of the results of having to run the farm on a no-money basis. Our home orchard gave us butter and milk, our eggs paid for the grain, our trees for the firewood; we rented some orchards to pay the income tax, others to produce meat and bread and the various necessities of life. Our apple crop not merely gave us cider and apple-jack but also a considerable sum for planting young trees and keeping the estate in running order.

Compared to the swift work of George's gang, the Besnard trio proceeded slowly, continually looking surprised. They had obviously not realized the immense difficulties of taking eighty-year-old pear-trees up by the roots. Towards the end most of the hard work was left to Marcel. Besnard during this time measured up the orchard to find suitable places to plant a dozen young apple-trees which he had ordered from the Maine-et-Loire. In principle we planted our orchards with trees ten yards distant from each other, but occasionally when an apple-tree was reaching its sixtieth year and gently dying, a young tree would be planted near it to step into the ancestor's place. The young trees would be seven years old when they came from the nursery.

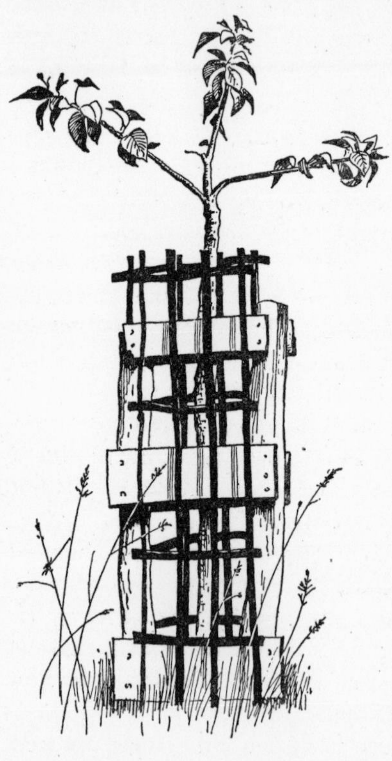

This gradual replanting was a work of love. One had to think in terms of Bobby. The trees Besnard would soon plant would grow up with my son. He was nine. They were seven. At twenty youth and trees would reach their full vigour. At sixty they would have to think about retiring in favour of their offspring.

For my part I needed some immediate satisfaction. I had asked Besnard to order eighteen tall rose-trees from the Loire for the garden in front of my house, two more peaches for the wall under my bedroom window where they did so remarkably well, and a number of greengage-trees and large black plums which in Normandy they call *Monsieur*.

These were the luxuries which, in my opinion, made my muddy existence pleasurable. One afternoon, just when I had washed and set my hair, I saw Besnard arriving with my rose-trees. Fourteen of them were planted like little soldiers in a newly dug bed outside the windows of the big room. I would have liked to go out, but because my hair was still damp I feared to catch cold again, so I opened the window and engaged M. Besnard in conversation.

'The wireless predicts another cold snap,' I said. 'It seems colder already. The tits have eaten all the bread and butter I hung outside the window.'

'It looks to me more like rain,' said M. Besnard from behind his spectacles and blue apron.

'More mud, I suppose,' said I.

'Whatever the weather is,' said M. Besnard, 'we always complain.'

'Yes,' I agreed. 'We ought to be glad enough to be in good health and about. That 's the only thing that matters.'

'I, more than anybody,' said M. Besnard, pushing a clod of earth off his shining spade with a stick. 'It 's a dreadful thing living with a dying man!'

'How does M. Duclos sleep at nights?'

'He sleeps because they give him drugs, but lately he complains of his stomach, though if it isn't that it 's something else. He hardly eats and so he is always cold. All day he 's with my wife in the kitchen, getting in her way, but then he 's so lonely, so afraid to be by himself, and I suppose her presence compensates for the loss of poor Mme Duclos. The daughter recalls the wife. What gets her is the heat. She has to keep the place so hot. Sometimes, not to faint, she leaves the door ajar or opens an inch of window, but immediately the old man shouts: "Close the window! Shut the door! You 're making us cold, deathly cold!" She hasn't the heart not to obey. The cold for him is the cold of the tomb. And so she closes the window and the door and goes on feeling faint. He was always so active. It 's a shame to see him shuffling round the kitchen, watching her pathetically in case she might put it in her head to go off and buy a packet of salt, and leave him. I feel sorry for her. She misses her mother. It wasn't that Mme Duclos went out much, especially towards the end, but they did like to gossip. They understood each other. That 's the way it was.'

'I can well imagine that,' I answered.

From the direction of The Point came a mighty rending sound as another elm crashed against the hill. Marcel, who was in the high branches of a cherry-tree, pruning it, jumped as if nervous about his own position. I said to M. Besnard:

'Poor Marcel had a shock!'

'Those elms coming down make a big noise,' said M. Besnard thoughtfully. 'Have you been round to see them to-day, ma'am?'

'No,' I answered. 'I 've just washed my hair, and secondly, from what my mother tells me, the Poulains' pony is loose, prancing up and down the lane. I think I would be afraid.'

'Funny,' said M. Besnard, puzzled. 'Don't you ride?'

'I wish I did. When I was in a position to learn, I was not young enough. I think one should start as a child.'

'On the other hand, you 've doubtless been up in an aeroplane, ma'am?'

'Oh, yes, many times.'

'Well, that seems to me brave. I would like to have a try, but Mme Besnard would be afraid. Marcel up there in the cherry-tree has been in one, coming back from Germany where he was a prisoner. I asked him to explain what it felt like, but he couldn't remember any of the emotions.'

'There are not too many, M. Besnard. I think you would be all right.'

'Things happen curiously,' he went on. 'A gentleman and a lady who own a fine villa here called ten days ago to bid us good-bye before returning to their estate in the Indre. My father-in-law was particularly touched. I think there were tears in his eyes and you should have seen him, so frail, standing in front of his gracious customers twiddling his cap between his poor fingers. He said it was very considerate of them to call on their gardeners. Last night we read in the newspaper that while they were standing with twenty-five other people at a level crossing near their home, the woman in charge gave them permission to cross. The gentleman arrived safely on the other side, but his lady and their daughter were caught up by a Micheline cutting past at nearly seventy miles an hour, and from what the paper said they had a job to find enough to put in a coffin!'

M. Besnard spat in his hand, took up his spade again, and added inconsequently:

'These young rose-trees will need props. If you 'll be so kind, ma'am, I 'd like to go to your small wood and cut two dozen hazel sticks.'

Perhaps because of thinking about Mme Besnard spending so many hours of the day with her doomed father, I asked suddenly:

'Is your wife a strong woman, M. Besnard?'

'Yes,' he said thoughtfully, picking a piece of dead wood off a rose-tree, 'except during the war. She had Clément when she was eighteen, with the forceps, and afterwards she was never quite well, but while the Germans were here, with the standing about in the queues, not feeling at all good, she went to see a doctor who told her she was beginning her change of life. Her change of life, and she was only thirty-six! Nobody believed it. It was insulting a fine young woman! We sent her to another doctor, who gave her so many drugs to take that there were not hours enough in the day to take them. Another prescribed injections, jabbing needles into her arms. She went to Cabourg, to Trouville, to Lisieux. "Ah!" she exclaimed at last. "I 've done with doctors! I 'd rather die than see another. They hurt me too much!" But she was getting no better and a cousin of ours said to her one evening: "There 's a new doctor at Caen who is quite remarkable for that sort of thing. You really must consult him." "Oh, no!" she cried. "Not for anything! They are all alike. I said I would not see another, and I will not. I 'm tired of being mauled about." But you know what it is, ma'am, we put it to her that she should go for our sakes, and as we never gave her any more peace, she consented, and we took the coach to Caen, she having to stand all the way because of the German soldiers who only gave up their seats to women they thought worth while.

'This doctor at Caen, when he had examined her, said: "Well, I did not hurt you, did I?" "No," she answered, "you didn't hurt me." "Because," said he, "if you had told me the contrary, you would have been the first, for never, never have I hurt a woman!" There was a sort of ecstasy in his voice. He spoke like a visionary. I suppose there are doctors like that. "Now," said he, "though I did not hurt you, I shall tell you exactly what is wrong," and in very clear language which I shall not try to repeat he told her about a fibroma which would have to be removed with the knife, but first, while she was waiting, he would give her an injection to prevent her from having any more pain. Ten days later, ma'am, she was feeling so well that she did not want to have the operation, but he said to her: "By now you should have faith in me." She melted at that and went obediently to Caen, and since then she has never been ill again.'

'Who was the doctor?' I asked.

'It would be no use if I were to give you his name,' said Besnard. 'The Germans came one morning to take him away. He has not been heard of since.'

'The brutes!' I said.

VII

My husband and Bobby arrived home well pleased with their visit to London. The film star had recorded a talk about what he did on his farm in Normandy, mentioning specially Michel Gilles and André Poulain. It was to be broadcast in French by the B.B.C. at 9.30 on Saturday night.

The three other elms which George had cut down did not yield as much lumber for the mills as I had hoped. The largest was hollow for a distance of two yards from the base. The second, when the ivy was removed, proved thinner than it had looked at first, whilst in the third, half-way up the trunk, there had been at one time, perhaps twenty years ago, a swarm of bees which had been burned out, and this, with the passing of time, had done much to kill the head.

My hopes of balancing the cost of the logs by the sale of the lumber accordingly diminished. I was tempted to bring down more elms in an effort to restore the balance of lumber in my favour. Three more trees, for instance, with healthy trunks and not many top branches would quickly have done it, but if, on the other hand, I were to strike unlucky again, I would be plunged into debt!

The idea of throwing my seventy-foot-tall elms on a baccarat table filled me with shame. I decided therefore to keep them as so much money in the bank, even if, like the three I had just cut down, they were mostly hollow.

I had another reason to be careful.

That morning Jacques had arrived with the horse and cart to take the pear-tree logs from where they lay next to the filled-up holes in the orchard, to the north side of the well where they would be built up into a long wall six feet high. After breakfast, making a tour of inspection, I discovered Clément and Marcel helping Jacques to fill the cart with logs whilst Bobby sat on the horse. After the usual exchange of courtesies, Jacques said that George was also in need of the cart to bring in the logs from The Point, those which they had made from the second batch of elms, but that he could not place himself at their disposal till the next day. We could hear George and his partner wielding their axes rhythmically.

The logs from the first two elms, in a double row because they were eighteen inches long instead of three feet, stood against the north wall of the stables, and a fine sight they made. The

previous night, George, reporting that his stack measured twenty-seven *stères*, three more than he had estimated, asked me for several thousand francs on account, which, knowing that he and his companions lived precariously from week to week and had furnished rooms in the village to pay, I gave him.

'I imagine it will take you the best part of to-morrow to bring home the elm logs,' I said to Jacques whose plaited whip was curled round his youthful neck. 'George says he has at least another twenty-seven *stères* up there.'

Jacques blew air into his rosy cheeks and answered:

'We won't be so long if they are anything like the *stères* against your stable wall.'

'It won't that!' echoed Clément, laughing.

'Oh!' I exclaimed. 'Have you measured them? Are we short?'

'I haven't measured them,' answered Jacques. 'I haven't a yard-measure.

'There 's a tape-measure in my work-basket,' I answered. 'Shall I fetch it?'

'I don't think it would be of any use,' he answered. 'Those lads wouldn't trick you in that way. It would be too obvious. Exteriorly the stack looks fine, but if you look inside, up against the wall, there 's little more than air and twigs. I know. I was there when they did it.'

He threw the reins over the mare's mane, kicked a log under a wheel, and advanced slowly towards the buildings. When we had reached the wall in question he uncurled his whip and, pushing the handle between the logs, showed me the holes against the rough cement.

'If I were to pull this stack to bits and build it up as it ought to be,' he said, 'it would not measure more than twenty *stères*.'

'That 's right,' said Clément. 'You would have done better to have them stack the wood in the open so that you could walk round it, like the one my father and I are making for you with the pear logs.'

'What a nuisance!' I exclaimed. 'I almost wish you had not told me. They 'll be furious.'

Jacques shrugged his shoulders.

'And here! And here!' said Clément, walking slowly along the wall and poking a stick through the cracks.

'Why didn't you tell me yesterday?' I asked.

Jacques pouted.

'We couldn't, not in front of them,' he said.

I foresaw that this piece of trickery would upset my peace of mind for the whole day. My highly strung character dislikes anything of a ruffling nature. I was already, contrary to my desires, starting to feel indignant, and I recalled with vexation that the previous evening Bobby, hidden from view by a pile of faggots, had heard one of them refer to me as 'the bitch.'

I did not at all feel like going to The Point and accusing them of dishonesty. They might insult me or think out some particularly unpleasant form of vengeance. On the other hand the Déliquaires and the Duclos would now have their eyes on me. I did not dare let the matter drop.

I went slowly to the top of the field, and as I approached the gate the sound of their axes grew louder. I entered the lane and soon, through a break in the hedge which they had made when felling the trees, I saw them both, stripped to the waist, the red winter sun lending to their naked bodies, pearly with sweat, the high colour of bronze. The elder of the two particularly held my attention. His axe, held high above his head, his feet wide apart, was being brought down repeatedly on a wide ring of the trunk upon which five, six, seven times the shining blade made not the least impression. With each downward movement of the arms he appeared to spit out all the breath in his lungs with a horrible sepulchral sound, but whether he did this on purpose, or whether it was the effect of his immense effort, I had not the experience to tell. I marvelled to see how the axe came down, at each swing, on the same part of the wood. The piece of trunk, too heavy to move, yet had elasticity. Eight . . . nine . . . ten. Automatically I counted the mighty strokes. At the eleventh, as the lungs hissed with an excess of effort, the axe split the wood in two. One piece went rolling down towards the lane.

George wiped the perspiration from his forehead. His features were blotched with pink and I remembered with a twinge how many of his young comrades, exerting themselves beyond reason, catching too easily cold after being too hot, had become wrecks, merely fit for the sanatorium.

Why did these young men drive their bodies at such a furious rate? They made big money sometimes, when work came their way, but seeing the flush on George's face, I felt immensely sorry for them. The younger one who was scarcely grown up had two children—two children already and a wife hanging round his neck. She had apparently come to fetch him at the farm last night, which was the reason for the request for an advance. George's wife had come also.

They looked my way, and before coming down put their shirts on out of politeness and because of the wind that was treacherous. I said to George:

'You came to ask me to hire you and I agreed, against everybody's advice. Down at the farm some people say your elm logs are a bit loose towards the wall. Unless you want to make me look a fool, it might be a good idea to stack them again. I didn't expect you would do that to me, like a barrow man who put a layer of good fruit over the bad. I can't believe it was your idea, George!'

'We stacked the wood here, on The Point, first,' said George, looking down at his feet. 'It 's here we measured it.'

'The two men you employed stacked the wood they had cut here, and you paid them just half what I paid you. Their stacks were honest. You saw to that. When the wood was brought to my place you restacked it loose to have a double profit.'

'Maybe it 's a little loose, but not all that, ma'am.'

'I 'll tell you what,' I said. 'I 'll make a bargain with you. Take down the wood and stack it right, and I 'll pretend it never happened. I wouldn't even let it affect things if I wanted to employ you again.'

He looked up.

'We 'll stack it again, ma'am, before night.'

'Come and tell me when it 's done.'

On my return to the orchard I discovered Clément putting corsets round the freshly planted apple-trees and said, a trifle sadly:

'I suppose you 'll be glad to leave us. I am afraid it was harder cutting down those pear-trees than you expected.'

'Oh, no,' he answered quickly, 'I 'm not so glad as that it 's finished, ma'am. Where we are going to-morrow will be harder. Lopping off branches from very high trees—with ropes.'

'That 's funny!' I exclaimed. 'It never struck me you did much work of that kind. I imagined you more often pruning rose-trees.'

'Here there 's room,' he said, allowing his eyes, blue and dreamy, to roam across the orchard. 'At least one can see what one is doing, but in gardens round villas when one can hardly move! In summer it 's even worse. The trouble is that people who own villas often don't think to trim their trees in winter, and then, arriving in July or August, suddenly find a branch or two pushing in through the bedroom window. They send for us to trim the tree, and the leaves being thick one risks kneeling on a dead branch. That 's what happened to me on the 18th of August last. I fell. The branch swivelled round and cracked me on the head. I lay on the grass a quarter of an hour unconscious. Getting well again was not so hard, but when I had to climb up a tree again I was so afraid, that seeing my father underneath, I called to him like I used when I was a little child. I cried, I think. It was silly.'

'Not so silly,' I said.

'Oh,' he exclaimed, twitching his fingers, 'since that 18th of August, everything with us has gone wrong! It was as if suddenly the luck of a long, long time had turned. First, it was a cousin at Caen, a real genius. We all loved him. He had cancer of the lungs and was gone in six months. Then it was my granny, Mme Duclos. You know, Ma'am Henrey, she had so often rapped me over the knuckles, so often kissed me, that I could not believe it when she went. Then there was my father's mother who died at Falaise at the age of ninety-three, so tough that she never complained when, during the invasion, she had to hide for six days in a pigsty. No, what upset her was that the French or the English or the Americans—she was not sure which—stole all the linen from her house—the linen she had woven as a little girl at Elbœuf.'

'I saw your mother yesterday in the village,' I said. 'She told me that your grandfather, M. Duclos, had slunk off to the hothouse in the morning, and by lunch had planted all the carnation cuttings!'

'He 's amazing!' agreed Clément. 'It 's the spring-like weather that gets him. Already, a week ago, when the sun came out for the first time after the storms, he said to us one morning after breakfast: "As you 're all off to do a job at Blonville, I shall prune the vine. By the way, Marcel, do you mind lifting the ladder for me. I can't think why, but I find it a little heavy!" When father heard that he gave me something to do in the hothouses so that I should be around in case anything happened, but my grandfather pruned the vine without help, and I tell you, ma'am, it 's a ticklish job at the best of times.

'You know, it will be a terrible thing when he goes. I don't know whether you remember him well enough, but he was a real terror for giving orders. Even though he and my father discussed a thing beforehand, it was M. Duclos who told each of us what to do. I was thinking the other day that soon it will be my father and I who will talk things over beforehand. We do already, but we can't get used to it.

'It 's the same thing with my grandmother. In her beautiful hand she wrote out every estimate and bill, and never once did she make a mistake, either in favour of a customer or in favour of us. She spent hours, poring over figures at her high desk, her "ministerial" desk we called it, while mother went shopping or made the dinner, but if ever a customer walked in, however busy she was, she gave the impression, and I 'm not sure it wasn't true, that she was quite delighted to be disturbed. And what a dressmaker, ma'am! She made mother's dresses and all the shirts for us men. One feels the loss of her somehow.'

Since his return from London Bobby had been very busy in the carpenter's shop, and now, by the way he came to ask me to fetch the cider with him, I guessed he had invented something new.

A quarter of an hour before Matilda served lunch, it was his task to take a pitcher to the cider press and fill it from the barrel, and this walk through the prettiest part of the orchard laid so many temptations in his way that often the roast, exactly done, was obliged to await his return. For instance, at the foot of one of the oldest pear-trees, which was much too beautiful to remove, there was a grassy hole shaped like the mouth of a cauldron into which every year, according to a tradition so old that I would not know how it began, the farmers, after having made the cider, emptied two or three cartfuls of squashed apple husks. This picturesque spot was the rendezvous of the chickens, the ducks, and the turkeys on the way down to the stream which ran, so clear and cool, over rocks and moss, between high trees, at the bottom of the orchard. The members of our farmyard scratched amongst this brown sediment for apple pips, and the cocks, with their radiant plumage, could be seen strutting in front of their favourite hens, and with infinite grace, bowing and dancing, presenting them with the choicest morsels to eat. Here also these magnificent birds would occasionally fight in what I have known to prove mortal combat, with all the hens and turkeys ranged in a semicircle. I have often thought that what binds one most to Normandy is its prodigality. Nothing is ever made to yield its utmost. There is too much grass for the cows. The pigs roam from orchard to orchard, nobody caring. Some mother turkeys took their flocks for expeditions two miles distant, and if night overtook them, would sleep in the high branches of a tree. Our ducks paid visits to ducks on other farms, which in turn called ceremoniously on ours.

Holding the pitcher and the huge key to the vault, my son capered lightly in front of me. He said:

'It 's to do with the stream. You 'll be surprised.'

'A boat?'

'More complicated than that. It works. It will go night and day.'

'A waterfall?'

'Of course not. There is a waterfall already. Shut your eyes and think. First, the stream, coming from the direction of our wood, widens to make a little lake in which Mme Gilles's ducks swim. Then the water becomes clear, hurrying past white boulders we use as stepping-stones to go to the Déliquaires'. After that the stream plunges down to the lower level to run between elm and ash towards the Poulains' orchard. Now do you remember?'

He had stopped and was looking up questioningly into my face.

'Yes,' I agreed, 'there must be a waterfall, but the branches are so entangled.'

'So as there is a waterfall already, it is not that I've made.'

'An aqueduct?' I suggested. 'To water one of the young apple-trees M. Besnard has just planted.'

'No,' he said, interested, 'but why do you say that?'

'Say what?'

'About the aqueduct?'

'I was thinking of the story Jean Jacques Rousseau tells at the beginning of his confessions, that when he was a little boy of your age M. Lambercier, his tutor, planted a walnut-tree.'

'Yes? And so?'

My son often broke into what I was saying, with this breathless two-pronged interrogation, to show he was interested and that I was not going fast enough.

'Round the foot of the walnut-tree M. Lambercier dug a trench into which, night and morning, he poured a little water. Jean-Jacques, seeing all this, decided to do the same thing, and so about eight feet from the venerable walnut he planted a young willow, and, like M. Lambercier, made a trench round the foot of it. The trouble was to water the willow, for Jean-Jacques was not allowed to fetch any from the river, and so he devised a pipe-line covered over with earth which would bring to his willow some of the water destined for M. Lambercier's walnut. That evening M. Lambercier poured a bucket of water into his trench round the walnut. Jean-Jacques was standing with his back to the willow to hide it, but when he saw the water flowing into his secret passage he gave such a cry of joy that M. Lambercier looked up and, with a spade, destroyed the invention and the willow, crying out: "An aqueduct! An aqueduct!"'

'No,' said my son meditatively, 'I have not made an aqueduct.'

'A water wheel?'

'Not a wheel, but a mill like the one Landry made in Mme George Sand's story. You remember how Sylvinet found it after his twin brother had been sent to work on another farm, and it made him cry?'

'Why, yes, of course, but I always imagined a water mill had a wheel?'

'Now listen, mother,' exclaimed my son earnestly, showing me the palm of his hand, which is a Norman gesture he had picked up in some way from birth, 'my edition of *La Petite Fadette* has a picture of the mill. It 's from that I have modelled mine, and I don't think I would know how to make a wheel.'

He was walking backwards, preceding me. The water gurgled. When we reached the thick mud, churned by the cows when they came to drink, he turned sharply, and using his hand to cut the air in front of him as with a knife, he exclaimed:

'Now, look!'

He had taken one of George's elm logs, curiously shaped, and jutting out from what for all the world looked like a tower which he had taken pains to thatch, was an arm with four blades turning briskly in the sunlit water, which tumbled in a clear cascade from the boulders to the deep labyrinths partly hidden by the roots of mighty trees.

'Bravo!' I cried. 'Here, at least, is something to be proud of!'

He answered with satisfaction, plunging his hands in the water to verify the foundations of his structure:

'Yes, it 's certainly like the one in *La Petite Fadette*.'

At that moment our ducks, arriving from the orchard, took to the pool just above the boulders, and a beautiful thing it was to see the possessiveness of their action. They knew it to be theirs. They swum round proudly, contentedly, looking to right and to left, as if to make sure that no change had taken place in the disposal of the reeds or floating bark since their last visit. My *canette* was not only well again—she had recovered the use of *both* eyes. I admit that this statement may sound fantastic. Matilda first pointed out to me the sudden reappearance of the eye I felt certain had been gouged out, a shiny bead at first, then a fully wide-awake jewel of living intelligence. I can merely conjecture that the wound had in some mysterious way been inflicted so near the eye, temporarily hiding it, that I mistook the one for the other, or else it was a miracle. The nursing back to life of my duck gave me one of my most poignant satisfactions. Achievement comes so seldom. For a woman of intelligence the repetitive actions of life are apt to leave her with a terrible feeling of uselessness—the getting up each morning, the lighting of fires, the making of beds. Possibly this explains why we have bouts of depression more frequently than men. In giving life back to my duck, I had the elation of having done something creative. I fear less being laughed at for this confession since discovering how many farmers' wives in Normandy feel sentimentally about their animals. Mme Déliquaire, sweet soul, was not an exception.

We walked to the thatched building, Bobby turning the key in the lock and pulling the heavy door by a piece of string. It creaked, and against our cheeks blew a freshness of humid air, of sawdust, and casks seeped in apple juice. As Bobby drew the cider he tasted some from under the cherry-wood tap. Though a month had passed since Jacques had made it, we were surprised to find it still dark, sweet, and cloudy.

Towards five, after having written letters nearly all the afternoon, I came down to find a big fire in the low room and the kettle whistling from a dangerous position astride two logs. I was immediately told that George had undone all the wood and had now rebuilt it in two parallel ramparts which, owing to tight packing, had diminished the measure by six *stères*. A few minutes later George came to ask me for some more money. I told him he must first bring in the wood from the three elms which he and his companions had been cutting earlier in the day. His features were white and set. Jacques Déliquaire, Clément, and Marcel had watched the demolition of the elm logs, rejoicing at this sullen avowal of guilt. I felt no elation at my victory, for they had boasted in my son's hearing that they would yet get the better of me. Nevertheless I accompanied George to the stable wall and exclaimed, laughing, impressed myself at the difference:

'Amazing, George! A real conjuring trick! Well, let's not talk any more about it.'

He made a gesture of the hands as if to bewail a matter he could really not be held responsible for, and added that he would be back early next day with his partner.

I sent Jacques back with a message to his father, saying that if he cared to listen to Bobby's broadcast, we would be very flattered. We also invited Mme Déliquaire, though knowing she would not change her strict rule of going to bed at eight o'clock.

Bobby had previously warned the Poulains, who had a radio of their own, that André was going to be mentioned.

Encouraged by the pleasure *Treasure Island* had given us, my husband had brought back from London a dozen books to read aloud by the fire in the evening. We had some difficulty in settling happily into a successor. *Kidnapped* we started, but I know not why, our mood for brigs, pistols stuck into pockets, knotty bludgeons, case-knives, horrible faces, and still more horrible oaths had passed. *King Solomon's Mines* had insufficient feminine interest for me. We abandoned it after fifty pages and plunged gratefully into *Pride and Prejudice* and *Evelina*, both of which, I was glad to notice, enchanted my son.

If I mention this matter of reading aloud it is merely to illustrate the peacefulness of our evenings—round the fire with Baba, the brown and white kitten, which slept for hours on end on a folding stool. We grilled rump steaks on the hot embers and toasted long strips of French bread which we thickly covered with butter. We all three felt, probably in different ways, that this period was as good as we were ever likely to have. For two of us, having age and experience, our intelligence, pointing to the example of others, suggested that moments of calm are seldom of long duration. I would have liked to plan against the future. Though I had rich land upon which many cows grazed, it would have been nice to have a cow of my own, to milk morning and night, to look after when it calved, to hear in the dark against the side of the house.

The looking after a cow would have given me the illusion of holding tighter to a good fortune I never quite believed in. My son's success dazzled but frightened me. The fact that in 1940 I had lost not only the farm, but all my linen, my books, and hats and dresses, my pictures and photographs, my most personal treasures, had taught me in a way I could never forget that what we hold to-day can disappear in a night. What I owned on that sunny July morning when the roses bloomed in my garden, was gone completely the next day. No woman was less sure of success, therefore, than I. In my girlhood I was brought up on stories of women who, though poor, were rich because they owned a cow on the field in which they lived A herd of cows did not seem to me as certain a bulwark against sudden distress as a single one. Doubtless a herd is impersonal, whereas one cow, which I could handle and milk, was different.

This cow I could have had any day for the asking. I was prepared to get up when it was still dark to milk it. The work it would have given me would have prevented me from so often feeling useless. It would have been nothing to pass the milk through the electric separator, to have made the butter. But a cow argued a pig, indeed made it imperative, in order not to waste the whey. There would have been piglets and calves, and soon I would be wanting to take back all my land from Déliquaire to give full scope to a model farm.

I had only to look at my diary to realize the impossibility of this dream. Ahead of me were two important engagements in town; for one of them I would wear the dress Mme Delanghe had made me for the Command Performance when I had presented Bobby to the Queen. I would go to the hairdresser on my way through Paris, do my hands, wear my jewels. And who, during these three or four days of metamorphosis, would milk my cow and plod through two feet of mud to look after my private pig? Matilda's hands were crippled with rheumatism. She found it a sufficient effort to look after the farmyard and cook the meals. If it were just for once or twice, Mme Beaudry would milk my cow, but when Bobby was sent for to make his new film, who then would take my place? Last November, when Bobby and I had been in Paris during the dubbing of his film in French, we had gone one Sunday by car to the Petit Trianon at Versailles, walking all the forenoon in Marie Antoinette's model dairy farm, as pretty, as bewitching, or nearly so, as in her own time. There was nobody but ourselves. The ground was full of moss and fallen leaves and smelt magnificent. I had cried there, as if her suffering had been recent, and all the way home I was silent and afflicted.

We were reading *Evelina* when Déliquaire knocked at the door. He stood on the threshold wearing a sou'wester and holding a lantern which made him look as if he had walked out of the past. He said he had the Italian influenza, but that it was better and his wife had sent him to report on Bobby's broadcast.

He drew his lantern level to his face and, opening the little door, blew out the flame. I asked him what he would like, and he said China tea with lemon in it and some English biscuits. He hung the lantern to a nail on the beam of the low room and said, by an association of ideas, that it was a job milking the cows now that they were sleeping indoors. What he meant was that his cow-house was too small for his magnificent herd and that Mme Déliquaire and he were obliged to milk by the light of this same flickering lantern. I had myself been a witness to this picturesque scene only a few nights earlier and indeed it was strange and beautiful, making one think of the scene in Nazareth so many Christmases ago.

But Déliquaire, filling a teaspoon with tea and drawing the liquid into his mouth vigorously, said:

'What we need is electricity.'

Though only two orchards, with the stream in the middle, separated Cathedral Lane (the Poulains, Victor Duprez, and ourselves) from the road to Saint-Vaast (the Déliquaires, the Gilles, and Mme Beaudry), only those of us in Cathedral Lane had electricity. Victor Duprez had paid for the transformer which stood at the western extremity of his land, during the Occupation, and it had been made to serve our three farms. Déliquaire's farm remained as it doubtless was during the reign of Louis XIII. The Poulains, who this very week-end were inaugurating their electric milking apparatus, were the symbol of progress. The contrast was interesting. As both flourished exceedingly it was hard to tell which rested on the most solid basis.

'Lamps are picturesque,' I said, 'but electricity is cleaner.'

'I dare say half a dozen pylons would be sufficient to carry the cables from your house to mine, across the stream,' said Déliquaire almost aggressively, 'but I 'm told you won't have them on your orchards.'

'Who said that?'

'M. Louette says it is written somewhere in the town hall.'

'I don't see why it should be written anywhere. I merely told M. Louette that I would be stupid to allow the company to stud my land with pylons if the government were soon to electrify the road to Saint-Vaast. On the other hand, if it were a question merely of running some wires from me to you, as a temporary measure to save Mme Déliquaire a little work, I would be delighted.'

'We would have to pay,' said Déliquaire dubiously.

'I had to pay too,' I answered. 'So did the Poulains. As for M. Victor Duprez, I imagine it must have cost him a great deal of money.'

'To bring the electricity from you to me,' continued Déliquaire, gnawing at his biscuit which he held genteelly in my honour, 'would cost, M. Louette says, more than a hundred thousand francs.'

'The cost of a good cow,' I answered. 'It might be worth it.'

'Ah, but wait!' exclaimed Déliquaire, putting down his cup and saucer and preparing himself for an important explanation, 'it wouldn't be I who would pay. Oh, no! The landlord would have to pay. He charges me a high enough rent.'

'Surely not high enough to recuperate a hundred thousand francs!' I said, laughing. 'If I know anything about farm leases, you get the house for nothing.'

'The house is included with the orchard, of course,' he said, 'but I pay too much for the orchard.'

'Not so much as that,' I replied, 'for when we signed our lease the other day before Maître Vincent, you asked me to let you off a bit to make what you pay me the same as what you pay M. Sandret, the owner of your other orchards, and because I am a silly woman I agreed.'

'The landlord is always responsible for repairs to the house and buildings,' said Déliquaire, returning to the problem near his heart. 'Putting in electricity is his business.'

'That would certainly simplify matters.'

'He would not pay,' answered Déliquaire.

'If I am kind enough to allow the company to put pylons over the bottom of the orchard to take the current to your house, you at least could pay for the installation.'

'Ah, no,' said Déliquaire craftily. 'It wouldn't be right. I tell you what I shall do, ma'am. I shall ask M. Louette to bring the current across your land to my farm, and then he can distribute the light to the other people round about who will defray the expenses.'

'Ah, no!' I cried shrilly. 'That I will not, M. Déliquaire. Deface my fine orchards for you and Mme Déliquaire is one thing, but to do so for all the inhabitants of the road to Saint-Vaast, certainly not!'

He smiled at me with disarming affection.

'I knew it wouldn't work,' he said.

Matilda, Déliquaire, Bobby, and I listened to the voice on the radio, and when it came to the part about Mme Déliquaire teaching Bobby how to milk the cows and how, of all of them, the one known as Bouboule was his favourite, Déliquaire leaned forward in such excitement, his hand trembling so, that I thought he would drop the cup of freshly poured out tea which I had just given him.

'Bouboule!' he said, much impressed, when it was all over. 'Fancy M. Bobby mentioning Bouboule!'

I do not know why my son had such a curious love for this particular cow, which I recognized because of strange white markings that gave it the appearance of wearing one of the new tight-waisted corsets.

Déliquaire had risen and was rekindling the wick of his lantern.

'About Bouboule,' he said, 'that talk on the radio puts me in a bit of a fix. I was going to sell her owing to the fact that she takes so long to milk, and also she 's ten years old. But I reckon now that Bouboule is famous, almost a world character, I am afraid we shall have to keep her, Ma'am Henrey.'

VIII

LAST spring, for the first time, I had started to learn the names of the wild flowers. My ignorance had come to me, while picking them, as an unpleasant shock. It was as if I had discovered suddenly that I was inarticulate. I had taken a bunch of different flowers hurriedly to M. Beaudry who was planting seeds in the kitchen garden, and asked him to enumerate them. He leaned across his spade and said: 'Madam, they are like primroses but different.' I stamped my foot angrily and felt like throwing them in his face. 'You are a gardener,' I said, 'your son is a gardener. Don't you know the names of the different flowers?'

'They are not flowers,' he answered. 'They are wild flowers.'

I had sent to the London Library for books with illustrations in colour. Gradually I became as enthusiastic as a herbalist.

Going down the steep lane which leads to the village during this third week in January, the hedges were quite blue, and kneeling down on the moss I discovered a great quantity of periwinkles.

There was quite a crowd of women at the butcher's where Mme Vannier, from behind her copy-book in which she kept the accounts, was discoursing on the subject of cats. A woman had said: 'Mme Vannier, you should keep a dog,' to which she had answered:

'I don't like dogs, except perhaps Mme Trémois's dog Bobby, who comes round here when he is tired of looking at cabbages and eggs. When our garden gate is closed the wretch rings the bell with his paw, and though when I hear it I suspect him, he catches me every time.'

'You see,' said the woman, 'if you like one dog, you like them all.'

'No,' objected Mme Vannier, 'I love cats. I have loved them ever since, as a very young woman, I was in service in Paris.'

M. Vannier smiled behind his sharp knife. What was nice

about him was that he never laughed at his wife's stories, but looked understanding.

'What happened when you were in service in Paris, Mme Vannier?'

'The lodge-keeper had a cat which died while having kittens, and only one lived, which was going to be put down the lavatory, when I pleaded for it. I took it up to my bedroom on the sixth floor and fed it with a toy feeding bottle, the sort they sell for dolls, and in due course it grew up fine and sleek. The cook being agreeable, the lady of the house gave me permission to bring it down to the kitchen and it never left me. Since then I 've had a child, but I can tell you that I 've never so much had the impression of being loved as by that kitten whose life I had saved.'

'They are pleasant to have about the house,' said the woman.

'It 's not that,' Mme Vannier went on. 'Not that only, I mean. One day the cat jumped up on a high ledge. Somebody came into the room, pushing open the door violently, and the cat, being afraid, jumped down, but in doing so upset a bottle which, falling quicker and breaking on the stone floor, ripped open its belly. I took it round in a blanket to the veterinary surgeon, who put stitches in and bandaged it up like a baby. Seeing how at night it kept scratching the bandage, I knitted it a pair of pants. But it died.' Mme Vannier wiped her eyes, and added: 'I still have the—the little thing I knitted for it, amongst my relics.'

'There!' said M. Vannier quietly. 'Who is next?'

When I had bought the meat I went to Mme Trémois to sell her three dozen eggs, but as she was engaged I looked round the shop as one does on such occasions. Mme Trémois kept her money in a cash box at the extreme end of the long table on which she displayed her modest goods, and most customers, while they were waiting for their change, used to edge up to her and enjoy a few moments' gossip. I was unable to recognize the woman all in black who was now talking to Mme Trémois in a low voice, but once or twice, as I pretended to examine some tinned peas, I was certain my name was pronounced. Out of politeness I pretended not to hear. After a few moments, having closed her purse, the customer whom I now saw to be wearing a very 1900 black felt hat and a worn but genuine astrakhan coat, said to me:

'I was just asking Mme Trémois if you were not the lady who had written *A Farm in Normandy*.'

I smiled politely and said that I had indeed written it. She went on:

'I went up to your place during the Occupation when I was in charge of the Relief Society. A young nephew of your farmer's had fallen from a cherry-tree. Perhaps you know about it?'

'Yes,' I answered, 'vaguely. So many tragedies happened there during my absence. The little boy died, I believe?'

'At Blonville. But, my dear madam, if you could bring me a copy of your book one day. Not that I speak English, but one can accomplish miracles with a dictionary.'

As soon as she was gone I said to Mme Trémois:

'If I 'm not mistaken that lady must be Mme Sauvalle. I have an idea my mother went to her for a docket to buy a mattress when, after the war, she had nothing at the farm to sleep on.'

'That 's right,' said Mme Trémois, counting the eggs.

'Hasn't she had rather a tragic life?'

Mme Trémois laughed ironically.

'*Rather* a tragic life! Dear. madam, that is a strange way to put it. Her husband was assassinated by a bandit in the Paris express between Lisieux and Serquigny! Her daughter and son-in-law were brutally murdered in a forest at night!'

A shiver ran down my spine.

'Where does she live?'

'At the "Commanderie," a great sleepy mansion surrounded by trees as you go up to your farm from the post office.'

'Is she then so wealthy?'

'Once upon a time extremely so, but now she is very poor.'

'Surely not so poor as all that if she lives in a large house?'

'She 's a saint, madam.'

'Do you know her well?'

'Nobody better. Originally my husband and I were her gardeners.'

'Oh, I understand.'

I was itching to ask her more, but while speaking she had counted the eggs and paid me, and Mme Sauvalle herself, in showing such a polite interest in *A Farm in Normandy*, had given me an excuse to call on her. I did my shopping that morning with my mind entirely centred on the little woman in black who bore on her frail shoulders the weight of such cruel memories. I wondered who she could be, and marvelled that I, who prided myself on knowing so much about what went on in the village, knew so little of the life of this tragic character.

At lunch I asked Matilda:

'Who exactly is Mme Sauvalle?'

'Except that she is charitable and pious,' answered Matilda, 'I

know nothing about her. I was to ask her for a mattress but she was away, and in the end I borrowed one from Mme Roginsky.'

The next evening, on my way down to post the letters, I found myself suddenly in front of the 'Commanderie.'

There were some white gates on which, roughly, in German, were written the words 'NO ENTRANCE,' a semicircular drive, some rose-beds and fine trees, and a tremendously tall end-of-last-century house with red brick façade and white balconies, Venetian shutters, and a magnificent tiled roof. My son, for once, had offered to come with me to the village, and I asked him: 'Shall we go in?' 'Why not?' he answered, and gently pushed open the gate. A bell, fixed to the woodwork by a strip of resilient metal, started to ring noisily at which a girl, rather pretty, put her head and shoulders out of a circular window right at the top of the house, under the roof, calling out to know what we wanted.

'Does Mme Jacques Sauvalle live here?' I asked.

'Yes, madame.'

'Is she at home?'

'Yes, madame.'

'Could I see her, do you think?'

'Use the side door, to the left, by the bushes.'

I went forward with a curious apprehension, as if in some way I were introducing myself into an atmosphere of tenebrous misfortunes, and I was not altogether reassured when, upon pushing open a narrow door, I found myself at the foot of a steep winding stair which Bobby and I climbed, step after step, without help from banisters or landings, to the very top of the mansion, where we were met by the girl who had looked down on us from the round window. She asked our names, and going along a carpeted corridor disappeared through a door already half open. There followed some low undistinguishable words by which it was clear that Mme Sauvalle was trying to place us. I therefore called out:

'Forgive me, madam, I am the lady you spoke to at Mme Trémois's shop yesterday morning.'

'Oh, yes!' she cried. 'How kind of you!'

We came forward to meet her, but as soon as she saw the child she made a gesture with both hands to drive us back, exclaiming:

'I did not know you had brought your son. My little granddaughter is in there with the whooping cough.'

As she approached I saw her quite differently from when she was in the shop. She was still in black, a cardigan and a woollen dress, but without the coat and the top-heaviness of the old-fashioned hat, she surprised me by a youthful figure, eyes that were still beautiful, and an assurance that made her immediately mistress of the situation. We stood all three for a moment at the head of the winding staircase while she thanked me for coming.

I said: 'Madam, you have known so much sorrow, my heart goes out to you.'

'You are very well informed,' she answered.

'Mme Trémois told me about—about your husband,' I said,

colouring. 'It is so dreadful that since yesterday I have scarcely thought of anything else. In the train—in the train between Lisieux and Serquigny? Is that possible?'

'Yes,' she answered. 'He was returning from here, from this house, to Paris, where we were living, by the express which was due in at midnight. The man murdered him as he was sleeping in a darkened first-class compartment.'

'Why him in particular?'

'He was alone. He looked easy to rob and the sort of person who might have some worthwhile money in his wallet. As a matter of fact he had just sold his car, here in Villers, and he was bringing the money back to me in Paris. I expect it amounted to quite a lot. I forget just how much. But the murderer never even took it. He got frightened because the train was slowing up. The trains always slow up at that place. There 's a dangerous curve or something. That 's how the man got caught. He jumped out on the permanent way and sprained his ankle.'

'It was just a sordid crime.'

'All crimes are sordid. If only people who are so keen on reading about murders knew how sordid they really are!'

'This house must be full of memories. You must see him everywhere. I don't think I could live in a house where I had been happy with my husband, not after a thing like that.'

'We have to accept what God wants, my dear. It 's no good you saying you wouldn't do things. Perhaps that 's because nothing has happened to you yet, nothing terrible.'

'I 'm sorry. I 'm a silly woman.'

She smiled and put her hand on mine protectively.

'I didn't mean it that way,' she said.

'Why did one person have to bear so much?' I asked in a whisper. 'And the others? When did they get—murdered?'

'At the end of this war when everything was practically finished. During what they call the "liberation."'

'Oh, I see. You mean that it was a political crime?'

'Dear me, no. Just a crime under the cover of chaos. If blood, my dear, has marked my passage through life, it has always been attracted by envy.'

'May I know, from you, how it happened?' I asked softly.

'My daughter had married a staff college officer,' she answered with a continuance of her calm objectivity. 'They had a large house in rather a lonely spot on the outskirts of Nevers, and everything that two young persons, delightfully in love, could dream of. She, for instance, had lovely clothes, jewels, a luxurious home, and sweet children of the most exciting ages. He had come through the most gruelling examinations with high honours. One evening, like any other evening, they were sitting talking after supper, enjoying probably not having to go out, when the bell rang. Four soldiers had arrived in a military car. One of them gave my son-in-law a message. He was wanted for something in Nevers and they were waiting to drive him back. For some reason my daughter decided to go with him. She changed her dress, put on a hat and a fur coat, and told her maid she was not to wait up. They were laughing as they left the house. The children were asleep. The night was calm. My daughter must have been proud to go on this expedition.

'They did not go to Nevers. The car took the opposite direction, through the forest. In a clearing the four men fell upon their victims. My young son-in-law must have fought like a lion. He would have done, wouldn't he? You can imagine what they were going to do to my daughter. A man would fight to his last to prevent that, wouldn't he? His last moments must have been terrible. It is nothing to die. God who gives us life takes it away. But for a man like my son-in-law to see his wife on the point of being raped. Can you imagine it? Raped and murdered. And then for him to know that his tiny children were at their mercy. My son-in-law was a man of honour. They must have torn him to pieces. Dying, he certainly continued to spit at them. Obviously. Besides, there were the marks on him afterwards. She was naked. Naked, with only the leaves to cover her, the moss for her bed.'

'How horrible,' I whispered.

'The assassins drove back to the house, where they let themselves in with my son-in-law's key. They ate and drank by the fire. They went up to my daughter's bedroom and took the dresses and furs from her cupboards, opening her jewel cases, even ripping the sheets and blankets from the bed. The babes saw it all happening. The little girl remembers. She is the one in that room with the whooping cough.'

'Were they caught?'

'Not yet. The police say that we must first wait till certain people are dead. In five or six years we may learn something. But what good will it do?'

She began to talk quite calmly about herself, as if grateful to have somebody in whom she could confide. She was born in a château near Evreux which had now passed out of the family.

I whispered to Bobby in English:

'Go down and play in the garden.'

He had heard too much of this story already. He disappeared obediently and she opened some double doors that creaked and suddenly we were on a landing on the top of the grand staircase.

She said: 'I keep the house closed in winter because it is difficult to heat. Please forgive me, madam, if I lead the way, but the place is untidy. I have been drying beans on the carpet.'

The scene, as we went down, was magnificent and shabby, the superfluity of another age, tattered and damp, but nostalgically reminiscent. We crossed the vast entrance hall with a steel gate, padlocked, across the front door, and entered a room stretching the full length of the mansion, the farther end overlooking the garden, the near windows shuttered, but which she vigorously opened, throwing the fading afternoon light on a billiard table, books in high bookcases, leather chairs, paintings, and oil portraits dusty and sometimes pierced.

She was bending over, in a corner by the window, rummaging amongst albums and books, some of which from time to time she handed up to me and which, impatiently curious, I opened, turning questioningly the pages.

'Oh,' I exclaimed suddenly, 'what a superb château!' Then reading the title underneath: 'Chambray!'

'Do you know it?' she asked, looking up quickly.

'No,' I answered. 'I was merely struck by its grandeur, its strength!'

'The Marquis de Chambray was my father's greatest friend.'

She rose from her stooping position, and looking over my shoulder:

'There is my father!'

What, I think, in those days men called mutton-chop whiskers descended, snow-white and crinkly, from either side of his square features. His eyes, under semicircular eyebrows, smiled but were authoritative. He wore a velvet hunting-cap, a white stock, velvet waistcoat, and over his left shoulder he carried a hunting-horn. His name, under the photograph, was written: 'A. Morgon.'

'Morgon,' I repeated slowly. 'Is that a Norman name?'

'No,' she answered as if I ought to have known. 'My father was from the vineyards of the Beaujolais. Is the famous vintage not familiar to you?' Then, more patiently: 'It was my mother who was Norman.' She continued to turn the pages: 'Now here is the Château Les Vaux, as magnificent as Versailles, and here is ours, with the moat and the old wing. This part'—pointing with her finger—'was rebuilt.'

My eyes, quickly turning from architectural splendours to people, darted to a fine young woman wearing a lovely dress, striped, tight at the waist, wide at the hem.

'Her?' she echoed, laughing at my insistence. 'But it was I, as a young woman, twenty-five to be exact. It was taken, as you can see, on the steps of the château.'

The books, the albums, pictures, and photographs were massed round me now, and immediately, forgetting everything else, we were both in the past, I by evoking all I had read of novels and memoirs, she by recalling real happenings of her youth, and because, without quite knowing why, we felt sympathy for one another, I listened engrossed, she talked on confidently, opening up her soul. These people, in these châteaux, aristocratic, wealthy, lived on a princely scale, the men as occupied with stag hunting as, at that time, people in the English shires thought of so little else but fox hunting. The pictures, the drawings, fell like leaves on the table—the whoops, the flourishing of the horn at the deaths, taking place in forest clearing, on railway line, on empty racecourse, even in the most sacred part of the village church of Gaudreville. Seeing these magnificent animals, hunted over eighty square miles of country, towards Lisieux, towards Serquigny, seeing their pathetic eyes, their graceful exhausted bodies, revolt surged in my breast. But I could not come to hate, on this account, the people of the period, admiring the courage and honour rising above their cruelty. She said, and I heard her as in a dream:

'Here is the Marquis de Chambray, the master. Those who

hunted with him called him Le Grand Chef. He hunted the stag over four departments: the Seine-Inférieure, the Eure, the Eure-et-Loir, and the Orne, a vast territory with Domfront, Rouen, Vernon, and Chartres at the four corners. Everywhere he went, there also went my father. There was not an inch of forest, of woodland, of river bank, where their white and orange hounds did not pass. Great seigneur, the Marquis de Chambray had a prodigious personality. Himself owner of thousands and thousands of acres, he had business dealings in one way or another with nearly all the farmers on the territory, and where he and his friends passed, hunting the stag, you may be sure generous gifts followed. Look now at the various châteaux—and here is Bois-Normand, our own. Here are the companions of Le Grand Chef—the Count of Rostolan, the Marquis of Boury, whose dogged, square face looks as if it had been cut out of a piece of oak, M. Méry de Bellegarde with his fine pointed white beard, and my father again, flourishing his horn! Great men, great horses, great dogs, great times, in a way. Here they were finishing a hunt on the banks of the fish pool in the great Trappist monastery. See how courteously the marquis and my father bow, how rubicund are the three monks, side by side, their hands hidden in the wide sleeves, the other monks passing in single file with spades and picks over their shoulders, to work in the fields. This is a print of a stag hunt in the seventeenth century, under the reign of Louis XV, returning to the château of Chambray. Nothing much had changed between them and the days of my childhood, but from that time to now everything has altered.'

She suddenly left all these books and photographs as if they annoyed her, and, indicating with a wave of her arm the spacious room, said:

'In summer you must bring your little boy to play with my grandchildren. When our château of Bois-Normand was sold, my mother bought this house for me. I said to her: "It 's much too large. I would rather have had something smaller." But she answered: "When your children have children and you want to invite them to the seaside in August, I 'll warrant this house will hardly be big enough." Well, madam, believe me, last summer when I had twelve grandchildren under my wing, I can assure you that my house did not seem too large.'

I said: 'Madame, what surprises me is how you can laugh. You are like a tree that no tempest can uproot. If I had suffered as much I don't think I could talk about the summer.'

She looked thoughtful and answered:

'When I was little I would have given anything to be a boy. It seemed to me that men had all the fun. I think, also, I looked like a boy. I liked to mount astride and do daring things. I hated it when I was made to wear frilly dresses and look demure. Once when I complained bitterly to my mother she said: "It is perhaps because in life you are going to have a lot of things to stand up against. God has equipped you on purpose with a virile character."'

A few days later I had gone again to post some letters in the village. By the parvis of the church, outside his shop, I met M. Trémois, who very politely said good evening and passed some remark about the spring-like weather. I told him I had called on Mme Sauvalle.

'I know,' he answered. 'She told us.'

I asked quickly: 'She wasn't angry, I hope?'

'On the contrary, madam, she was touched.'

I looked at him inquiringly.

'There was a little girl of five or six who had whooping cough. I would have gone in but I had my son.'

'That was Mlle Chantal, madam. She would have been two and a half when Mlle Jacqueline and her husband were murdered.'

'Mlle Jacqueline? Yes, of course, you would have known the poor young woman since childhood. Was she pretty?'

'If madam had a moment to spare . . .?'

'Of course,' I answered, 'I always have a moment to spare.'

'We have photographs.'

He led the way into his shop, and through the shop into another cottage, which was their home. In the parlour Mme Trémois was running up a curtain on her sewing machine. She rose at my arrival and made a fuss of me. By the window there was a round table resting on a single cloved leg. Its shining surface was covered by a dull red material with tassels. An oil lamp stood in the middle. On this table M. Trémois placed a bundle of newspapers and photographs, and one of these showed Mlle Jacqueline in her bridal gown.

'She was indeed a fine young woman,' I said. 'I gather the little girl with the whooping cough is her daughter.'

'Yes,' answered M. Trémois. 'There are three children—

Mlle Chantal and two boys. The little boys are at boarding school.'

'Were the little boys in the house also when the bandits came?'

'They say that young M. Bertrand, who must have been about four, was in his cot, and one of the bandits, when the gang had come back after the crime, said to him: "If you make any noise, sonny, we 'll hit you on the head."'

'Mme Sauvalle told me they took away the valuables.'

'Oh, madam, more than the valuables. They first sat down to a big meal in the room where the child was asleep, and then they fetched lorries and took everything.'

'Were there no servants in the house?'

'Nobody knows. There was anarchy, madam, under the cloak of the resistance movement. The poor souls were buried like paupers.'

'How did Mme Sauvalle manage to live through it?' I exclaimed.

'She hides her sorrow, madam, but I, who sometimes have business in the house, see her kneeling at the side of her bed, crying her heart out. She's religious. That helps. For example, the day she was told about the murder of her husband, she was coming back from mass. Not a muscle of her face moved. No, madam, not even a twitch. She went back to her room and locked herself in it for days.'

M. Trémois handed me three newspapers, saying:

'The first two describe the crime; the others the trial.'

He glanced at me almost ashamedly, and added:

'It's the *Petit Journal*. We used to take that rag in those days.'

'But why not?' I asked. 'It was a very good paper. I often read it myself.'

IX

GEORGE and his lads had now finished stacking the elm logs of which there were forty-three tightly packed *stères*. Nobody any longer questioned the fullness of the measure, but, as I should have expected, a new vexation arose. The merchant, chosen by them, who was to come to collect the trunks and pay me cash, had mysteriously changed his mind. George himself blandly gave me this news, while demanding that I should immediately acquit myself of the large balance due to him in wages.

This paltry vengeance made me so angry that I told him he should not have the money till his merchant changed his mind. He looked down at his shoes and answered nothing, but two days later I received a registered letter from a solicitor at Dozulé saying that my presence was required the following week in the law courts to inform the magistrate why I withheld payment. The plaintiffs, in addition, claimed a thousand francs damages.

I was put out by this procedure. George was legally in the right. My mistake had been to employ him. My refusal to settle his balance immediately was due to a feminine pique. I had sensed that this was the revenge he had boasted of to make up for our discovery of the loosely packed wood. I was more angry with myself than with him.

I hurried down to the village to consult Maître Vincent, the notary. Not to obey the summons to go to Dozulé would, I knew, be contempt of court, but I was not anxious to spend an entire day dancing to George's tune.

'Madam,' said Maître Vincent, politely smiling, 'you must learn not to worry. How long is it since the work was finished?'

'Four days.'

He was holding my summons delicately between thumb and index, and, with a gesture of shaking these troubles away from both of us, asked:

'Do you dispute the sum?'

'No, indeed. It is quite exact. It was the way they countermanded the merchant which vexed me. I tried to telephone him. He was not in the book. I don't even know his address.'

'I shall be seeing him to-morrow,' said Maître Vincent, who knew everybody. 'Shall I ask him to come after all?'

'Yes, do,' I pleaded. 'Supposing the trunks went bad or anything. It would be such a loss.'

He smiled indulgently at my inexperience.

'But, madame, they could remain there for years without coming to any harm.'

'I did not know. But the point is that I need the money to pay the woodcutters.'

He smiled again. I was beginning to feel he scarcely credited me with the intelligence of a schoolgirl.

'As you agree to their little bill, I shall write to the magistrate and send him a cheque.'

'That would be a great relief. I will bring you the money.'

'No,' he corrected quietly, 'I have enough. Your tenant's rent stands to your credit in my books.'

Small of build, beautifully dressed, eyes alertly darting this way and that out of a finely cut, birdlike head, Maître Vincent was feared. The peasants said of him that he bit with a smile. Though near his sixtieth year, age had merely given a smoother polish to an already luminous skin. His voice attuned itself melodiously and with apparently no effort to the varying circumstances of a conversation. With me he was gallant, respectful, slightly patronizing, as if I were not old enough to seize the finer points of knavery or law. To my farmer, Déliquaire, when on occasion we were together in his presence, jocular but severe, marking with cruelty the distance which separates a man of law from a peasant whose heavy boots still bear damp traces of liquid manure. The notary administered for me a small fund composed of the moneys Déliquaire paid me twice a year, at the St. Jean and the St. Michel, from which he extracted the many provincial and state taxes. As the amount paid to me varied with the fluctuations in the price of butter and beef, the custom in this part of the country, I felt incompetent myself to deal with it. In Maître Vincent's integrity I had unquestioning belief.

After many polite questions about my family, he smiled me to the door, and when I came out into the clear, spring-like air, I felt lighter for having so easily rid myself of this unsettling annoyance.

The approach of evening coloured the western sky with streaks of delicate pink. I climbed back to the farm. Birds of magnificent plumage were poised on low branches. The trees, nobly bare, but to those, looking carefully, showing signs of soon breaking into bud, were full of sweet noises. The smell of moss came up from under dead twigs in the ditches, and rotting leaves filled one's nostrils with vigorous perfumes of this still unspoilt country. At a turn in the lane, just ahead of me, a little woman all in black was hurrying forward; by her frail back but quick movements I recognized my neighbour Mme Castel, Yvonne Poulain's mother.

I was surprised how small she looked. On the stone floor of her farmhouse she was the dispenser of energy and wise mediation, the much-listened-to grandmother, the woman of great and precious experience who never lost her temper or used a harsh word. Now, as she looked up with kindliness into my face, I felt my heart beat with regard for her and a little because of her age and frailty, which seemed suddenly, in the lane, to appear more marked. I supposed she had been to confession, for she was very religious, but whether it was that or not I felt surprised she had not taken advantage of her business in the village to bring back André, whose school hours would be finished.

'André is in bed with a chill,' she said in answer to my inquiry.

'The weather is treacherous,' I answered, 'and there is this Italian influenza about.'

'No,' she answered, referring to the influenza. 'It was yesterday at a funeral. Something happened outside the house of the deceased person. The coffin was a quarter of an hour late, and I expect André had not enough underclothes.'

I was puzzled, and, after a moment's confused thinking, said: 'I don't understand.'

She answered chattily: 'André is a choir-boy.'

'Yes, I think I did know that.'

'He attends nearly all the funerals. Have you never seen him? Generally he walks a few paces ahead with the holy-water basin. He walks very fast. He is apt to out-distance the procession.'

'I begin to understand.'

She trotted along happily by my side.

I asked suddenly: 'How does he know there is going to be a funeral? Who warns him? Does he hear the bell toll, and run down?'

'They go to fetch him at school.'

'At school?'

'Why, yes, Mme Henrey, André goes to church school. It was I who insisted on that, on account of the religious education.'

'I see.'

After a few moments I asked again:

'Surely he is not the only choir-boy? Why does he attend nearly all the funerals?'

'You know what he is, Mme Henrey. It 's not that he is clever, but he is so very quick. The other evening, for instance, he left all his home-work to the last moment. Ten minutes' concentration and then he recited it all off pat!'

'Oh, yes, I know he 's very quick.'

'You 've no idea, quick as a monkey, but a bundle of nerves. At night, asleep, dreaming, he recites his lessons. If before bed-time I read him a story about a shipwreck, at midnight he will clutch at his pillow and call out that he is drowning. But at school he is always top of his class. The masters, and mark you it 's not because I 'm his grandmother I am telling you, say he is brilliant.'

'I am still puzzled about the funerals, Mme Castel.'

'When somebody dies they choose the boys who are at the top of the class. The sharp ones can better afford to miss the next day's lessons.'

'How curious! The more intelligent a boy, the less he needs to be taught! I had never envisaged that form of education.'

I was very intrigued. I tried to picture André, such a terror on the farm, agile, crafty, against whom Bobby was no match, dressed up in a lace surplice, demurely carrying the holy-water basin. I asked inquisitively:

'Does he like it?'

'Like what, Mme Henrey?'

'Going to funerals.'

'I like him to go,' she answered pensively. 'It keeps him out of mischief.'

'You mean that they do not always take place during school hours?'

'Well, no, and they go as far as the cemetery.'

'Poor child!' I murmured.

She said brightly: 'They pay him fifteen francs a time.'

'Do they? And what does he do with it! Do you allow him to spend it on sweets?'

'Why, yes, but you know what they are, Mme Henrey, if he gets half a chance he puts the fifteen francs in his money-box and makes me pay for the sweets. Not that he is mean, but thrifty. He says he is saving up for when he has a farm of his own.'

We went on to talk of other things, and at the low stone wall in front of the tall modern farmhouse I left her. I think I have already mentioned that the Poulains rented the farm from Maître Bompain, a notary at the inland village of Le Breuil-en-Auge. Maître Bompain, now a man of fifty, was born in this brick house which his parents, then the chemists in the village, had acquired partly as an investment, partly as a country retreat. I am not sure at what period they ceased to live in it. During the First World War the tenant farmer was a M. Anger who married one of three beautiful young women who, when they went to mass in their pony and chaise, were known as the 'Three Graces.' The other two also married prosperous farmers: Mme Lermarchand had the reputation of making the best butter in the neighbourhood. Mme Lamidet's husband was the mayor of the medieval hamlet of Saint-Vaast. Shortly after the first war M. Anger hanged himself from the rafters of my cider press and his widow moved to the important farm she still owned beyond our hayfield, the Bourgogne. The Poulains, the father and mother, who both died before we bought the farm, had come from Touques in the very early twenties leading their four cows by a rope, their children by the hand.

The sun was now disappearing over The Point.

Henriette, the serving-maid, with a stick raised above her, was driving the geese across a corner of the orchard. She now wore a pullover and a skirt, and her hair was cut according to the fashion. She looked like any other young woman of eighteen who works on a farm. But in August, when she had first arrived from I know not where, she had presented a strange picture.

Her long hair was dishevelled, the colour of brown leaves, and she wore only an uncouth chemise of the same earthy colour. It was a veritable shroud of poverty. Her body was curiously shapeless except for the exposed whiteness of legs and feet. She came into view, along our leafy lane, astride a high white horse

led by Émile, the Poulains' farmhand. I stopped, fascinated and speechless, at the sight of this girl, who looked like a young witch of medieval times being led to the stake for practising occult mysteries. She passed slowly, her hips swaying, her eyes wild. I looked back. The tattered brown garment revealed patches of naked flesh, and its insufficiency made one suspect that she was a stranger both to modesty and vice. A few days later, after Yvonne Poulain and Mme Castel had clothed her in a normal manner, the spell was gone and I knew she was a human being.

A lazy smoke, smelling of peat and wood, coloured by flying sparks, rose from an open-air fire on the other side of the stone wall, where a washerwoman, stout, and with a blue apron and her hair done up in an old-fashioned bun, was boiling the week's linen. The dogs jumped up at Mme Castel and licked her gloved hands. She scolded, then good-naturedly patted them, and with tiny, quick steps passed from the gravel of the path to the stone-floored farmhouse. I went on along the lane, following the low wall in the direction of the hedge, studded with cherry-trees and elms, which divided the Poulain farm from mine. Henriette was still driving her geese picturesquely to the place where they spent the night, safe from the roving fox, a little square house with a front door and a chimney exactly like the one that appears amongst the tree-tops for Wendy in the last magnificent scene of *Peter Pan.* The base was of Caen stone, the sides were half-timbered, the roof had shimmering slates, the chimney-pot was of red brick, and on the front door was a horse-shoe. The first of the geese waited for the girl to open the door. He then walked in importantly, followed by his wife and the family, making at the same time a great deal of fuss and noise. Henriette closed the door and threw her wand into the adjoining drinking-pool covered with green slime which the cattle no longer used, but which continued to make a pretty setting for the fairy-tale house where the geese lived at night.

When, after several days, there was no sign of the timber merchant, I began to feel unhappy about the large sum I had paid out to the woodcutters. I then remembered the existence of M. Cauvin, and I was even surprised and angry that I had not turned to him earlier for guidance on a subject on which he was certainly a great expert.

On the afternoon of Roger's wedding, on our return from the magnificent farm with its medieval château administered by Déliquaire's brother, we had stopped for tea at a villa M. Cauvin owned on the road between Trouville and Pont l'Évêque. I think the Cauvins had taken this modern house for the sake of their daughter who was of marriageable age. In ten minutes by car they could be at the casinos of Trouville or Deauville, at the races, or on the sands. Somewhere at the bottom of a handbag I had a slip of paper on which he had marked his telephone number, and I determined to ring him up.

To my surprise and pleasure, he promised to come over and have a look at the timber himself. He asked if I was in the habit of getting up early, and suggested Friday at eight-thirty.

On Fridays and Saturdays the power station at Caen had lately been cutting the current off from eight in the morning to six at night, and accordingly on these days I tried to get the fires lighted and the house swept and polished before being put into darkness, for though each week the sun was rising earlier, it was not yet usefully light till half-past eight.

At about twenty minutes to nine on the Friday morning, the house shining and the fires crackling, breakfast finished, I went out into the garden and saw Cauvin and Déliquaire coming up the orchard from the direction of the stream. I went immediately to meet them, and it was decided that we should go to The Point.

Cauvin explained that he was interested in buying lumber himself, partly to give employment to some of his farmhands who had insufficient work at this time of year, and partly because it gave him an excuse to leave his own estates and look up friends. Our Norman farmers, though so imbibed with the peasant tradition, yet loved, when they grew wealthier, to drive about the countryside, 'their bottoms in a car,' as their womenfolk picturesquely said. Cauvin was allowed a car because he administered more than a hundred acres. It entitled him to a monthly issue of petrol coupons.

The two men, over breakfast, had undoubtedly had a little talk about my trees. Déliquaire was this winter in need of logs for burning, and though I had made a present to him of two cart-loads from the forty-three *stères* George had cut, this would obviously not be sufficient for Mme Déliquaire's hearth.

After measuring up the trunks lying on the hilly side of The Point, M. Cauvin inquired if there were any other trees to cut down. I explained that I had paid out enough money and now wished to make some.

He said: 'That is excellent sense. Choose some trees you don't want. I will buy them as they stand.'

He added that he would keep the trunks and sell the heads and branches to Déliquaire.

I welcomed this arrangement. I knew secretly that Mme Déliquaire would be grateful. She liked her man to do as little as possible. She had an oriental affection for him. She disliked any person who brought him work, and correspondingly loved all those who said to him: 'Don't bother.'

We went to both the large and small woods. As we walked back the sun, gathering strength, touched the hilly country and the distant estuary of the Seine with fingers of gold. I seldom visited the distant orchards so early, closing myself in my room every morning till lunch to write. I exclaimed suddenly, amazed by the beauty of the scene:

'Isn't it lovely?'

Déliquaire looked at me curiously, saying:

'But it 's yours.'

He meant by that, I suppose, that I should have been tired of what I saw so often. On the mossy banks, hiding behind leaves and twigs, there would soon be violets. Matilda knew better than I where to look for them, and was more patient.

M. Cauvin said: 'These narrow lanes that go up and down like switchbacks are not as handy as ours at Tourgeville.'

When we were in sight of the farm I asked Déliquaire what he thought about putting some artificial manure on the grass, and I added, as an after-thought, that Ernest Poulain was treating some of his orchards during the next few weeks.

'I bet he 's not paying for it,' said Déliquaire guardedly. 'I bet Maître Bompain will have to pay for it. Basic slag this year costs seven pounds a ton.'

'You should buy it quickly at that price,' put in M. Cauvin. 'I am having to pay as much as ten pounds.'

At the thought of doing the merchant down, Déliquaire's eyes brightened.

'I might talk to M. Sandret about it.'

I asked how many tons I would need for the orchard on which my house and farm stood. M. Cauvin said that I would need at least three.

The next afternoon, hearing that Bobby had forgotten to fetch the milk from the farm, I took the can and set out myself. Our two establishments were less than five minutes' walk from each other. I merely needed to go down to the bottom of my orchard, past the long thatched cider press, cross the stream by the stepping-stones, and climb steeply another orchard, and then, on the other side of the lonely road to Saint-Vaast, under the boughs of a great oak, was the iron gate leading to the Déliquaires.

Whereas the Poulains lived in a modern brick house, the Déliquaires had a home as old and picturesque as our own—the same foundations, half-timbering, and shining slate roof. A vine, which gave magnificently sweet grapes in August, grew against it. A flower garden was divided from the orchard by white posts and wire netting. The house was just as it had always been. The water came from the stream. An oil lamp and candles flickered at night through curtained windows. The activity of the house took place in the central low room with its ever cheerful hearth, its cauldron hanging blackly from a hook in

the chimney. To the right was the buttery; to the left, the parents' bedroom. A ladder, through a hole in the ceiling, led upstairs to where the boys slept.

When the sun was hot, three or four cats, black and well fed, basked one beside the other on a long narrow ledge built specially for them. If the east wind blew, they would all hurry indoors, and with their tails up advance to the hearth where they would find a comfortable corner. In other parts of the low room, on cushions, rugs, on chairs, dogs slept contentedly. Mme Déliquaire loved them all. The midday roast was equally divided between humans and beasts. The cats drank unhindered from the milk churns.

Round the house, on the other side of the white garden posts, the young heifers and the donkey came up, eager for the sound of human voices. The cows lay lazily under the pear-trees. The chickens and the ducks threw splashes of colour against the timbered cowsheds lurching with age. The sow arrived from time to time from long expeditions from the farthest ends of the orchard.

Pushing open the garden gate, puffs of inhabitated warmth blew against my cheeks from the interior of the low room whose door all day was never closed. Mme Déliquaire, whose joy gave a rosy quality to her cheeks, was with Jeannine, busy talking and ironing the men's shirts. They looked up in a neighbourly way at my arrival, drawing me without words into the genial atmosphere of the room. Great slabs of crusty bread were toasting on the hearth against red-hot embers. A mountain of butter stood on a dish to be spread thickly on the golden toast for what the women called their afternoon collation. Coffee was percolating odoriferously. Cream was in a jug.

'Bonjour, Ma'am Henrey.'

The welcome, twice repeated, now took vocal form, the eyes and gestures having first invited me to enter. I placed the milk can on the table and asked Mme Déliquaire for news of her father who had been unwell, and of the eldest Gilles boy whom she saw more often than I did, and who, according to Mme Beaudry, had spent two days at home with boils. I then turned to Jeannine for information about Roger.

'He 's over at your place,' she said nasally, putting down the iron and making a vague gesture in the direction of the road to Saint-Vaast.

'At my place?'

'Cutting down trees with one of M. Cauvin's lads.'

'Why, yes,' said Mme Déliquaire in a happy drawl. 'M. Cauvin has employed him.'

'Oh!'

Presumably Déliquaire had asked Cauvin to employ his eldest son. I was glad to think my trees were proving of use to so many people. Mme Déliquaire, unhurrying, put down the knife with which she had been buttering the long pieces of toast smelling deliciously good, and wiping her hands went off to her bedroom from which she returned with a bundle of one thousand franc notes.

'There 's this,' she said, offering it to me, 'that M. Cauvin brought last night.'

The sight of the money made me blush. I felt curiously the excitement of having earned it, or at least of having by quick action repaired a large hole in my budget. I stayed talking about other things. Déliquaire had gone shooting in the forest of St. Gassien. The family hoped he would bring back a hare. I exchanged the empty milk can for the full one, and returned slowly to my own house.

M. Besnard had arrived with some plum-trees. He looked out of sorts, and in answer to my inquiry said that M. Duclos had been in greater pain than usual during the last few days, the laudanum no longer proving strong enough to deaden it. He had probably not slept much himself, and suddenly, as if anxious to blurt it out, exclaimed:

'Have you heard of the tragedy, ma'am?'

'What tragedy, M. Besnard?'

'About M. Des Houle, the man who came with M. Louette to mend your high-tension cables? The man who climbed down from the pole to help us pull down the pear-tree that first morning? You remember?'

'Of course, I remember. Though we all tugged together, we were not strong enough. Clément and Marcel were obliged to saw off some more of the root.'

'That 's right, ma'am. He was mending some cables by the station. The pole was rotten at the base. He had just taken off the last wire, when he went up again for something or other. They are accustomed to it, sitting up there, joking, smoking a cigarette. I suppose the weight of his body, and the fact there were no more wires, made it crack like a dead tree. He saw it coming, ma'am. It appears he shrieked horribly. They picked him up on the asphalt road with his spine broken.'

'How horrible! I can still see him walking froglike, because of his curved steel-spiked shoes, towards us. We were just there, by the pear-tree which—which has quite gone. There's nothing to show where it stood but the turned earth not yet covered with grass. Yet it was only a few days ago. I talked to him a few moments after breakfast. He said his father had once lived in my house, fifty years ago, and he was born in the room upstairs where I work. That shows he was over fifty.'

'Over fifty, ma'am, and a grandfather. His dad only died a few weeks ago. In fact, they would have mended your cables earlier but for the funeral. An important funeral it was too. The father was an old man. One morning at the beginning of the First World War he received a cable to say one of his boys had been killed at the front. "Oh," says he, "if it 's like that I shall go and kill a German." He had to lie about his age to get accepted, but within a week he was in uniform and fought right through till the armistice. That made his funeral important. All the veterans went to do him honour. It 's always the same when death knocks at the door. He calls twice.'

The next morning, almost as soon as I was downstairs, the bell started to toll. Perhaps it had something to do with the wind, but the sound came louder than usual. It tolled when the coffin left the house, when it entered the church, when the man's soul knocked at the gates of heaven, when his mortal remains left the church for the cemetery by the station where the accident happened.

From my bedroom window I could see distantly the road leading to the cemetery—the procession snake-like, a small figure in a white surplice going faster, faster ahead. Fifteen francs for André Poulain. Would he put it in his savings box to buy a farm when he was big? Or perhaps, more likely, he would buy sweets.

X

THE ground was hard, and the ruts made by the cart when our logs were brought from The Point remained deep and black, crested here and there with frost and ice. The grass of the orchard was tinted with brown. The birds were hungry. I had made them a little table nailed to the top of a hazel stick, and placed it amongst the rose-trees in my garden, and on this every day I put a long crust of French bread with butter laid thickly on, and occasionally a slice of cake. From my seat by the fire, while sewing or reading, I could look up to see my bold visitors.

Farther away in the hedge, perched on high branches of elm or ash, the carrion crows, between exhibitions of air mastery, soaring and wheeling at a great height, came to rest, to be observed through glasses, their blackness tinged with blue, bills hooked and cruel. The turkeys would start to gobble, the entire farmyard rustle in agitation, for sometimes, with rapid swoops, these powerful birds would descend with darkening wings and carry off newly hatched chicks or baby ducks, leaving Matilda impotent and furious. Woodpeckers continued to use the pear-tree beyond the garden railings, and parties of magpies flew from tree to tree. To my table above the rose-trees came the robin, the yellow siskin, the chaffinch, and all the tits with their pretty bibs and becoming waistcoats. They hopped down from the boughs of the greengage in which, unmindful of my bread, a fine bullfinch wickedly attacked the precious fruit buds. He would arrive, as fat as a city alderman, swaying and puffing out the red feathers of his breast, shaking his important head, and then in the warmth of the sunshine start busily nipping off every convenient bud. At first, watching intently, I did not realize the harm he was doing, noticing only with puzzlement how, after each bending of the head, particles of tender green fell from his beak.

What a pretty problem these magnificent gentlemen set me,

for soon the tree became full of them! I would count as many as three on a single branch and my greengage, in its winter garb, took on an exotic appearance. Anger and delight filled my breast alternately. I could not decide whether to enjoy their colourful presence and lose my black plums and sweet greengages, or to attack them as common bandits. Matilda had no patience with me for being sentimental about birds. In summer they stole the cherries just as she was ready to make jam. They also ate the hard-grown vegetables in her kitchen garden. Sleeping late because of her rheumatic pains, she did not hear their musical awakening at dawn. She was not touched, as I was, by the luxury of their garb. Matilda preferred her black cat, Tilly, who followed her as she moved thoughtfully about her yard. He had the cleverness of all black cats. The others were put out of the cottage when Matilda closed her door at dusk, but he pretended not to be there at all, curling up in the half-open iron drawer built to slide under the hearth. Warm and satisfied, indistinguishable from the blackness round him, he would dream happily. This drawer was a curious contraption. Goguet, my first tenant, asked me to put it in, when ten years earlier I had built the cottage, claiming it was a peasant custom for the family to put their clogs and felt slippers in this drawer on going to bed, so that close to the glowing embers all night, they would be warm and comfortable to wear in the morning.

The drawer, though of steel, had warped, or perhaps it had been banged. At any rate it was now always half open, providing a comfortable bed for Tilly between the hearth on which Matilda stored short logs and the wood-burning stove which had replaced the open fire. The cat had lately been gorging himself with heat. While stalking rabbits by moonlight a snare had trapped his front paw, keeping him a prisoner in a distant wood for four nights and days. He returned late one evening with a limp and a parched throat. The night was cold and Matilda's door was closed. She told us the next morning that the pekinese heard Tilly and barked, but at the time she did not understand. He must have roamed round the buildings all night, searching for food. Just before dawn I heard a strange noise under my window, something light but rough being dragged quickly across wood. I noted the hour but fell asleep again. In the morning, walking out into the garden, I saw that the long strip of French loaf which I had so securely tied with wire to the bird table had entirely disappeared. I imagined that a great crow had swooped down and carried it off to a distant aerie. The next morning, hearing the same noise, I sprang out of bed and switched on the powerful lamps which floodlight my garden. Tilly, having been put out of the cottage by Matilda at midnight, had climbed the greengage-tree and jumped from a low branch on to the bird ledge, from which he had quickly pulled the bread which he was devouring. I was very angry with him, but he looked up at me with a look which seemed to say: 'Put the light out and go back to bed.'

I did as he told me, reflecting that Tilly and my tits were, alas, as incompatible as bullfinches and tender greengage buds. The cruelty of nature is so continuously apparent that, to the unthinking, God gives a very bad example to thieves and assassins. After breakfast I replaced the buttered bread, and as it continued cold the tits and robins feasted all day.

As Matilda's ducks had not laid an egg for nearly three weeks, I was asked by many allusions to the cold, sunny weather, so ideal for a brisk walk, to pay another visit to Mme Déliquaire, whose advice on the matter would be valuable.

I found my farmer's wife bending over a black saucepan, whose boiling mixture filled the low room with the smell of mint. At first I thought she might be making a stew for supper and I advanced inquisitively, but she answered with a magnificently contented smile:

'Oh, Lord, ma'am, it 's not that at all, but a potion for one of my cows who has been seedy these last two days.'

'Not Bouboule, I hope?'

'Not she, ma'am, one we call Bijou. They are so lazy, these cows'—Mme Déliquaire rolled her words on purpose very slowly, as if she were saying these things aloud as much for her enjoyment as for mine—'so lazy, ma'am, that they won't even trouble to go down to the stream to drink, and so it happens that when they do at last find themselves accidentally by the water, they drink so much, ma'am, they give themselves the bellyache.'

'So Bijou drank too much water and gave herself a pain?'

'Why, yes, ma'am, that 's how I reckon it was, so for the

last two days I 've made her wear something warm round the tummy.'

'What sort of thing, Ma'am Déliquaire?'

'A dress, Ma'am Henrey, and very becoming.' She winked. 'A piece of warm sacking? Tied with a double knot under her waist, but they are so artful, those cows. She 's gone and shaken it off somewhere, and how should I know where to look for it?'

'How did you know she was ill?' I asked, not ashamed to show my ignorance.

'Why, that 's easy!' exclaimed the farmer's wife, opening her mouth wide. 'She kicked when I tried to milk her, and, anyway, her udders were dry, but by the same sign I know she 's better, for this morning I milked her again.'

'I wish I could have seen her wearing the dress!'

'There are other things for you to see, Ma'am Henrey.' She added quickly: 'Two little she-calves, one born to Bouboule's sister at midnight, the night before last, and the other born without us knowing it by the stream yesterday at ten in the morning.'

'Two she-calves! Aren't you lucky? Please show me them, Mme Déliquaire. What I like best about baby cows are their eyelashes.'

She laughed.

'I like them myself,' she said, 'but, bless me, cows are surprising animals, always more intelligent than people take them for. Now, Bijou, the one who was ill, came to the barrier in front of our house yesterday morning and made such a stamping and a mooing, looking so serious and worried in her brown dress, that just before lunch I said to my husband: "You 'd better go down to the stream, just in case something has happened and she is trying to tell us." So off he goes, taking Jacques with him, and Bijou, all dressed up, follows a few paces behind. When the reached the stream, there was Bijou's girl friend with her new-born!'

'Why do you say Bijou's girl friend? Were the two cows particular friends?'

'Why, yes, of course. There 's nothing more usual than for a cow to have her best friend. It 's like when we were at school.

One would choose, maybe, some girl who had come the same term.'

'How delightful! Why don't people teach us these things? Did Bijou stop mooing and stamping?'

'Why, yes, immediately. I even think it put her tummy right, on account of the fact that I was able to milk her again this morning.'

She showed me, in two separate warm compartments of a rather dilapidated half-timbered building, the she-calves, not yet very steady on their tall legs.

'And there 's another one due to-night,' said Mme Déliquaire as she closed the door.

'Which is the mother this time?' I asked, very aware of their different names on account of Bobby's affection for Ma'am Déliquaire's cows.

'Surprise,' she answered, dragging the name, and arranging the scarf over her hair because the wind was blowing at the curls. She paused under a tall, curiously shaped tree which in summer yielded quantities of tiny sweet pears, and said in a tone of exasperation:

'I hate the mud, but I do wish it would rain just to fill up the rain-water tank in the garden. I 've been saving it all I can, using it only for ourselves, for filling up the kettle and that sort of thing, but I 'm down to my last drop. We send the cattle down to your stream, and my husband and Jacques take Jeannette, the donkey, with a churn on either side of her pack, to fetch up water from our stream. It was easier when my husband used to deliver the government milk in the village; he would take milk down in the truck and bring water back. Between ourselves, Ma'am Henrey, I 'm almost glad that Ma'am Beaudry, being ill, hasn't been coming to clean my house. She has no regard for water, throwing pailfuls over the stone floors as if it was there for the turning of a tap. It 's on account of the fact she has that big cistern in her garden. She forgets the value of it. Then, with two cows having calved, and a third on the point of doing so, they have to have their drinking water brought up from the stream and warmed to take the chill off. There 's always something to do. Lucky I 'm not a complaining soul!'

Her eyes were sparkling with happy malice.

The Déliquaires' home orchard, instead of being sloping like ours, was on a plateau, and one had from where we stood a magnificent view of the blue bay, Trouville, Honfleur, the mouth of the Seine, and, curving round like a protective arm, Le Havre with its docks and flattened city.

Waddling towards us across the grass, like sailing boats in a choppy sea, came the ducks, not the fat table fowls, but the small highly coloured males, all blue and green about the head, and the dull brown females. The farmers kept this species for wild-duck shooting in the marshes down by the sea. I asked:

'These are no good for eating, are they, Mme Déliquaire?'

'Some like them quite a bit,' she answered. 'They will have two for a meal instead of one. I know of men who like them better than the fat Rouennais. They claim the flesh has more taste to it.'

'These cold, frosty February nights, with bright stars in a clear sky, are just what the men like for duck shooting? Am I right? Does your husband go down to the marshes this winter?'

'My husband has never been a great one for wild-duck shooting. Roger went down once or twice last week.'

'How do they do it, exactly?'

'There 's nothing to it,' she answered. 'They tie the males on one side of the water and the females on the other. When the teal fly over, the males come down to the females, and the females to the males. That 's when the men take aim.'

'Can the wild ducks see them in the dark?'

'Of course they see them, because of the water. Besides, these ducks call all the time, the males more loudly than the females. They never stop calling. They have a language of their own. When there is a fox around, for instance, the men can tell at once. Sometimes they come home in the morning with a fox instead of a wild duck.'

'It must be a cold sport these nights?'

'Lord bless you, no! Between ourselves, it 's just an excuse for the men to eat and drink. They have cabins, all camouflaged so that the birds can't see them, and nicely heated inside, with bunks to sleep if they have a mind. Each man provides a basket of eatables. You don't need to pity them. Nor even the wild birds, for few come over these times. Every year the coast is less wild.'

'That reminds me, I really came to ask you about our ducks, who have not laid an egg for three weeks at least.'

'My guess would be they are laying in the orchard, where you will never find them,' answered Mme Déliquaire. 'Now, I will tell you my way of thinking. Close the gates of your inner courtyard in the morning, and do not let the ducks go out into the orchard till each has laid her egg.'

'That is certainly a fine idea. I already apply that principle to Bobby. No running wild till he has done three arithmetical sums and copied out a page of *Pride and Prejudice*.'

'One has to be hard sometimes,' said Mme Déliquaire, smiling.

'Oh, and there is something else,' I went on. 'I have a broody hen.'

'Where is she sitting?'

'On some hay in the corner nearest the door in the stables.'

'That 's not agreeable,' said Mme Déliquaire. 'I have one also. You shall see her. She is sitting in a wooden box lined with hay, in a rabbit hutch.'

'Have you no rabbits?'

'Only two, the female who is waiting for a family, and the male which I shall kill. See! There is the female.'

'She 's enormous!'

'She is happy.'

'And here'—drawing aside a curtain—'is the hen.'

'How many eggs have you put under her?'

'Fourteen.'

'If only I had a box like that!'

'You shall have one, Ma'am Henrey,' she said, as if it were but a matter of course to satisfy my wishes. She plodded off in her clogs to the back of the cowshed, from some dark corner of which she brought me a neat box. Then, as she put hay into it: 'The chemist keeps them for me in return for a drop of milk from time to time and some butter. Your hen will do fine in this. Remember now. Don't let her impose on you. Pick her up firmly by the wings and she will sit here as quiet as gold. A little exercise once every two days is quite enough. No, no, you 'll not take the box with you. Jacques will bring it round to your place with the milk this evening, and now it is time for me to prepare the soup for supper. We are really old-fashioned that way. I 've never known my husband grumble about his food, but his soup in the evening must be regular as clockwork. Lord bless me! I scarce know what would happen if the soup was not ready.'

'What sort of soup will you make to-night?'

'Potatoes and leeks,' she answered, smiling. 'There 's practically nothing else for the moment.'

We parted in front of the cowshed where the liquid manure, oozing from the strong-smelling heap, ran under the cartway, losing itself in the green grass of the orchard. At the iron gate I looked back. She was opening the door of the house. I thought: 'There, at least, is a really happy woman!' I felt almost jealous of her equanimity of mind.

Standing under the high oak-tree which grew like a giant postern to the gate, I had a sudden desire to go a few paces up the road to Saint-Vaast, perhaps as far as Mme Beaudry's house where I could inquire how she was. The sun was beginning to unfreeze the stiff earth, and in the hedge opposite the Gilles' modest farmhouse I saw the first violet of the year, pale, but the prettiest picture in the world on a February afternoon.

A little farther on there reached my ears repeated blows from an axe, and I quickly guessed they must be coming from deaf M. Gravé's garden. I had not seen him, except distantly, since that pre-war summer and autumn, when with the other carpenters he had made the parquet floors of my house and all the woodwork for the adjoining cottage, and though I knew that he lived all alone in this bungalow overlooking the road to Saint-Vaast, rumour had it that he was ill-disposed to visitors.

The loneliness of his existence gave me a great wish to look over the fence and bid him good afternoon. I wondered if he ever troubled to make his bed or lay a cloth for supper. By the hedge which divided his small garden from the orchard which he also owned, there had stood, until the recent gales, a very fine Scottish fir which I could see from my bedroom window. The news that it had been blown down about an hour before the mayor's oak fell on the high-tension cables had sent me running upstairs to look upon a view which henceforth would no longer be tinted with the familiar red bark. I was genuinely grieved at the time, though since, I had not given it a thought. Now I beheld deaf M. Gravé making with his axe a large notch, preparatory to bringing down what was left of the trunk, which I judged to be about twelve feet in height. I shouted to him, but of course he took no notice. Nevertheless he put down his axe after a few moments and, mumbling to himself, came along a gravel path in my direction, so that I had no great difficulty by shaking the gate and rattling the heavy chain in making him look up. He received me in a very civil manner, inviting me into his domain, and telling me with much detail how his tree had been smitten down.

'But, you know,' he said, 'I 'm not altogether sorry, for it was giving too much shade.'

He showed much concern that I should not go too close to that part of the trunk which he was cutting down. He felt, I believe, that it might crash down at any moment, and I was amazed how little, for a carpenter, he could know about felling a tree. I had seen him so expert making doors and windows, that I imagined that timber in all its conditions, from the living tree to the finished product, rubbed and polished, had no secret for him. I must confess I was somewhat pleased to find him so awkward a hand at this operation, which resembled greatly what I would have done myself. He had made a pretty enough notch with the saw and the axe, but the steel wedges, of which there were no fewer than six, were fixed all round the hewn circumference, as if he had wanted to prop up the tree instead of guiding its descent.

'I am a trifle anxious,' he said with good humour, 'about the spot where I should make it fall. First, there are the two apple-trees which I must certainly avoid, but the trunk is still so tall that if I bring it down exactly between the two apple-trees, the top of it may well demolish my rabbit hutches.' Then dismissing the problem altogether, he said: 'The great thing is to keep active. Have they told you I am seventy-two?'

'A fine age for an apprentice woodcutter!'

He was very neat, sturdy, and square-jawed, and stood looking at me with eyes as beautiful as those of his daughter, Mme Gilles. He answered without any particular inflection in his voice:

'Maybe that is so, but you will have noticed I have moved up three places since the start of the year.'

'How so?' I yelled.

'Did you not hear of the death of M. Des Houle, the elder, the one who volunteered in the last war?'

'Come, come, he was much older than you?'

'Why, yes, he was ninety, but there have also been two others a trifle younger than him. He mentioned their names, but I had scarce heard of them. 'I tell you I have moved up three places. There are not so many now who are more than seventy-two.'

We were standing on the gravel path outside his bedroom window, which was open. A high bed with the ends of walnut took up nearly all the space, though behind it was a stove so close to the crumpled pillows that if he slept with the window closed he must at times be nearly asphyxiated. A pair of trousers with braces attached sprawled over the unmade sheets. This glimpse was much what I had expected of a bachelor recluse.

'Look after yourself!' I said loudly in his ear.

'Thank you, ma'am,' he answered, in his deep strong voice. 'I do very well. The house is soundly constructed. It was brought up here from the village, beam by beam, one might say, sixty years ago, before the road to Saint-Vaast was thought of.'

'From the village?'

'Because of some piece of litigation which escapes my memory. The house which, although sound, cuts no great figure now, stood, when I was a lad of twelve, very proudly in the village square. The approach here was by the lane that leads across to your hayfield and thence at right angles to the sea, and very rough walking it was. Tall grass and rushes grew on either side. As school lads we used to take the grass from either side and tie it in the centre, so that grown-ups passing would catch their feet in it and trip up head first!'

His eyes, brimming with the memories of boyhood, twinkled happily. He led me back to the white gate and added:

'Thank you for coming. I enjoy a visit now and again. The truth is, I don't see many people these days, and the farthest I walk is to Mme Beaudry's house to buy an egg.'

'But surely your daughter——' I began.

'No, no,' he said. 'It would not be fair. She would likely give me her eggs if I were to ask her, but I would not rob her of the money.'

'Good-bye, M. Gravé.'

'Good-bye, ma'am, and thank you again for coming.'

The pot-holes in the narrow road were filled up with newly broken flint, over which earth and moss from the hedgerows had been laid. I soon came upon M. Beaudry with a wheelbarrow and a rake, and as he was within fifty yards of his own house, whose green shutters and red façade were clearly to be seen, I said I was indeed glad that his road-mending had brought him so near home at a time his sick wife would doubtless be so much in need of his help.

'Next week,' he said, 'it will be on the far side of M. Babluche's farm, on the road which leads to the castle.'

He did not sound altogether sorry at this prospect, and I remembered what his wife had so often told us, that every farmer along the dusty white road invited her husband, being a popular man, for a yarn in the cider press, or if it were after lunch at the common table for a cup of coffee with a generous nip of *calvados*, so that by evening he would, as likely as not, come home in a brawling temper.

I asked him if his wife was better, and he said that she was so much on the mend that she hoped to come and pay her respects to me at the end of the week. I then asked if I could count on him to turn over the ground for our potato crop, but he said he had no desire to work any longer, and that if it were not for the pension he would not lay another flint on the roads.

I said encouragingly: 'Perhaps for an hour or two on Sundays?'

He said he would think about it, but that I must not count on him.

Two days later, after lunch, Mme Beaudry came to see me, not to work, but as a courtesy visit to show she was up and about again, with almost as much ceremony as if she had just risen from an accouchement. She even brought me a gift from the woods below her strip of orchard—a wicker basket full of primroses whose roots were hidden in a bed of damp moss.

I exclaimed: 'Oh, Mme Beaudry, how wonderful! These are the first of the year! How do you manage to find them so quickly?'

She answered: 'Well, madame . . .!' with an expression which meant that without prejudice to her respect for me she never had entertained any illusions about my cleverness regarding country matters.

I answered lamely: 'I suppose you know where to look. Anyway, I am delighted to have them. They shall have a place of honour on my sewing table.'

I then asked a trifle anxiously how her husband was doing, for generally this question brought a flow of bitterness, but to my pleasurable surprise she answered:

'He 's been a lamb, and what would you say, madame, if I told you he even did the washing? Then again, this morning, on my way up from the village, where after all these days in bed I had to go for the shopping, he met me half-way to carry up my parcels in his wheelbarrow. For once his work on the road was very useful.'

'Yes, I saw him laying flints in front of your house.'

'There 's no better husband when he 's nice,' she said, 'but, between ourselves, I am afraid it will not last long. I called on the Poulains last evening, a visit of convalescence like I am paying to you, and incidentally they took me along to see their cows being milked electrically, so that it was dark, or more exactly moonlight, when I crossed the stream, and I clearly saw

Beaudry walking along arm in arm with a friend with whom, I much fear, he will soon be celebrating my recovery.'

She looked round authoritatively, and remarked:

'The kitchen could do with a good scrub and your mother wants me to kill a rabbit, so I'll be here to-morrow.'

The magpies, tempted near the houses by the hard frost, came as near as the black boughs of the greengage outside my window and remained there a moment, as large and as gracefully white as a liner riding the seas. Jays, two or three together, normally shy and careful, occasionally flashed past in pursuit of a white owl which woodmen, felling a tree, had cast out of its warm bed. Our evenings and nights echoed to the sad cries of the white owl, but nocturnally one never saw them. Superstitious farmers, believing their presence prophesied a death, would catch them and crucify them on a barn door. Rettol, the best woodcutter in the village, often saw them fly out, terrified, from the trees he cut down, and one evening, when during the gloaming we were walking on the outskirts of my large wood, I saw him quite affected, even afraid, when one of these birds glided past us, a noiseless shadow. 'The bell will toll to-morrow,' he said.

I was seeing quite a lot of Rettol just now. Mme Michelin, whose house was not far from ours on the path to the village, had unwillingly given orders for the cutting down of a three-hundred-year-old elm, which if it had fallen might have done great damage, for it was the tallest, greatest tree of its kind the imagination can picture. She loved it, as we all loved it, conscious that it must silently have witnessed the history of our hamlet, of our orchards, of my house, since the reign of Louis XIV. Owners of old trees were, however, becoming alarmed by the vast sums they were obliged to pay if nearby roofs and cables were damaged. Modernity, with its comfort, was uncompromising with the kings of the forest. Mme Michelin's elm was so thick that four men sawing at the same time, two at each end of the cross-cut saw, required an hour to make each cut. We might have saved this venerable elm if we could have proved that the trunk was not hollow. A method, highly picturesque and as old as the tree itself, was used by Rettol, a fine stature of a man, rather red in the face and bald of head, to discover the condition of the foot. One of his apprentices, a fine tall youth wearing a dark blue sailor's jersey, having an aquiline nose and honest blue eyes, lay across the roots at one side of the mighty tree with a loud-ticking alarm clock. Rettol lay at the opposite side, with his ear close to the bark. The clock ticked like the one in the crocodile's inside in *Peter Pan*. Rettol's face grew redder from the uncomfortableness of his position. If he could hear the clock ticking through the trunk, then there was a cavity whose size he must determine by the loudness of the tick. If, on the other hand, the sound of the clock travelled round the giant trunk, instead of through it, then the tree's life was to be saved.

Alas, the tick-tock arrived with alarming clarity by the shortest route to the woodcutter's ear. All the village waited the next day for the mighty, sickening crash.

XI

FEBRUARY was half through. The days seemed to be rushing past, perhaps because so little happened to make them important. The evenings were becoming quite long and the weather had turned mild, but it was not yet spring. When one looked closely at trees and shrubs, one saw buds, but the hills and valleys echoed with the woodman's axe. M. Besnard refused to prune my peaches, my vine, and the rose-trees, saying that we could yet have ice and snow.

Nature and my own affairs were in a state of gentle suspense. One Sunday morning Jacques Déliquaire knocked at my door, asking permission to take a dozen cuttings from the magnificent cherry-tree under whose largest branch Bobby swung gently in summertime. Every time Mme Déliquaire came to see me she said: 'That reminds me, Ma'am Henrey, I must ask Jacques to graft a few twigs from your cherry on ours.' He had brought one of those tall cutters which gardeners use to clip the tops of fruit trees. I asked him if he would do the grafting himself.

'Ah, no!' he said. 'The Trémois are coming after lunch.'

After our own lunch, the sun being pleasantly warm, I felt a sudden desire to sit for an hour at my farmer's hospitable table. Bobby was not much of a companion during the day. His boyish pleasures kept him busy till dusk. He was for ever hammering, or inventing new lamps for Matilda with flex and electric torch batteries. She had an amazing patience with him. They played like children. They had, also, long discussions to which I was not admitted. He made her read *Pride and Prejudice*, *Treasure Island*, and *Evelina*. Fanny Burney's novel had specially charmed them. They were united in rejoicing at each ill-mannered practical joke played on Mme Duval, partly, I think, because they knew that my sympathy had lain with the unfortunate woman, partly because my son being very young and Matilda old, neither had a great fund of pity.

I therefore took the pekinese and, crossing the stream, went to my farmer's. The new motor van was drawn up by the gate, and Déliquaire arrived looking smart and awkward in his Sunday overcoat.

'It 's a fine truck,' I said admiringly.

'It is that,' he agreed, putting his large hand lovingly on the bonnet.

'I suppose you are off to a football match?' I continued.

He considered me with naïve surprise, and answered:

'How do you know?'

In the low-raftered room of the farmhouse Mme Déliquaire, corpulent, slow and deliberate in movement, but silent in carpet slippers, was making pancakes and apple fritters, which she sprayed thickly with castor sugar before putting them on a large dish in the centre of the table covered with a worn American oilcloth.

'I am sorry!' I exclaimed, pushing open the door. 'I see you are still at lunch.'

'No, no,' answered Mme Déliquaire in her long, friendly drawl. 'We 've finished some time ago. These are just to eat from time to time as anybody happens to feel hungry. You 'll taste one yourself, I hope.'

At the table sat Roger, with Jeannine on one side of him and Mme Déliquaire's sister Marie on the other. The room, as usual, was full of well-fed cats and dogs curled up on chairs, or sprawled out on the red-tiled floor in front of the fiercely burning hearth. Bobby Trémois, the mongrel terrier who had learnt to ring at the butcher's gate, bringing Mme Vannier down from her housework, had arrived with Jeannine, and was now playing with the Déliquaires' terrier of the same name. The farmer had left his spaniel, Mireille, at home, fearing the crowds at the football; there were four black cats on the bench in the garden.

Roger and Jeannine were gentle lovers. She would look at him with large inexpressive eyes. He was happy to be sitting beside her, saying nothing. From the little black stove came the sizzling of batter as Mme Déliquaire made the pancakes. Through the half-open door could be heard the song of birds, and the quack, quack of ducks waddling across the grass in single file.

I put my teeth carefully into a hot apple fritter, compared it mentally with those I made myself, and said to Jeannine:

'I suppose you are learning to be a good cook?'

She opened her mouth very wide and answered:

'Our garret is not commodious for cooking.'

Her strong Norman accent made her sing in a loud-pitched tone. She looked at her husband with devoted eyes.

'No,' he confirmed, mopping with a large coloured handkerchief an ear scratched by a thorn in the wood, 'where we lodge is not favourable for anything.'

'You 're lucky to have any sort of lodging,' said Marie, whose features were drawn by comparison with those of her sister, Mme Déliquaire, and whose cheeks lacked that apple rose of the farmer's wife. 'The thing to fear is that they put you out into the street after Easter.'

Home hunting in our sleepy Norman village was a sad business. In London I knew the difficulties. Here one would have hoped to find matters easier.

'It 's not a fear,' said Roger resignedly. 'Why don't you say it 's a certainty?'

'To begin with,' I asked Jeannine, 'where do you lodge?'

'On the third floor above the Turk who is such a good photographer,' she answered. 'The shop next to the passage in front of the tobacco store. His wife dresses their baby the Turkish way, one nappy over the other.'

'Just two rooms, a bedroom and a kitchenette,' said Roger. 'No space for anything, not even for the furniture we were given for our wedding. But as they will turn us out, it hardly matters.'

'They 've had to crate their furniture,' said Marie.

'It 's not the way for a young married couple to live,' said Mme Déliquaire, turning a pancake.

'That it isn't,' thought I. 'Married last spring. By rights they should have a baby by now.' I counted the months quickly on my fingers, under the table; glanced at her to make sure there was yet no sign.

Aloud, I asked: 'Why should they want to turn you out?'

'The tourist traffic. They can't decently ask a workman for more than a couple of pounds a month. People who come for a holiday by the sea, Parisians and that sort of thing, pay more than that a week, not counting the breakages, the replacements, the little ways there are to fleece them.'

'Is that allowed by law, to keep an apartment empty, I mean, for eight months in the year, just to rob the holiday makers when they come?'

'You can't have it both ways,' said Marie. 'Where would we be without the holiday makers? The shopkeepers make enough in three months to keep them for the rest of the year. Ask Madeleine'—her sister, Mme Déliquaire—'if her butter and milk would sell so dear if it were not for the crowds who come to the sea. The farmers inland get nowhere near so good a price.'

'They make it up in other ways,' said Mme Déliquaire, wiping her frying-pan. 'They know what each month brings. I 'm not the one for gambling.'

'I thought your parents owned a little house on the road to Caen,' I asked Jeannine.

'At Albertville?'

'That 's right, at Albertville.'

'My father bought it three years ago for the orchard. There are no fruit trees in the neighbourhood to touch the ones at Albertville. He never looked to the day when he might need the house. It 's a family full of children. They were there before the war. He 's not allowed to put them out. Families with children are sacred. We went to the municipality to ask for an ejection order, there being no lease. The man said, turning to me: "When this young woman has as many children as your tenant, perhaps we 'll consider your application."'

I thought Roger looked little disturbed at the prospect of being turned out into the village street at Easter. I guessed they would not try again to lodge with the Trémois opposite the church, for Mme Déliquaire would always find a corner for them in the farmhouse. Everybody used the farmhouse as a friendly haven. I asked Roger if he was still determined to drive a lorry as a living. He said it was all fixed with the cider merchant and that he was beginning on the first of March.

Mme Déliquaire, silent in her carpet slippers, had put away the frying-pan and cleaned the stove and, with a passing smile, she slipped out to fetch two heavy logs to put on the hearth. She was always working, but never absent from the unhurried conversation. Her sister Marie, angular, her curved chin stuck out so that her face took the form of a crescent, sat stiffly on the edge of a chair. Her head moved whilst her body remained stationary. Unhappily married in their native village in the plains south of Fécamp, she had turned up one day at the Déliquaires', where she was given a room above the farmhouse. At that time Mme Beaudry worked for a haberdasher, Mme Petrel, in the village, but finding the steep walk, twice a day, too much for her, she persuaded Marie to take her place, and soon Marie, earning a decent wage with Mme Petrel, took a modest room near the cross-roads, coming to her sister each Sunday for lunch.

I think it was I who turned the conversation on Mme Beaudry, who had boasted just before her recent illness that her husband had knocked her head three times against a brick wall and turned her out to feed the rabbits in her chemise.

Mme Déliquaire immediately put in: 'She exaggerates. He 's not near so bad as she likes to make out. She dreams most of the things she tells us.'

'In her "kemise"!' exclaimed Marie. 'No, I do not believe it. Mme Beaudry is too chaste a woman to walk in her garden dressed only in a "kemise"!'

'But does he never beat her?' I asked, disappointed. 'He does get drunk, doesn't he?'

'Oh, that, yes!' laughed Marie who, turning to her sister, inquired: 'There was that time after the christening of his grandson—do you remember, Madeleine—when he came up the road to Saint-Vaast with you and me each holding him by an arm. And she never ceasing to scold him!' Marie rose with a little jolt from her chair, and, dancing this way and that to show how Beaudry collapsed alternately against the two women, added with more excitement than I would have thought her capable of: 'When we reached their little house, Mme Beaudry sat her husband on a stone step and came back with us to milk the cows. "Mme Beaudry," said Madeleine, "are you not worried to leave Beaudry in the state he is alone on a stone step?" "Lord, no," answered she, "what business has the idle man to get drunk? If I can work, so can he."'

'I remember,' said Mme Déliquaire thoughtfully. 'She milked the cows and fed the calves just as unconcerned as any day.'

The terrier, Bobby Trémois, cocked up an ear and ran to the garden. We saw another dog arrive, a black animal belonging to Jeannine. M. and Mme Trémois walked up rather sedately, Mme Trémois in a fur coat, holding a violet between her thumb and forefinger. She was much taller than her husband, who looked docile and kind.

Mme Trémois's fur coat reminded me suddenly of Mme Beaudry. I was standing next to her while she wrung the boiled linen. Without looking up from her work, she was telling me a story, every word of which now came back quite clearly to my mind.

'Last night the firemen held their annual dance,' she had said. 'Déliquaire, being a town councillor, felt it was incumbent on him to arrive accompanied by his wife, but Mme Déliquaire, as you know, is for going to bed at candle-time, just as soon as her hens are locked up, and it needed a rare amount of persuasion to make her put on her finery to dance a rumba in the village hall. Nevertheless, the firemen's annual dance being a very important affair, and Mme Déliquaire not being able to refuse her husband anything he really sets his heart to, climbed next to her man in the milk van, and there they go clattering down the road to Saint-Vaast. When they entered the hall and saw all the people, Mme Déliquaire said to Déliquaire: "I 'll not dance just yet. It would give me palpitations." They sat by the door, watching the people coming in. After a while Roger arrives with Jeannine, who was showing off her new fur coat, the one she had bought after Roger had been breaking stones that time on the road. He had seen a shot-gun that pleased him so much he took half of what he had earned on the road to pay for it, whereupon Jeannine had said: "If you 're going to buy a shot-gun, I shall buy a fur coat." That was the history of Jeannine's coat. I 'm not saying Mme Déliquaire wasn't a trifle jealous at the time, but Jeannine, being a young woman and her daughter-in-law, Mme Déliquaire did not show it, at least in my presence. Roger and Jeannine, therefore, swept past their parents looking very fine. Next came the mayor and some of the dignitaries. I can just see M. Déliquaire, smiling and looking important. Then, timorously, M. Trémois, with his wife, not at all shy, wearing a fur coat just like the one her daughter Jeannine had bought. "Bless my soul!" exclaimed Mme Déliquaire. "To think I scrub and drudge all day, never asking you,

Déliquaire, for a thing for myself, and that this family who haven't yet paid us for their share in the wedding feast, flout me with their expensive furs! My heart is cold, Déliquaire. You will drive me back to the farm this very moment!" And so he was obliged to do, my dear Ma'am Henrey. She who is so even in her temper was jealous for once, jealous like the rest of us.'

I remember laughing at this droll tale. But now, seeing Mme Trémois advancing slowly along the gravel path, wearing her 'expensive fur,' holding a violet between her finger and thumb, not at all shy beside timorous M. Trémois, and recalling at the same time what Mme Déliquaire had said about Mme Beaudry's veracity, I felt, I must confess, a tinge of disappointment that the story about the fur coats at the firemen's dance might not, after all, be true. What in the world were my reconceived ideas coming to? Mme Déliquaire not a tiny bit jealous after the manner of the rest of us? Mme Beaudry not beaten by her husband? I bethought me of the saying that there is no smoke without fire. The heroine of a novel I was then reading by an outstanding Spanish woman writer, Carmen Laforet, said of another character: 'Generally speaking, she tells amusing lies, mixed up with exactitudes.' The words had stuck in my memory. So much for Mme Beaudry! Mme Trémois was advancing towards me. To me she held out her hand (the one with the violet) and said:

'Good afternoon, dear madame.'

'I see you have been picking violets, Mme Trémois.'

'The first ones,' she smiled. 'My husband spied them in the hedge. He has a keen eye.'

'The sun brings them out,' I said. 'The sun and the mild spring-like weather. You are not too hot in your fur coat?'

Mme Déliquaire, without a trace of jealousy, was beaming.

'Come!' she exclaimed to Mme Trémois. 'The fritters and the pancakes are still warm. I took them out of the pan not five minutes ago.'

On my return to the farm, going up to my bedroom, I again put it into my head that what I needed most urgently were new floor boards. The large half-timbered room at the end of the corridor which I used as a study, shutting myself up there to write, had a fir parquet which deaf M. Gravé had put down in 1938. Highly polished it had the look of a golden guinea, and I would have been satisfied to have another like it in my bedroom. But wood, cut into lathes, fetched prices out of all proportion to those paid for lumber. My mind, therefore, started to wrestle with the idea of cutting down some of my own oak-trees, which I would send to the mill.

My oak-trees were the finest on the plateau. They were in what we used to call the large wood which Victor Duprez had sold me before war broke out for the small change in my purse. Six months later, having acquired the farm where he now lives, he offered me a great sum for its return, but I had visions of my son, then a baby, playing in it when he grew older, and I refused. A clear stream divided it from another wood which formed part of his newly bought estate. I had no direct outlet, the orchards to the south and on both sides belonging to Mme Anger. Even the hedges and the trees in it belonged to my woman neighbour, who was very strict about her rights. The law, however, requires the owner of a piece of land to give a right of way for timber during certain months, and I foresaw no trouble to bring out what trees I cared to fell.

My oaks were magnificently tall, with wide trunks, unspoilt by a branch or a knot for three-quarters of their height. I wished particularly to have floor-boards of the exact length of my bedroom. In towns and even in country places this is practically unknown. The modern method is to cut the lathes short, so that they can easily be packed and carried by truck or rail. The old method gives a bold and pretty effect, and would fit in admirably with the beauty of my house.

The next day I sent for Jollivet, to know if he had yet made any inquiries. As he arrived in the low room, I thought he looked like the Mad Hatter in *Alice in Wonderland*. He took a deep breath and started on one of those explanations which I knew by experience to last for a long time. He said:

'But, my dear madame, if I were to be a dishonest man, nothing would prevent me from laying your green floor-boards immediately they return from the mill, but I must say that my conscience would forbid me to do any such thing, given that with your central heating and the monster fire you keep up day and night in your low room, the floor boards would soon warp and make a sorry picture, doubtless buckled in places and with gaps between them of half an inch or an inch in width.'

I cut him short and said: 'I was rather of the same idea.'

He was too surprised by this frank confession to resume immediately his interrupted phrase. I asked him how much a new floor in spruce would cost. He answered, after much argument, that he supposed, if I did not hold him down to it, that forty pounds would be an approximate figure. He quickly added:

'But I could not guarantee the wood, madame. I shall have to buy the planks unseasoned at the mill.'

The next step was to compute how much it would cost me to cut down two oak-trees and have them sawn. The lathes could dry for three years under the warm thatch in the cottage hay-loft.

The next evening, towards dusk, I was inspecting a pollard in the hedge, wondering if I would have the strength to saw it for firewood, for it was three years dead, when a short, sturdy man, rather red in the cheeks, with tufts of curls sticking up most luxuriantly on either side of an otherwise bald head, walked down the orchard, hat in hand. This was M. Rettol who had the reputation of great strength, a marvel of adroitness with the axe, and in addition of being extremely susceptible to women; quite a gallant in his way. Looking at the pollard with more interest than it seemed to merit, he declared that though a horse could not pull it out of the hedge as it lay, two of his men, having the knack, would have small trouble to tip it into a convenient position on the grass. I said it was a pity the pollard was so awkwardly placed because, though I had forty *stères* of green wood, I had come to the end of the previous year's supply, and needed sorely some dry logs.

'I 'll pop along with my son-in-law before breakfast,' he said. 'A real pleasure to be useful, ma'am.' He coughed self-consciously, and went on: 'The tall elm by the gate is withered in the head.'

'It 's the one I thought looked strongest,' I said, genuinely disappointed. 'Are you sure?'

'The two others on either side of it are in no better state: the ash, with its broken bough, will do no good; the cherry would cause a rare lot of damage if it fell over the high-tension cables. I would say there are at least ten trees that the wind will bring down for you during the next half-dozen gales.'

'I am tired of selling trees,' I answered angrily, 'and I 've enough logs to last me three years. When first I came here the lane, half-way down to the sea, was so thickly flanked with tall trees that it was like standing in the nave of a cathedral. Everybody is cutting down trees, but nobody replants any. The farmers say there is no point in replanting elms because of the disease. Mine are the last. You are too eager to cut them down.'

'Maybe you are thinking about your little boy, ma'am, but when he 's of age all these trees will have long since died. The fault is not with you, but with those who planted them, timing things for them to mature so soon after you had bought the place!'

I laughed at his cunning, but I reckoned him in the light of an enemy. Though I was delighted with the fifteen thousand francs I had received from M. Cauvin for the trees he had bought, I suspected he had taken advantage of my ignorance. I was no match against the clever son of a horse-dealer. I was no match against any man who has facts and weighty talk and treats one with a patronizing amiability. I was certain M. Cauvin must have laughed with M. Déliquaire at the fine bargain he had made. Déliquaire had admitted as much, saying that it was Cauvin's policy to place business above friendship. I ought merely to have been grateful that he came so quickly when I called him.

Rettol did not ask me how much Cauvin had paid for the trees. He merely offered me twice as much for those which had taken his fancy. The evening breeze, which was warm, played in his side curls. I was tempted by the money. Rettol put his foot on one of the immense pear-tree roots which Besnard and Clément had left untidily about my orchard, looking like ungainly octopuses, and said:

'These things should be split. They make fine burning logs.'

'Nobody will split them,' I said. 'Besnard told me it was not possible; Déliquaire said they should be blown up with a charge of dynamite.'

Rettol smiled.

'A charge of dynamite would more likely blow up your house than these roots,' he answered. 'Perhaps one would be split; the others would be sent a-flying round your orchard. Then where would you be? That is if you lived to tell the tale. Now, to-morrow, when I come here with my son-in-law, I'll split these roots up for you proper.'

'That, at least, is a handsome offer,' I answered, 'and between now and then I'll think about the elms and the other trees.'

'Good night, ma'am,' said Rettol. 'I'm always glad to help.'

As I watched him climbing towards the gate, I felt a good deal relieved by his visit. On my way down to the post office earlier, to post the mail, I had, as usual, looked in at Mme Trémois's shop with three dozen eggs in my basket, but to my horror she had refused them, saying that prices were tumbling and the demand was slight. Eggs had fallen from twenty-six francs before Christmas to nine or ten, and people who had come back from market at Dozulé told me that there were not even sufficient buyers at five francs to absorb the supply, with the result that many farmers' wives returned home with their eggs unsold.

The climb back to my farm in the evening took me twenty minutes, and as soon as I had posted the letters I would buy the bread, call at the newsagent's in front of the market for a newspaper and, on the right days, my women's magazines, and then load up with meat and groceries, so that I was quite exhausted on my return, weighted down by so many necessary provisions. The thought of adding three dozen eggs to the rest vexed me. I was for selling them at any price, and the first person I approached was the baker's wife, with whom I had become such an excellent customer. She told me, rather curtly, I thought, that she had her own sources of supply. I smiled, asked for news of her children, and pretended that I really did not care a bit about the eggs. But as I left her shop I knew that I did care desperately, my cheeks quite flushed with the dishonour of having been rebuffed twice within a few minutes. My honour was pathetically at stake. I had the impression of begging in the village street. My shame was quite pitiful, and yet I had put it into my head that I would not take those eggs back to the farm. As I passed the village ironmongery I remembered that Mme Deloges had not yet drawn up my bill, and it had been several times my intention to demand it, for I bought many things at her shop, like saws, steel fencing, paint, nails, and implements both for the farm and the garden. She was behind her desk, excused herself about the bill, and promised to attend to it within the next week or two. I told her the sad tale of my eggs, hoping she would come to my rescue, but she went out of her way to expatiate on her own lack of sympathy for this food and the general feeling in the village that as eggs were falling in price it would be absurd to buy any until they had fallen still further. I was about to express the hope that her own goods would decline in a like manner, when her husband appeared from the depths of the shop and told her, sharply, to relieve me of a dozen eggs. She obeyed so quickly, with such wifely resignation, that I could find no suitable exclamation of horror at this act of charity. I told her that for nothing on earth would I consent to the bargain.

'Oh, but you must,' she whispered. 'I can't go against my husband. Besides, I shall be glad of them to make cakes.'

She had become thoroughly good-natured. Her happy features had the usual ingratiating smile. Knowing how much cleverer she was at business than her husband, how entirely she ran the concern, I was full of wonderment that she who normally wore the trousers had so miraculously buckled under. To have refused at this juncture would have been to prolong an unpalatable situation. I gave her the eggs for much less than Mme Trémois sold them. At least I had the satisfaction of taking a smaller profit than she normally took with me.

A few moments later I walked into Mme Baudon's grocery shop. I had neglected her of late, and I suppose she feared I might take my custom elsewhere. She exclaimed loudly:

'My dear little Mme Henrey, how glad I am to see you, and have you brought me the eggs I perceive in your basket? That is a splendid surprise!'

'You surely don't want to buy them?' I asked, noticing a great bowl full of new-laid eggs. 'The price is dropping.'

'Not with me, Mme Henrey,' she said in her most affable tone. Then, turning to her little assistant: 'Take Mme Henrey's basket and credit her with twelve francs each for her eggs.' Then, business-like: 'What can I sell you to-day?'

I took the full value of the eggs in merchandise and promised to come back the next day for sugar, coffee, and chocolate. I felt suddenly as if my shame had been wiped away, and though I was tolerably certain that Mme Baudon had merely bought my eggs as a peace offering, my gratitude was genuine.

Other things besides eggs were falling in price, most important of which were barley and corn. Rettol, coming down my orchard to offer me money for trees which he was right in saying would blow down dangerously if not soon felled, seemed less of an enemy than at first I had thought. His promise to split the roots of the pear-trees had touched me. It was quite hopeless to count on the Déliquaires for anything which needed so much effort. Already I wondered by whom I ought to replace Beaudry to dig up the immense kitchen garden which he and his wife had so magnificently looked after the previous years, and, selfishly, I began to hope that if prices continued to fall, it was possible that there would be just enough unemployment in the village to make the men more anxious to work. A woman who wrote to me now and again from New Zealand, having read certain of my books, complained that the men had reached a state where they left all the work to the women. Though Mme Beaudry doubtless nagged her man, I could not blame her for being angry when he turned down work.

I decided, as a start, to dig up a large piece at the end of the kitchen garden and plant green peas, covering the seeds with fish nets to keep off, as far as possible, the frost, the birds of the air, and the members of Matilda's farmyard. The hens dug everything up, even my bulbs. I was full of good intentions, but the evening was the only moment of the day I could devote to these exertions. It would have been more convenient if, like Mme George Sand, I could have written at midnight when the house slept, instead of closeting myself up so much of the precious day. The gentle hours between dusk and supper-time I still employed in reading aloud, not only to amuse Bobby but equally to charm myself. I resolved suddenly to go on with *Kidnapped*, whose fights on the brig had disposed me against it, but the Stewart *maquis* in heather and brae greatly pleased my son, and I was myself quite won over by the sensitive friendship therein described between youth and man. Immediately afterwards we began our most gentle evenings with *The Mill on the Floss*, allowing George Eliot to describe for us in words superbly strung, cool streams and tall trees, as lovely and peaceful as ours. Tilly, the black cat, who had come back, hungry and slightly limping, after being four days in a snare, soon went off again, and this time had been absent for so long that we were bound to consider him lost. Our male cats, when they reached a certain age, would go off adventurously at dusk, like airmen to attack an objective, and one morning they would be missing. We had noticed this curious thing, that when a cat like Tilly was caught once and escaped, he would nearly always return, and that would be the end. I am afraid baby rabbits were too powerful an attraction. Innumerable poachers placed snares in our woods. It would have been impossible to catch them.

Baba also had experienced his initiation. One morning I found him soaked and miserable, and smelling horribly of liquid manure. His appetite had gone, and not even the fire in the low room was able to dry him. I wished greatly he could have told me what happened that night. Had he been chased by a fox or attacked by a man? It was about four days after Tilly's final disappearance, and for a moment I thought he might have discovered his brother at the bottom of a disused drinking-pool, guided to him by the same pitiful cries which once guided me to a young cat who had been trapped by a gin in a hedge. I imagined that perhaps he had tried to save him, sinking deeply into the fetid water. At all events, he quite changed after this adventure, no longer sleeping contentedly for hours in front of the fire while we read. After the first chapter of Maggie he would rudely leave us, even though supper had not yet been served, and we might not see him again till morning.

The difference of an hour between French and English time was the reason, curiously enough, why we went to bed later than we might otherwise have done. I had a radio by my bed, and we would generally lay aside the book we happened to be reading a

few minutes before the nine o'clock news from London. This was the signal for Bobby to put himself into pyjamas, and slip, with his teddy bears and dolls, into the bed against the half-timbering. He had a bed lamp, so that he could read as long as he wished without straining his eyes. He was alone and yet, because of the narrow corridor between our two rooms, we were together. We did not try to put out the fire in the low room, merely making certain that the logs upon it were of elm or apple, which burn safely, and thus it would often continue merrily through the night. I was also learning how to keep the central heating just sufficiently active for a draught to start it up again before breakfast. The all-night warmth of the house was one of the things I appreciated most towards the end of this winter. As my husband was away I could read very late, and come down to a welcoming fire to make tea if I felt so inclined.

Coming up to bed as Big Ben boomed nine made me entirely forget that it was ten in France. The result, of course, was to add an hour to each day. The radio did not play any great part in our lives except for this calling us to bed. As soon as my son had called me to say his prayers, putting his lamp out, and going to sleep at once, I read mostly in French, discovering occasionally some outstanding contemporary novel like Germaine Beaumont's *La Roue d'Infortune*, which she had dedicated to Colette. These warm nights of mid February had suddenly brought back the bats which during my sleep, the windows being open, would occasionally flit terrifyingly from beam to beam. Like the women in the south of France, I was pursued by a fear that one might catch in my hair and send me bald, a mere wives' tale, I fancy.

Rettol and his son-in-law arrived at eight, immediately setting to work on the first pear-tree root. I still lay comfortably in bed. The day before, at this hour, just a few birds, the thrushes beginning, sang in the garden. One or two, living in the roof and knowing me, hopped on the zinc ledge of the window facing the sunrise, to peck at the bread I always put there. But this morning, what a singing and chirruping and nest hunting and merry-making! My ears were nearly deafened. Lingerie blues and pinks streaked the sky above the Louis XIII château. In the higher branches of an ivy-covered oak, larger birds of the crow family were frantically busy. Above them others flew through the clear air in formation. My fruit trees were quite covered, and took on the appearance of aviaries. In the farmyard the ducks were quacking themselves hoarse, furious because Matilda would not let them go across the green orchard to the clear stream, but she kept strictly to the rule that they should not escape till they had laid three eggs within easy reach of her cottage door. The magnificent male turkey, gorgeous in black robes and scarlet wig, fan held high, side wings beating against the dusty earth, hissed with the noise of a piston moving in an engine before it starts up. The hens, one after the other, flew over the white gates into the orchard, and I could see them tumbling helter-skelter down the grassy slopes. Eight-week-old Christmas, the chick, pursued its mother with touching affection. When the hen found some comfortable place, like the dog's kennel or the various toy buildings Bobby built under the cherry-tree, to lay, the orphan would remain obediently outside till she had finished, even if the operation took an hour. He looked so pretty with his fluffy grey feathers, waiting. She might have said to him: 'Now stay here like a good boy. Mother will be back in a moment!' He would hurry up affectionately when she had finished. Off they would go after this, in search of the others.

Within twenty minutes Rettol had disposed of his first knotty tree, and had moved on to the next. Through glasses I watched the two men at work, the elder powerful as a steam engine, the younger tall, scarcely more than an adolescent, shoulders and bare arms gleaming like marble in the sunshine. I took little more notice of them till after lunch when, having dealt with my mail, I decided to do some more digging in the kitchen garden. They had finished all the pear-tree roots and were preparing to break up two pollards, one where Rettol had found me the previous evening, the other down by the stream.

My adventure with the eggs quite changed my life. In London, during the bombardments, I had been so short of them; on the farm hitherto we had sold so many to buy meat and groceries that I had never enjoyed the feeling of being reckless. Now, if nobody wanted them, I would have a fine orgy. I put three in a bread-and-butter pudding for lunch, three in a cake for tea, and I used a seventh to wash my hair which I set just before working in the garden so that the sun should dry it, for as the day had progressed the heat was like the most glorious summer day, its rays strong enough to burn one's skin, white and unresistant because of the long winter.

I noticed that Mme Beaudry had taken away her tools, though she usually kept them in a compartment of our half-timbered bakery, and from this I deduced that neither she nor her husband had any intention of doing any more work in the kitchen garden. Our own, intended for the farmers, were heavy for me, but I dug quite a large square and successfully planted several rows of shallots, this being the right moment to do so. Bobby, who had carefully watched Mme Beaudry at work, gave me the benefit of his advice, and in other ways also made himself useful, collecting the dry sticks from last year's beans and wheeling them away in his barrow. The Poulains' kitchen garden was on the other side of the hedge, and more distantly their magnificent half-timbered cow-house, now fitted up for electrical milking. Ernest, his wife Yvonne, and their various farm-hands, including the girl Henriette, touched equally by the spell of this mid-summer weather, were very busy.

The ducks, coming up to the fence which divided the kitchen garden from the undulating grass of the orchard, made a great to-do, wanting to poke their bills amongst the newly turned

earth, but I would not let them for fear they would entangle themselves in the fish nets over the green peas. Bobby made a bonfire, after which he ran to the cottage for a pitcher of cider, for we were both as thirsty as labourers. We then went, for a change, to the farmyard, where we took the sitting hen from her eggs so that she should take her food and exercise, and because one of the ducks was lame we put her, with a bowl of water and some sweet corn, under a steel cage to prevent her being attacked by the turkeys. A moment later my son hurried off to ride Levure, the white mare, the first of a team of two horses bringing Déliquaire's farm cart up the orchard.

Matilda did her ironing in the afternoon. She did not believe in electric irons, having been brought up amongst seamstresses and laundrywomen who, by a turn of their wrists or a thump and a bang where it was needed, could iron the magic way. Wives of American millionaires, when they came to Paris twenty years ago, could not believe the pleats and other miracles which the maids at the hotels put into their lingerie and blouses. Of all my accomplishments I am proudest that I know how to iron, but even if labour becomes cheap again there will be few of us competent to transmit this lovely French art.

The irons were put to heat on the stove in the cottage, the same stove upon which the bread was put to toast for breakfast. While they heated, Matilda sat very upright on a hard chair and read a novel, allowing a finger to hover over the leaf as if, the page read, she were afraid not to turn it fast enough. Matilda had always read like this, avidly, and when I was a little girl and we were poor, she used to paste together the serials in the Paris newspapers for her subsequent delectation.

A pile of beautifully ironed clothes now stood fragrant and warm on the table which a carpenter I once employed had made for me at a bench he had fixed up in the stables. Matilda, closing her book reluctantly, announced that it was the right moment of the year to gather dandelions for a salad. She put a scarf over her hair, and took her black-handled knife and an osier basket. She would carefully inspect the slopes of The Point and return by way of the lane past Victor Duprez's farm, being interested in a clump of cowslips which she claimed were nearly in bud.

Being left to myself, I went down to the stream to see how Rettol was progressing. I had not paid any great attention to this second pollard at the time of its fall, beyond noticing that it was thick and knotty, of a light grey colour, but almost entirely covered by tentacles of dead ivy.

Exposed naked on the grass, sawn into lengths about four feet, this piece of wood was giving the two woodcutters a great deal more trouble than all the pear-tree roots together. To break up each piece which looked like the vein-swollen forearm of a prize-fighter, they were obliged to use more than a dozen specially strong iron wedges, which they drove in with ten-pound hammers swung alternately with rhythmic sequence. I had not dreamed that elm could be so hard. Interiorly the wood of a deep chocolate, highly polished by two centuries' existence guarding our orchard from that of the neighbours. Each length was split into three logs for the fire in the low room, jagged, magnificent, fantastically shaped, and so heavy that I stumbled trying to carry one. The pollard, having been blown over with its roots, I said I supposed it was dry, to which Rettol answered: 'Lord, ma'am, it 's been dead these last ten years, and for that is all the harder to cut.' I felt ashamed to burn pieces so magnificent in strength and beauty of colour, but by the same token the romance of it touched my imagination. Many people had fine hearths; few indeed would watch giant lumps of aged elm, fit to have graced a galleon, simmer gently from morning till night on caverns of red-hot cinders. According to Norman custom, I had sent Bobby to the two men earlier in the day with the key to the cellar, so that they could freely turn the cider tap. They announced their intention of going there now, and on our way across the orchard we saw two men, one of whom I recognized as Jollivet by his long, spectacled features and curious amble, coming towards us. I asked Rettol if he knew the name of the second, but before he could say anything his son-in-law answered:

'It 's my brother.'

At this I exclaimed, somewhat shamedly:

'Nobody has told me your name.'

'Bouveau,' he answered.

The name of Bouveau was curiously familiar. I searched strenuously for a few moments, and then asked:

'Would it be some member of your family who, while hiding a Scots parachutist, killed five Germans on the roof of a villa and then ran bleeding to the house of Mlle Lefranc?'

'My brother,' he said.

The brother, some ten years the elder, but as fine a man, with blue eyes and ochre skin, as I think I have ever seen, ready for anything, and as strong as two lions if village rumour was true, walked a little ahead of his lanky companion. A dog, running here and there, but often returning to lick his master's hands, made the third of the advancing party. The Normans like to bring their dogs with them to work. Woodcutter, crofter, carpenter, are happiest when their dogs are sitting in the sunshine beside them; at lunch they share the meal. We were soon all on the sawdust of the cellar by the open door, the cider flowing from the polished yellow tap. The elder Bouveau told us, with words and gestures he must have used a hundred times before, the wonderful story of how Déliquaire had come to him one day, soon after the

Normandy landing, with news that a Scotsman was hiding near his farm. There was a second parachutist, I think, who found refuge in another farm. Bouveau took charge of both, put them into civilian clothes, and hid them in the attic of his tiny house, the 'Villa Lucie,' on a slope just above the post office. The Germans came to the villa late one night; Bouveau, crouching at the top of the narrow stairs with a machine-gun, shot five. The Englishman and the Scot escaped over the roofs. Bouveau was caught, and was on the point of being shot when a German officer gave a counter-order. He escaped, and though four times fired at, dragged himself wounded to the midwife's house.

Many people said that until this incident Bouveau was so involved in black market operations with the Germans that he planned the battle on purpose to save himself at the liberation. Many of the noblest deeds were done by men of adventurous spirit, to whom shooting and rapine came easily. I like to think that Bouveau helped the Britishers in a natural access of pity. The magnificent creature facing us in the cider cellar was of the sort to fear neither man nor devil. He was curiously Nordic in type; indeed he was very much how I had pictured Alan Breck in *Kidnapped*, and it would have been as pretty a sight to have seen him with lace round his cuffs handling a sword in combat, as mowing down those Germans in the staircase of his burning villa (for they had set the place alight) or helping his brother and M. Rettol to swing the sledgehammer over iron wedges in a two-hundred-year-old elm.

A curious picture we must have made—myself on the stone step, the four men gathered round the cask, and the dog at Rettol's feet. A bloodthirsty lot too were these fellows, though no doubt there was something of bombast in their desire to impress me. The elder Bouveau exclaimed:

'The next German, I filled his groin with lead!'

He clapped his hands against this part of his anatomy and made a fearful face as if it was he who felt the pain. Jollivet broke in:

'The moment you ran down the street—that's the time for me to carry on with the story. I was helping the police. We followed the bloodstains all along the cobbles. Mlle Lefranc came to the door of her house and said to us: "No, I haven't seen a soul!" We winked at her. The blood was all over the threshold.'

Rettol had been silent till this point. The light caught his blue shirt, put on clean that morning, as luminous as the sky above the orchard, and because he was corpulent, in the position he stood, the blueness of his shirt made a fascinating semicircle. Open at the neck, it revealed much hairiness; where it joined the trousers one saw, coming up to meet it, an inch or two of flannel underpants. Puffs of air coming in from cracks in the distant wall, where ivy had pushed itself through the overdry mud of the half-timbering, blew gently against the curls blossoming above each ear. As an example of rustic strength he was both admirable and frightening. Jealous, I believe, of Bouveau's declamatory success, he seized the right moment to begin a story of his own. Immediately after the landing the Germans had ordered the inhabitants in the coastal area to bury their wireless sets. Rettol had his under a cabbage patch, but in the evening, pretending to garden, would bend down, scrape the earth away, and listen. Whilst doing this a German soldier came along stealthily from behind and kicked him vigorously in the pants. Rettol, like a clown in a circus, acted both the kicked and the dispenser of this ludicrous justice. This pantomime in front of the giant vat was Fatty Arbuckle at his best, and I laughed with such good heart that the actor suddenly looked at me, astonished at his success. A professional clown would have exploited my hilarity. Rettol was anxious to do so, but my gaze had made him blush and he repeated *ad infinitum* the words:

'And the German soldier kicked me up the bottom!'

Jollivet, determined to take the stage again, warmed by the cider which was quite excellent, better than any we had ever made, returned to the subject of Bouveau's adventure, telling us how the young wife, seeing her husband running wounded down the street, jumped down from a back window and sought shelter with her husband's young brother, who was not yet married to Rettol's daughter. She undressed quickly, jumped into bed with him, and when the Germans came pretended she was his wife, but the sergeant, who knew them, said '*Nein, nein!* Wrong husband, wrong wife!'

All this, by different ways, brought us to the subject of my parquet floor, and from thence to an examination of the cellar and the cider press so urgently needing repair, and Jollivet, who in spite of a certain slowness and repetition in speech was a man of ideas, said reflectively:

'For you, Ma'am Henrey, who has a partiality for old-fashioned things, there 's a way, perhaps, of restoring this beautiful building not only as it should by rights be restored, but also without spending more money than is justified. It 's the cutting down of those oak-trees in your wood for your bedroom floor which set my mind thinking that maybe we could take some of your own elms and, without sending them to the mill, which is ruinous because of taking them there and bringing them back, haul them behind a couple of stout horses to the bottom of the orchard and fashion the beams by hand as our ancestors did, taking eighteen months or two years to do so.'

'A sound idea,' approved Rettol, 'and there would be little cost to it but my charge for felling, and your labour during the slack months of the winter. A deal prettier, too, than if the beams were made at the saw-mill.'

'In three to four years,' mused Jollivet, 'we could make this place look as it did a century ago.'

They began to inspect walls and rafters, promising to draw up plans and consult me in a week's time. Then, because night was falling, I bade them good evening and left them.

XII

LATE in the afternoon, on my way down to the post, I used to look forward to my first, refreshing sight of the sea.

Half my journey was countrified. Wearing a red knitted bonnet when it was windy, carrying a small basket with the eggs and the mail, and another, wider and less smart, for the bread and the provisions, I would climb to the top of the orchard, pass through the big white gate into the narrow lane, and follow it between my own fields to where it widened, the Poulains' magnificent farm on my right, the tall trees of Mme Michelin's estate on my left. If Mme Yvonne was not drawing water at the hand pump, washing at the open-air laundry, feeding the chickens, or making the butter, I would look into the stone-floored kitchen and bid her good evening. On Tuesdays, if she had been with Ernest in the pony trap to market at Dozulé, the most important of our inland markets, she would tell me if prices were up or down, and we might gossip a little longer than usual. On other evenings I would merely ask her about Mme Castel and the children, and hurry down along the lane.

A little farther on, to the left, where the three-hundred-year-old elm had stood at the corner of Mme Michelin's walled fruit and vegetable garden, a white, stony path turned sharply to the high road between Deauville and Caen, but I walked straight past this, pursuing my way along the more picturesque lane which was now flanked on the right by a fine estate called Bois Lurette, and on the left by the Bellay farm, a large mansion in neglected grounds now serving as a holiday camp for children from a communist suburb of Paris, and another property on which the house had been blown up during the Liberation.

The lane, all this while, thickly wooded on either side, very quiet except for the singing of birds starting to nest, had mossy hedgerows in which the first cowslips were already scenting the air. Victor Duprez, driving to or from his farm, or Ernest

Poulain standing whip in hand in his farm cart, were the only people who would occasionally overtake me. The holiday camp only functioned in the hot summer months, and the children used a gate opening on the main road at the far end of the property. But walking towards me, her face wrinkled like an apple, dressed completely in black, very sparse and tapping her way along, like a witch, with a tall stick which she held by the

pommel above the level of her tight waist, I often met the grandmother Bellay returning to her farm by this lane, tinted by the blood-red of the sinking sun.

Quite suddenly one came upon a meeting of four paths, a circular platform with the trees behind one, and a white road, as deserted as the lane one had just left, diving steeply down to the sea whose horizon appeared to be climbing up into the sky. Great ships often lay at anchor distantly outside the harbour of

Le Havre whose immense oil tanks, painted silver, gleamed prettily, the flattened docks behind them.

Rich villas stood on either side of the road whose flints and uneven surface tripped one's heels and menaced one's stockings. But the smell of the sea came up, and salty winds brushed against one's cheeks. Well-tended gardens preened themselves in readiness for Easter visitors. Almond blossom and japonica nodded gaily. Down, down the straight road one hurried, the sea coming nearer at each step. The weather being so lovely, Bobby, who was with me, took it into his head, after we had done our work, to go paddling. Except for some fishermen clambering out of their boats, we were alone on the immense sands.

Our village was at equal distance between the two extremities of a wide, majestic bay. In the direction of Caen, five black cliffs stretched hard knuckled fingers across the sand at rocks covered with mussels, which at certain seasons of the year the villagers gathered by torchlight. In the direction of Le Havre the lights of Deauville and Trouville hovered like fire in front of the violet haze covering the estuary of the Seine whose flat, muddy, grass-tufted banks pushed inland.

I was often sad not to take more advantage of these lonely stretches of sand and surf, the changing moods of sea and sky. My own duties, in the house and out of it, did not leave even enough time to tutor my son. When he came down to the village with me, I made him repeat his multiplication tables or the rules of grammar. On the sands I used to draw a map of the world. He ran over mountains, sailed between Le Havre and Rio, crossed the North American continent by railroad, flew from Seattle to Tokyo. He learnt too easily. I decided in future only to guide him in French and English literature, and to employ immediately for Latin, Greek, and mathematics some brilliant young woman graduate of an English or Scottish university, being strongly of the opinion that a clever woman teaches better than a man and that in a child of nine or ten careful and sustained tuition in his own surroundings can produce magnificent results.

'Let us come down to-morrow morning,' Bobby said, 'and walk along the sands to Trouville. You remember last summer?'

'We took a taxi to come back,' I answered.

'Would that be too expensive?'

'We might not find a taxi easily at this time of year. It would be wiser to have Fournier drive us there on market day. I need some tools for the garden. At any rate it would give us an outing.'

'To-morrow is market day,' he said.

'Who told you?'

'Mme Beaudry. She wants to visit her sister at Deauville and take her watch to M. Déliquaire's cousin, the watchmaker, but she says she is too fat to take the motor-coach.'

'We could ask her to come with us. I should feel less extravagant hiring the car.'

'Yes, let 's. I 'd love to go.'

We ordered the taxi from Fournier for nine o'clock. It was dark by the time we returned to the farm, and I was unwilling to let Bobby go alone along the road to Saint-Vaast to invite Mme Beaudry to join us. I therefore left him with Matilda, and taking a lamp and a can to fetch some milk from the Déliquaires, set off down the orchard.

As soon as I had crossed the road to Saint-Vaast and unfastened the farm gate, I heard the cows trampling in the wooden building. Mme Déliquaire came out with a lantern in one hand and a heavy churn in the other. I saw the lantern swinging as she moved slowly on the other side of the tall dung-heap. She turned, and not recognizing me in the dark, asked who it was.

'It is I, Mme Déliquaire.'

'Mme Henrey!' she cried. 'Bless me, I thought it might be Jacques. I 'm wanting him to skim the milk.'

She put down the heavy churn, while I picked a path cautiously over the dung.

'Tired?' I queried as, coming up to her, my lantern shone on her features, which I thought were drawn.

'It 's the digestion,' she said. 'I was so bad this morning, M. Déliquaire took me down to see the doctor.' She laughed grimly: 'You know me. I have to be pretty bad to see the doctor.'

The last time she had seen the doctor it was about a poisoned foot. He laughed at her because she squealed when he hurt her. French country doctors are apt to be rough, and Mme Déliquare was not good at enduring pain. I well imagined she had not wanted to see him again. She said her husband had been in my woods making faggots with Roger. He was not so strong as he used to be and needed somebody to help him press the four-foot-tall sticks round the branched twigs and then secure each bundle with a turn of steel wire. The farmers' wives, so much stronger than we townswomen, could toss such a bundle over their backs and carry it into the house, where they would put it in a cavity against the hearth for lighting the fires and giving them a sudden flare up under the black pot or the frying-pan. I, so much less strong, could just lift a bundle on the wheelbarrow. Unloading at the door of the low room, I would drag it across the tiled floor.

Déliquaire and Roger, in a hurry to finish their work, had not helped with the milking. The farmhouse door was partly open, throwing a beam of light across the garden fence as far as the dog's kennel at the foot of the gnarled tree. Mme Déliquaire said pensively:

'It looks as if the men are back. I suppose they came in whilst I was busy.'

She seemed glad to have me to talk to a moment before going in, and I asked her since when her digestion had gone wrong.

'Oh,' she answered, 'these twenty years.' She laughed, a little sorry for herself, and added: 'When it 's chicken for dinner, I have the bones and the parson's nose; when it 's a piece of meat, it 's the outside slice for me, that is, if I 'm lucky. Then, too, there 's really no sitting down to a meal unless for a moment, on the edge of a chair. When I 've served the men once, I 'm bobbing up to serve them again. It 's nothing for Jacques to have five helpings. We 're all the same, aren't we? The men come first. It 's natural.'

I suddenly recalled one evening when I had dropped in on them at supper. Mme Déliquaire was standing, as I so often saw her, with a hand on the frying-pan in front of the stove. The oil lamp threw a circle of light on the table. Déliquaire and his sons were eating fried herrings, loosening the flesh with the extreme point of their jack-knives which they held against their thumbs. The pocket-knive travelled with incredible speed between plate and mouth, though lifting but a tiny morsel at each lightning movement. I was fascinated, not shocked. What struck me forcibly was that soon nothing remained of the herring but the skeleton, cleaned to perfection, as if by a bird with a sharp beak. And as soon as the skeleton was clean, it was tossed on the floor for the cats or the dogs, and a newly fried fish, all steaming and glistening, was thrust on to the empty plate by Mme Déliquaire. When the men had finished, their knives were wiped and put back in pockets. They rose: Déliquaire to a dance in the village, the boys to the pictures, for it was Saturday night.

'The doctor has given me a regime,' Mme Déliquaire was saying.

'What?' I asked.

'Milk!' she exclaimed.

Poor woman, she could not stand it! The men, on the other hand, at each meal had bowls of milk beside their plates. From time to time, between eating, they would bend down and bury their faces in their bowls, drinking deeply and greedily. It was the funniest sight. Déliquaire's mesh of discoloured hair would curl round his bowl. Jacques would drink milk at all hours of the day; when he helped his mother to milk in our fields on summer evenings he would even drink from the top of the churns.

'You 'd better come in a moment,' said Mme Déliquaire.

I followed her cautiously, not to stumble.

Two logs were burning brightly in the hearth; Jeannine was at the end of the long table, embroidering a sheet for her home—when they could find one. She was still making her trousseau. Roger had a hand on the oil cloth, playing with the base of the oil lamp. A young farmer, with red cheeks against which an unshaved dark beard made an uncouth effect, a cap pulled over his eyes, was seated in front of Déliquaire, who was stroking the spaniel which had jumped on his knees.

Déliquaire informed me that the grain merchant at Dives had that very afternoon delivered five tons of basic slag, of which three were for my home orchard. He called Mme Déliquaire to show me the piece of paper on which the truck driver had marked the number of sacks and the cost, and when she produced it from under a piece of china on the mantelpiece he borrowed a pencil from his friend to work out what I owed him.

'Now,' he said, stretching out his legs and pulling the spaniel up by the scruff of her neck, 'let us see what it says.'

He made a great show of moving the paper to the right spot under the lamp where the beam would shine clearly upon it, but there was something in this play which reminded me that the other town councillors always had it that he could neither read nor write.

'They wanted thirty-seven thousand francs if I remember right,' declared Mme Déliquaire from the buttery, who thus dashed my hopes of discovering whether her husband could read.

'Yes,' put in the farmer, 'that would be the price.'

'If five tons cost thirty-seven thousand francs,' said Déliquaire, 'how much do three tons cost?'

Each morning after breakfast I set these sort of sums for Bobby, leaving him to work them out by the fire in the low room, whilst I disappeared to produce seven or eight hundred words of prose.

This question of manure was extremely complicated. Before the war tenant farmers were required by contract to manure the fields they leased. This clause, I think, still existed. These chemical manures, however, were only just becoming available again, and were so expensive that only the richest farmers would buy them. My home orchard, which was not rented out officially to Déliquaire, but which I merely put at the disposal of his cows for grazing in return for some butter and milk, gave unusually fine pasture. Lately, however, moss was here and there apparent, and I was always in the most stupid fear that the terrain would suddenly lose its emerald green. Behind all this, of course, was my eternal thought that one day, like old women in fairy tales, I would be obliged, owing to straitened circumstances, to retire with one cow on my piece of land. I therefore wanted my grass to remain beautiful.

The two men, quite forgetting I was there, began to discuss manures in general. The one said:

'The first year it 's better to put down natural manure, so the grass will grow tall and luscious. After that a little lime burns the weeds and kills the insects, and that farmer at Tourgeville, who is no fool'—was he referring to M. Cauvin?—'puts down salt, the same sort you add to hay when rain has made it unpalatable. It 's a wonder what salt will do. Kills everything that 's bad. This basic slag is good too. Brings up the clover something wonderful, but I would have put down natural manure first.'

'You mean I 'm doing wrong?' I asked, thrusting myself into the conversation, and suddenly thinking that I would be quite ruining my land.

'No, no, not doing wrong, lady, but don't make a habit of it. The Belgians are terrors for that. They cultivate the soil so intensely that they leave it flat—the grass won't grow no more. A real desolation. It comes from wanting to work too hard, to produce too much. That kills the soil. God didn't mean it to go that way. Put down your basic slag, ma'am, but don't do it again in a hurry. If it rains you 'll get a grand lot of clover for three years.'

'And after that?'

'Well, nothing lasts for ever.'

I felt increasingly stupid. I did not plan to settle on my orchard with my one cow within three years. I was therefore putting down artificial manure at the cost of over twenty pounds to fatten Déliquaire's cows, after which might not my soil be impoverished?

'It 's a pity you didn't put down the manure to-day,' said Mme Déliquaire; 'it 's starting to rain.'

'A shower maybe,' said the farmer, 'but the glass isn't for rain.'

'And to-morrow at dawn,' said Déliquaire, 'I drive to Yvetot.'

'Yvetot?' I queried, looking at Mme Déliquaire, for it was her part of the world.

'Yes,' she answered, 'my father is coming to spend a month with us. The dear man is tired. It will do him good.'

'Oh, I 'm so glad!' I exclaimed.

Mme Déliquaire's father, like the waif in George Sand's novel, was known merely by his Christian name because he had been found on the roadside. They called him the père François, and before Mme Déliquaire's marriage she had been known as Mlle Madeleine François. The père François was over seventy, a sweetly pathetic man whom I had seen for the first time the previous summer. The Déliquaires had come to milk their cows, which were at the bottom of my home orchard, near the cider press. It was a warm summer evening, and I had gone down with Bobby, who liked to drink a glass of milk from the churn and pat Bouboule on the flank. The père François was holding one of the cows by the horns. We were introduced by Mme Déliquaire, looking up from under the animal which she was milking. The père François smiled gently, and said to me in the softest voice:

'I 'm a foundling child, ma'am!'

The word 'child' in the mouth of this humble septuagenarian had moved me to tears. In his smallness he had some of the freshness of a child. I would have kissed his hand, so great was my sympathy for him.

On that occasion Déliquaire had brought back from Yvetot also a boy called Claud, related in some way to Mme Déliquaire—a nice lad, but who played all the day long, searching the hedgerows for birds' eggs, whistling jazz tunes, and kicking a football across the orchards. At meals he ate ravenously. He went back to Yvetot after the apples had been gathered, and the Déliquaires were not altogether sorry. As Mme Déliquaire said to me: 'A boy on a farm eats more than a man and does half the work. Therefore, while you are about it, employ a man!'

Déliquaire, who was still thinking about the basic slag, said:

'Don't worry, ma'am, to-morrow evening, when I 'm back from Yvetot, I 'll borrow a spraying machine.'

'I thought you had one?' I exclaimed. He had told me so only a week earlier.

'Bless me, no,' he answered. 'They are expensive machines.

I only know of two or three this side of Dozulé. And when I say I 'll borrow one I ought to say *hire* one. I 'm likely to be charged two thousand francs a day.'

'I know something about that,' put in the farmer, 'for I had an experience a year ago. It 's not two thousand francs just for the day you use it, but from the word "go," from the moment you borrow it to the moment you take it back. So if never a rainy day comes along . . . You get my meaning?'

'If there 's no rain, only wind,' said Déliquaire, 'the manure flies away, and then I reckon your money goes down the drain.'

'You might do it by hand?' I said nervously. I remembered flying once between Paris and Brussels, and seeing men sowing corn as in biblical days like the figure which in my girlhood adorned French postage stamps.

'Not on your life!' said Déliquaire, making a terrible grimace. 'I tried it once. Ugh! Ugh! Never again.' He became calmer, and thinking perhaps he had painted too black a picture, and that it would be wiser to give me a little more hope, added: 'Don't fret, ma'am, to-morrow I 'll borrow the machine, and the first sign of rain will find me in your orchard.'

Already Mme Déliquaire was at her frying-pan. She said, looking over her shoulder at Déliquaire:

'Ma'am Henrey is thinking of her eggs.'

'And the pigs I 've been fattening up!' said the farmer. 'The price has slumped! Slumped, I tell you! Would you care to buy my pigs?'

'If it goes on they will have to bring the rents down,' said Déliquaire, not so much for my particular ear as for the relief which the expression of such heartfelt sentiments gave him. 'They 'll see, by gum! They 'll see!'

'There 's ways and means,' said the farmer.

'There is that!' agreed Déliquaire.

'And if it doesn't pay us to produce butter we 'll give it to the pigs!' said the farmer.

'The pigs would be glad enough!' laughed Mme Déliquaire, who had a gift for preventing the men from getting angry. 'Now, how about staying for a bite to eat, Ma'am Henrey?'

'No, really,' I protested, 'I was on my way to Mme Beaudry.'

The road to St. Vaast was so black that I was glad of my lamp. I could hear M. Gilles sawing in his orchard. The locksmith, working in the village all day, was obliged to do much of his farming in the dark. I have known him plant his young trees by the light of a hurricane lamp. Deaf M. Gravé was at home. I could see chinks of light through the boarded-up window of his dining-room. I wondered what he did all by himself in the evenings.

A five-barred gate, beautifully kept, led into the Beaudrys' narrow orchard, the gravel path having a hedge on one side and

the flower and vegetable garden on the other. The Beaudrys never used their front door. They entered their pretty green-shuttered house from the back. There was a wicker gate and a tinkling bell, and the dog sprang out of its kennel by the chicken coop, and barked, dragging its steel chain.

Having passed through the wicker gate and knocked for some moments unsuccessfully at the kitchen door, I began to call Mme Beaudry by name. After a while a window was opened and her husband appeared, his braces hanging from his waist, his neck and face looking curiously withered, his lean arms outstretched, for he had thrown aside the wooden shutters. He gave the impression of an apple-tree in winter garb. He asked thickly what I wanted. He sounded angry, and I wondered if he had been drinking.

His chilling welcome quite put me out, and I could only explain in the stupidest way the purpose of my visit. However, I said that if Mme Beaudry came round at nine in the morning I would take her in a car to Trouville.

'Why should she want to go?' he asked aggressively.

'To see her sister for one thing. And it 's market day. And it would give her a change.'

'She hasn't time to go gadding around.'

'Is she at home?'

'She 's in her nightdress.'

'I don't need to see her. Just give her the message.'

'You didn't come just for that?'

'Yes, of course.'

He looked at me with still deeper suspicion. I said good night, thinking it was most unlikely he would give her the message.

But at a quarter to nine the next morning Mme Beaudry arrived at the farm, dressed in black, and very neat. She sat on the edge of a kitchen chair, her bag on her ample knees, watching us finish breakfast. It was the first time I had ever seen her doing nothing, and she was not at her ease. She said:

'I 'll go and fill the coal scuttles.'

'I 've done them already.'

'I 'll fetch some hot water for the washing-up.'

'You 'll do nothing of the kind. I can hear a car. I 'll go and get my things.'

Fournier had sent his brother-in-law and partner, an Italian, who used to tell us in his charming accent how it was no longer considered a reprehensible thing in his profession for a man to do a month or so in jail because the government made life so difficult for the haulage contractor and grain merchant.

As we bumped off down the lane Mme Beaudry told me that as soon as I had left their house the previous night her husband had asked:

'Are you going?'

'Of course.'

'I shall expect my lunch to be ready as usual.' Then sulkily: 'I suppose you 'll be tired for your work in the afternoon?'

'Have you ever seen me tired for my work?'

She seemed rather pleased to be setting forth on this holiday, and in her barking voice commented on the various landmarks. When we came to the sands, for instance, she told us that only the other day deaf M. Gravé had walked all the way to Deauville by the seashore, and after looking at the shops in the town, came back the same way. She showed us the camouflaged hut in the swamps where Roger Déliquaire and his friends passed the night when they went duck-shooting. She was of the opinion that in another ten years the ground would be built on.

'We know to whom it all belongs!' she said with an informed laugh.

'And so do I,' broke in the Italian from his seat in front. Maître Vincent was a sharp fellow to have bought it when nobody wanted it. One day he 'll likely make a fortune.'

This led to a discussion about the unwisdom of building villas on the edge of the sand, the winter gales destroying the foundations and the salt eating the cement, for cement was a commodity our Italian bought and sold, and he liked to expatiate on various aspects of his business. Within a quarter of an hour we were passing through the wide avenues of Deauville. Then came the pretty station gaily painted, and the bridge into Trouville, where all along the quay, as far as the plage, the market splashed vivid colours as in the days of Boudin. When, at Sotheby's or Christies', somebody bids a thousand guineas for one of the artist's small canvases of Trouville, so very nineteenth century, I can smell the tar of the sailing boats, I can hear the beating of clogs against the cobbles, and I can see the geraniums and camelias in their pots set in rows on the quayside between the vegetable and clothing stalls. In the distance shines the casino and the powdery golden sand.

We went first into those narrow streets that criss-cross picturesquely between the market and the sea, rich merchandise invitingly displayed under gabled houses, in front of garbage water running tumultuously over cobble-stones. In one of these, with shutters closed because it was still early, was a small jeweller's, the name painted boldly across it: 'DÉLIQUAIRE.' We knocked and rang and soon a window above the shop was thrown open and the jeweller leant out. I recognized immediately one of the most jovial guests of Roger's wedding luncheon. He had not sat at the same table as I had, but quite at the other end of the hotel dining-room. Nevertheless, from time to time his voice, surmounting all the other noises of the eating and talking guests, would apostrophize the blushing Jeannine, who would look up, wide-mouthed, bursting out of her bridal dress, holding tightly in close fists her knife and fork. The wedding ring had been purchased at his shop. Doubtless he had sold it to Roger at a small discount. Mme Beaudry, doing the washing-up or plucking a goose at the Déliquaire farm, must have heard many keen discussions about the ring before it was placed on Jeannine's finger. Perhaps that is what gave Mme Beaudry the idea of giving the jeweller the watch when it went wrong, but since then she had apparently never had an opportunity to go to Trouville to get it back. Seeing the jeweller looking down upon us from his open window, I recalled how his voice had risen high during the wedding lunch: 'I 've a splendid range of alarm clocks for young married couples!' He was told the mayor, when kissing the bride after the ceremony at the town hall, had put a parcel in her hands and that the parcel, since opened, was found to contain an alarm clock. 'Then,' cried the jeweller, undaunted, 'she must have another kind. There are not only alarm clocks to wake you up, but also to tell you the hour to go to bed.' Massive laughter greeted this sally, and somebody asked: 'Perhaps you 've also got an alarm clock to make babies?' 'No, no,' said the Déliquaire cousin, 'but I 'll take the matter up.'

Seeing Mme Beaudry's massive form as she stood with her back to the gutter, straining her neck to explain her business, the jeweller shouted for her to wait. The window was closed again, and a commotion could be heard as he prepared to hurry down. Having a few things of my own to do, I said quickly to Mme Beaudry:

'The car will wait for us by the fish market. Take all your time, and when you have finished go and sit in it.'

Bobby and I took the first street leading to the sea. After so long in my bog, it was fun looking at the shops, for those in our village were apt to appear monotonous. The knitting wool, chiefly, filled me with the sort of admiration that children show in front of confectioners at Christmas-time. Suddenly, in all the most tender colours, in pinks and blues of every description, it had come back. Skeins hung from the highest parts of the windows, cascading down like the spray of Niagara when the sun plays upon it, tumbling over each other in colourful softness, landing pell-mell on the loosely wound balls of baby wool which only six months ago one could only obtain with rare coupons. This sight, more than the falling price of eggs, more even than the buttery *croissants* at the baker's, gave me an impression of returning plenty.

'Come on, mummy!' exclaimed my son, cutting my enthusiasm in a way that made me turn with exasperation upon him. 'Come and look at the sea.'

But how cold and grey was the beach, compared to the previous evening after the heat of an almost summery day! Our sand goes out a mile, is smoothly damp, and covered with the prettiest shells; here it was powdery, and the waves came in angrily. The beach at Trouville seems always to sigh for the gay nineties. The wind wails, and the magnificent hotels, so typical of the period, had not recovered from being boarded up by the Germans as part of the Atlantic wall. The towers and minarets of the Trouville Palace, where in old days one would have entered with a saucy straw hat and a parasol, were daubed with black paint for camouflage. One or two bedrooms, or perhaps sitting-rooms, were sliced open, revealing Victorian mosaic on the walls. The Hotel de Paris was a little reminiscent of a plaster Louvre. In the foreground, on the soft, golden sand, was a once elegant bar, barricaded against winter seas by nailed planks. Trouville attracts and repels me. I love it for what it once represented. One must have had a lot of fun being a young woman at the end of the last century, before the seas of shortages and shop queues. The novels and plays of the period are full of references to Trouville. I have the same impression, visiting it, of discovering the age of Guy de Maupassant and Toulouse-Lautrec as, at Herculaneum, of treading the vestiges of a former civilization. I dislike it because, coming here for the first outing after my confinement in 1939 with a number of friends staying at my farm, one of them, a Paris broker, foretold the war and the collapse of France. I hated him for being a bird of such ill omen. I have never quite recovered from the chill his words gave me.

Mme Beaudry was waiting for us at the fish market. We bought some seeds and gardening implements and drove to

Deauville, where Mme Beaudry's sister kept an hotel at the corner of a smart shopping arcade, opposite the casino. Pauline, as she was called, had proved the most successful of the fourteen children of whom Mme Beaudry was the sixth. Mme Beaudry claimed that she herself had been the least lucky, and for this she blamed Beaudry's timidity.

'If only he could have left me to my own devices,' she said, 'but he was always butting in.'

'Does your sister Pauline look like you?' I asked.

'Yes, but she 's fatter,' Mme Beaudry answered.

Pauline, when a girl, had chosen Paris as the place to try her luck. Only the brothers remained in Brittany. The girls were sent out into the world to look for husbands. Happily, nature had built them all of a pattern, buxom and strong, not knowing what it was to sit down. Pauline was a cook. She could make the most succulent dishes, a gift she can hardly have learnt in her native Brittany, where there is seldom anything but a potato or an onion to make a dish, so meagre is the soil. Pauline, seduced and jilted, was left with a fatherless son. Life was cruel in those days, but Mme Beaudry, who had much hidden kindness, took her sister's baby and brought him up with her own son in the green-shuttered house on the road to Saint-Vaast.

After the war Beaudry came home and Pauline went to this hotel at Deauville; first as a cook, then as housekeeper. Soon her capacity for hard work started to reap its just reward. The place was not large—there were but fifteen rooms—but it was open all the year round and magnificently situated. The richest people went to it in the season; their stewards and secretaries arrived in the winter for a week or two to supervise the decoration of their masters' villas.

Pauline felt the need of male protection and married a man who, like M. Beaudry, tidied up the roads. But Pauline's husband had the good sense to realize that his wife was much cleverer than himself. He allowed her to get on with her business, merely being there when she wanted him. It was also much better for her son to have a stepfather. The boy turned out wise, sober, hard-working like his mother. The German Occupation found Pauline in charge of the hotel; her genius for cooking enhanced her fortune.

Mme Beaudry, with many dignified expressions of thanks, got out of the car, and said she would only remain a moment with her sister, just the required time to kiss her on both cheeks and inquire after her health.

'Stamps cost so much these days,' she explained, 'I hardly ever write to her.'

What a fortune a woman like Mme Beaudry ought to have made properly guided! She was successful, of course, in a way. She owned her house and a bit of land. That was not so bad for a girl who had come at the age of sixteen from Brittany, pennyless, obliged to send back each month part of her wages to her parents. Mme Beaudry had little regard for people who did not own the houses they lived in. Of her brothers in Brittany, she once said to me: 'They have done well. They are all *chez eux*.' It took me a moment to understand what she meant by this expression 'at home,' but I then realized that we are none of us quite at home until we own the house we live in.

I left Bobby with the chauffeur, to walk along the avenue. How lovely it was! Here perhaps is one of the last manifestations of a plage built only for the rich. Trouville in the nineties, Deauville between the wars. Will fashion one day forsake these twin cities of elegant pleasure? What beautiful villas! What a fabulous fortune it must now require to keep them up. Our Italian chauffeur had pointed out one in particular, saying that the owner had just spent several million francs on repainting it. The gardens cost thousands of pounds every year.

'Who is he?' I asked. 'An Indian rajah, an Egyptian cotton king?'

'No,' he answered. 'A rag-and-bone merchant from Paris who did well during the Occupation, joined the Resistance movement just in time, and bought a mountain of American scrap metal.'

Consider that their owners only live in these villas for one month in each year! Behind Pauline's hotel there was such a pretty house with green lawns and a thatched gate with irises that would bloom in May. It was called 'Indiana.' Surely it must have been built by an admirer of George Sand.

Mme Beaudry, returning, seated herself comfortably at the back of the car, her bag on her knees. She said a little breathlessly:

'I saw her. She was in bed. She heard me come into the room, but at first didn't look round. She was expecting somebody else. I said to her: "Is that the way you welcome your sister!" She would have liked me to stay for lunch.'

'Why didn't you? You could have come back quietly in the bus.'

'And Beaudry?' She chuckled. 'There *would* have been a fine to-do!'

'Is your sister's husband still alive?'

'No, he died at the beginning of the war. The more 's the pity of it. Pauline is feeling the strain. She 's done so much. We 've *all* done so much.'

Mme Beaudry barked out these short sentences. I found her very tiring to converse with.

'You said your sister was in bed,' I queried. 'Is she ill?'

'Not ill, only tired.' Then, clutching her handbag vigorously: 'I was right glad to see her.'

We bumped a bit climbing the steep hill over Blonville. I asked our chauffeur what he thought of the market at Trouville.

'Not so wonderful,' he answered, 'except for the salads. I 've several under the seat—dandelion, corn salad, and chicory. We southerners need plenty of fresh salad. What good is there in butter? Meaning no offence, ladies, butter is a woman's food. I dare say you can get along with it, but a man needs olive oil. That 's the foundation of a man's food—olive oil!'

'Nonsense!' said Mme Beaudry decisively.

'I wasn't meaning to be personal,' said the Italian.

'I like butter well enough,' I said, 'but I was brought up on salads too. If people ate more of them they would have prettier teeth.'

He smiled back at me, showing me as fine a set as one could wish to see. We arrived back at the farm just after midday. Mme Beaudry was so flustered that I whispered:

'Don't worry to help us with the things, Mme Beaudry. Run home as quickly as you can. Your husband will be waiting for his lunch.'

'It 's all prepared in advance,' she said, 'but if he arrives home first there 'll be a fine to-do.'

'Then don't waste a minute! Hurry!'

'I'll not be asking if I owe you anything for the drive, madame?'

'No, no,' I answered, 'of course not. Do please go!'

She set off heavily down the orchard. What tyrants men are! I felt as if we had both done something wrong. But the Italian, because of what I had said about the salads and the olive oil (and doubtless because he had been able, at my expense, to buy so many) beamed and said:

'Go in front with the little boy, madame; I'll bring everything down.'

Already he had unloaded from the top of his car a scythe, a sickle, a hoe, and a tripod for my fire.

XIII

The various signs of spring were now coming on so fast that I could not keep abreast of them; Matilda was always returning from her wanderings with bunches of sweet-smelling violets, snowdrops, cowslips, and primroses. A woman of eighty-seven wrote to me from Torquay enclosing me her recipe for cowslip wine. She thought I could be no sort of housewife without this valuable knowledge. I was delighted and decided to pick a large quantity of these sweetly named flowers in the meadows near my smaller wood. To go walking before lunch was to transgress my rules about working as soon as the house was swept and the fires lighted. However, the proofs of my novel *Philippa* had also arrived to unsettle my usual routine, so I took a basket and some scissors and set forth.

I have an orchard planted with young apple-trees, which runs between my wood and the stream. The meadows higher up communicate with it by a steep declivity of fern where foxes and rabbits have their lairs and where, in early summer, but not yet, the grass is full of wild flowers, the cattle not disturbing them because of the fern.

The trees of the wood overhang the orchard, and steal the sun from the young apple-trees. An oak at the tip of the wood especially does this, forming with its boughs a wide arch under which it is pretty to see the horse and cart slowly passing. I have it in my contract that its shade should not be clipped, for it leads to my favourite walk down to the stream which runs ice-cold between rushes and alder-trees, pillows of dew-kissed refreshing moss, and watery plants, such as Herb Paris, Bog Asphodel, and marsh Orchis which, if this hot weather continued, might soon, I thought, make their appearance.

The narrow strip of grass between the wood and the stream runs steeply down. From the stream, orchards of the tenderest green climb steeply up in the direction of the road to Saint-Vaast. The stream with its thick undergrowth therefore forms the bottom of a valley, the sun is imprisoned between the banks, cold winds are kept away. The wood, widening to form the thick part of a wedge, gradually reaches the stream. Here there is a pool for the cattle to drink, and a hedge dividing my property from that of Mme Anger.

In this valley, heated by the morning sun, I found Jacques

seated on a tree stump, whittling a stick, an occupation most dear to boys and youths, whilst crowded on the green carpet between water and dark wood were eighteen or twenty cows, the white horse, Levure, the brown horse, Miquette, and the donkey, Jeannette, with grey and black markings, adorably fluffy ears, and gentle eyes.

The trees I had sold to M. Cauvin were ready to be taken away—the trunks across the grass where they had fallen, the branches and heads cut into equal lengths and very neatly stacked between supporting sticks hammered into the ground. The young alder-trees and hazels had also been cut down from the water's edge, and now lay, leaning branch against branch, all the length of the narrow orchard, perhaps a quarter of a mile in length. This undergrowth, cut once in seven years, by the renting farmer belonged to Déliquaire, and was being turned by Jacques into bundles of faggots of the kind I have already described.

The young man touched his cap and rose, hand outstretched:

'Good day, madame.'

'Good morning, Jacques.'

Our meetings, though cordial, did not give much scope for conversation. Partly because he was so soon to be a man, partly because he had no enthusiasms, at least no enthusiasms in matters we could talk about together, my questions too often were blunted.

'How is your mother this morning?'

'Oh, she 's all right.'

'Did she sleep better?'

'I don't know. I suppose she did.'

'What day does she see the specialist?'

'To-day.'

He continued, quietly, to whittle his stick. The cattle trampled the water in the pool, fouling it, drinking it. The grass, being short, handfuls of hay were strewn here and there under the boughs of the wood. The donkey went from one little agglomeration of cattle to another, wedging her soft head fearlessly between the sharp horns, though she kept away from Miquette who, a few days earlier, being annoyed by her teasing manners, had dug strong teeth into the skin of her back, lifting her off the ground and depositing her some yards distant. The wound must have healed. I looked for it in vain. From the hazel-trees, not cut, an almost imperceptible breeze shook pollen in yellow clouds from the cylindric grey catkins hanging down like Chinese lanterns coloured golden by the sun. I said:

'Cauvin has not come for his wood and lumber.'

'It 's on account of him being caught in the falling price,' answered Jacques. 'He can't find a buyer.'

'It wasn't that he paid me too much for it,' I said, defending myself.

'He paid too much to sell it at a profit, with things as they are,' maintained Jacques. 'Of course, there wasn't only you. There was the labour cutting it.'

'All the same,' I said, 'I hadn't imagined Cauvin being caught.'

'It isn't that there are no buyers,' Jacques expanded, 'but simply no buyers whose price will give him the profit he wants. With coal being off the ration, and not too expensive, one can understand. The price is tumbling.'

'Like everything else.'

'I suppose so,' he said.

He had now finished whittling his stick, and putting it to his eye looked along it as men sight a gun. I did not ask what he wanted it for. I thought it better silently to find out for myself. There stood by his elbow a wooden cradle, but open at each end, on legs, with steel chains hanging down from either side. At each corner there was a hole for a stick to be placed upright in. Three holes were filled with sticks, the fourth was waiting for the one Jacques was finishing. I said:

'I know. You are going to make faggots.'

'Yes, ma'am. I made a few with my father the other evening, but I 'm not very expert yet. There 's a knack. Most things have a knack.'

'I 've always wanted to see how they were made,' I answered.

He looked flattered.

'There 's nothing to it, ma'am, except it 's lengthy. I expect I shall soon get into the swing.'

He had made a chopping block out of three joined branches planted in the reeds legs downwards. The thicker pieces of alder and hazel went on the cradle first. He tried to make them as near to four feet in length as he could guess. Then came the thin branches. A great many of them. Finally some more thicker pieces. This work took him at least twenty minutes, perhaps half an hour. He was very attentive to the cutting, that they lay flat and comfortable. When he judged there were sufficient he brought up the two steel chains and tightened them round the faggots by a curiously archaic, but effective device. When they were very tightly compressed he bound some wire round. The chains were taken off and the bundle cleaned up, rough ends and untidy pieces taken off with smart blows of the chopper. He asked me smilingly to lift it, and when I was unable to said:

'A bundle of faggots ought to weigh eighty pounds. When they are ready for putting on the fire you will have less trouble about taking them up owing to them being dry.'

'You 'll take many days to finish this lot, Jacques?'

'A good many,' he echoed.

'How long?'

'About a month, perhaps more. It all depends how early I come down in the morning. A man, working from dawn to dusk, expects to do thirty-five in a day. But you know what we are. We don't get up so early in the morning, in our family. I don't generally get out into the fields till ten. Then again, my father is always calling on me for one thing or another. And if it isn't him, it 's my mother. I 'm the one to fetch and carry. There 's nobody left but me, but I hardly think it will be for long.'

He looked up quickly as if having said too much, and exclaimed:

'There are the cows at the brushwood. I knew it. When they have finished the hay they go for the tender pieces in the hazel. They like the green buds, but they mustn't eat sticks for fear they get choked. Hey, there, Bouboule, off it! I shall have to move them. There 's always something to do when one is doing something else. I 'm getting tired of this life.'

'So early, Jacques?'

'It isn't a life!'

'There might be worse.'

'I 'll have to chase those cows.'

'I mustn't keep you,' I said; 'I must be going. I ought to have been working myself, only the sun tempted me out.'

'Working yourself?'

I looked down at the grass, conscious how idle the existence of a woman writer must appear to him, to his parents, to the Poulains. I had no cows to milk. On Sundays I could have breakfast in bed; in the afternoons knit, a cup of tea in front of the fire with the cat on my lap. My orchards brought in money automatically. Until a relatively short time ago I had not known the difference between a heifer and a bull calf. They had been obliged to teach me how to saw, like women on the farms saw, the female way, holding the steel frame between the knees, drawing the wood to be cut backwards and forwards across the teeth. Compared to country women I was lazy, spending too much time reading and writing. Instead of trying to explain, I said clumsily:

'I don't see any wild flowers. I can't think where my mother finds them.'

'There are some,' he said, 'but I see them without noticing them. We don't use them much. Some women, of course, are like you. Jeannine, for instance. . . .'

His brother's wife always had next to her while she sewed in the farmhouse a bowl of violets or primroses. When her eyes looked up from embroidering her post-marriage trousseau, they rested bovinely on these fragrant bouquets. I could see he was comparing me to her. I rather felt he despised us both. She was perhaps getting on his nerves, always being about his parents' house, seemingly doing nothing but sew. She never milked the cows, not having learnt to, having no desire to learn. I never even saw her help with the washing-up, though I am not sure about this. From his silences, from the way he looked, I felt certain that Jacques was angry with his brother and his sister-in-law, out of harmony with his parents. I said:

'I really must be going. I must look after the lunch.'

This excuse sounded more valid than if I had told him I had a bundle of proofs to read, but it was a lie. Matilda always made the lunch.

I went down to the village, according to my custom, just before six. On my way I met a gardener tending some trees in front of a villa and I asked him the name of one already in blossom. I thought it might be almond but he said not, and gave me the name in Latin.

'I don't know the names of trees in Latin.' I said simply.

He looked at me in surprise and answered: 'A sort of wild plum. The flowers come out before the leaves.'

'I have two plum-trees in my garden,' I objected, 'and neither is yet flowering. If I remember rightly, the leaves come out first.'

He said: 'But this is a *wild* plum! Are yours wild?'

At the bottom of the road the sea was deep blue, and there were ships on it. Correcting proofs in the morning and after lunch had given me the feeling that everything I had done up to now was little. My first books I had asked my husband to sign because I was bashful. In *A Farm in Normandy* I made it appear he was the narrator and I even composed a dedication from him to me. I was sure of my emotions but nervous about my English. Though I continued this rather stupid subterfuge in *A Village in Piccadilly*, gaining, I suppose, something in restraint, I soon found it impossible to prevent my femininity from coming out. I was never comfortable writing like my distinguished compatriot George Sand in the masculine gender. Now that on each new title page the prefix Mrs. preceded my name an immense thankfulness had taken hold of me. I had never been so proud of being a woman. I felt immediately capable of deeper thought and altogether more serious work. Reading *The Mill on the Floss* aloud to Bobby in the evening, however, I was both jealous and utterly dejected. Here were descriptions of orchard and stream written with a strength still far beyond my reach. Why should I not admit these disappointments which other women perhaps feel equally who try to write? I was like Anne Lady Winchelsea who, born in the year 1661, sang:

> Each woman has her weakness; mine indeed
> Is still to write tho' hopeless to succeed.

On certain mornings I was so confident, but always about what was still in my head. In this hot sunshine I felt horribly afraid that I would never succeed in taking a place, even the smallest, amongst the women writers of my generation, and I so wanted to! I wondered vaguely where the ships on the horizon were going to, and on the whole I was pleased not to be on them. In another garden another gardener was lopping trees. I suddenly recognized Clément, waved a glove at him smilingly, and looked automatically for M. Besnard, who was probably not far off. He had a rake and was preparing a bonfire. I asked him how the grandfather was.

M. Besnard came up, touching his cap, then held out his hand over the evergreens dividing the garden from the road, and murmured:

'Bad. Very bad. He 's not getting up any more. If it were not for his heart being so strong, he would be dead. It 's a sad thing to see him lifting a teaspoonful of liquid to his lips, slowly, with such an effort, then, when a few drops have passed his lips, throwing back his head to swallow like a bird. Just like a robin drinking. That 's what he has come to.'

M. Besnard threw back his head to show me. His neck was already furrowed. When M. Duclos was gone M. Besnard would be the head of the family, and, in turn, would be known as the 'grandfather.'

I asked how long M. Duclos's suffering was likely to last. He said that the doctor thought he might live ten days, but because of the heart nobody was certain of anything.

I went into the post office by the side door, giving the letters to the postmaster's wife just in time. I then bought a four-pound farm loaf, and in the market-place, in front of Mme Petrel's shop, saw Déliquaire. I waved to him, asking if he would give me a lift back to the farm.

He came up to me rather mysteriously and said:

'No, I 'm not going back now. We 've just been to Trouville. Ma'am Déliquaire has been to the doctor.'

He looked so grave and preoccupied that, feeling guilty at having thought of myself first, I exclaimed:

'Tell me quickly! What did the doctor say?'

This time my anxious question had the opposite effect, for he answered with a show of lightheartedness:

'Oh, there 's nothing wrong with her! Nothing at all! And this man we went to see is very important. He 's a specialist. You can read for yourself his qualifications on the brass door-plate. This man 's not like the others. Mind, we were only just in time. He said that if my wife had gone on taking the medicines of the other doctor, she would have died in a week.'

'I 'm very relieved,' I said. 'I do hope you understood everything in the right way. Are you quite certain about that? I mean, that there is nothing at all the matter with her?'

'The other one said she had the beginning of a cancer,' he muttered angrily. 'That 's what he said.'

The words burnt my cheeks. I exclaimed:

'No doctor would ever say that! I 'm sure, I 'm sure you heard wrong. Oh, please, never say that again.'

He answered: 'That 's what he said. But there 's nothing wrong with her. I 'm sorry not to be able to wait. I must take these four prescriptions to the chemist.'

'What! Four different medicines? What exactly did the specialist say?'

'He said there was nothing, only an ulcer in the stomach. In a few days she will be quite well again.'

'Perhaps not so quickly as that. I 'm afraid one worries a little, even about an ulcer in the stomach. But don't repeat the other thing again, ever. You might get into trouble. Cancer, ulcer. The two words might sound the same to somebody who was not used to them. That 's what must have happened. You heard wrong. I 'm glad the specialist has reassured you. There 's no reason why it should be any worse than he says. I shall go to see her.'

'She 's not at the farm. She 's with her sister.'

'Well, if not to-night, to-morrow. Ask her if there is anything I can do for her.'

The furnace chimney, encased in a buttress, passed through the big half-timbered room where I worked each morning. This room had the full width of the house. The window, a narrow slit in Caen stone two feet thick, overlooked the garden and the tenderest green of the orchard. I was always intending to pierce a window in the opposite wall, also of stone, which would then have given me a view, from my table, of the farmyard and, more distantly, the kitchen garden. In the place of this dreamt-of window was the buttress, faced with plaster, and a radiator which it was my pride to keep as hot as possible, for writing and sewing are two occupations that need warmth.

On the morning following my talk with Déliquaire in the village, Bobby, coming into my room, noticed smoke curling up from a crack in the plaster. The weather was unpleasantly damp and cold, and the wind, blowing down the chimney, was sending smoke from the furnace through this split in the buttress. Very soon to sit in the room became impossible. I telephoned to Giles Matthieu who, coming immediately to inspect, declared that the buttress must come down and the chimney be remade. The furnace must be put out, and we should be without water for two days. I wrung my hands despairingly at the thought of this turning upside down of my house, the coldness, the inconvenience, the tramping down of plaster upstairs and downstairs, the impossibility of working for several precious days. As soon as lunch was finished a man and a boy arrived. Their heavy boots filled the house with mud. Their cigarettes, bringing a strange odour to my nostrils, made me feel I was harbouring an army; stubs, ground in with toe-caps, littered the parquets. Songs and whistling echoed. Heavy footsteps blew duststorms. Broken plaster and cracked tiles were heaved through open windows on tenderly sprouting hydrangeas which, as the work progressed, were smothered in white powder.

That evening, and during the night, as if on purpose, the weather became windier and colder, and the next day there were rumours that snow had fallen for a few moments at Caen and in Paris. To make my house habitable I kept an enormous fire in the low room, using the largest of the logs split by Rettol out of the elm pollard. The plumber's lad passed and repassed with sacks of plaster and pails of water. I could not read or knit. Then I saw Rettol peering through the window. He said:

'I 've come about the trees, ma'am.'

'What trees?'

'The ones you were going to sell me—the elm which is dry in the head, the ash from which a branch has fallen showing the tree is not healthy, the wild cherry a bit too near the high-tension cable, and the others we talked about.'

'I thought you would not come because prices are falling so fast. I imagined I should not see you again.'

'I made a price and I stick to it.'

Taking a pencil and a piece of paper from my knitting basket I drew a plan of where the trees stood, marking against each tree the amount Rettol offered, and adding up I thought it would be stupid to refuse, especially if things were to become more difficult.

'When would you pay me?' I asked.

'On Saturday,' he answered. 'On Saturday, before dinner.'

'I suppose you would be starting quite soon?'

'To-morrow morning, ma'am. I 've finished the other things I was doing. I need something fresh.'

I nodded assent, and he held out his big hand. Though it was said he was short of money his big hand and his round face gave me confidence. I simply said:

'Start when you like.'

I had made tea when Déliquaire arrived.

'I 've come to settle our little account,' he said.

'Ah?'

'Here it is all written down.'

He pulled a grubby sheet of paper out of a pocket, and read out the items. On my credit side there were some apples and pears he had sold for me in the autumn, also a pair of corduroy trousers which he had asked me to buy for him in London. He said he had looked at similar garments at Dozulé the other morning and found that those I had brought him were cheap in comparison.

'They 'll come in useful,' he added reflectively.

On the debit side there was his fee for making our cider and scratching and airing the apple-trees. The result of all this was that I owed him two or three thousand francs.

'Then there is the basic slag,' I said. 'It might be a good thing to pay everything together?'

'Yes,' he agreed, 'it might be.'

We bent our heads over the table, and spent a few moments working out the total to our mutual satisfaction. Whilst fumbling in my bag for the wallet I asked:

'Do you still intend to spread the manure to-morrow?'

'To-morrow or the next day. I 'm off to fetch the machine to-morrow morning.'

'I do hope it rains.'

'Oh, you know, it really doesn't make all that difference.'

'That 's not what you said the other evening.'

'The thing is, you have no choice. The machine has to go back on Monday. The best you can do is not to worry.'

'I suppose you are right. Well, at any rate, here is the money. You owe me five hundred francs, but that can go towards renting the machine.'

'Just as you like,' he said, counting the notes.

He put them slowly in his pocket, but his hands were not sure of themselves, and he fumbled. I suddenly realized that up to this moment he had only remained calm by a considerable effort, a controlling of his nerves, but the excuse of his visit being spent he was on the point of exploding. I tried as one does, on these occasions, quickly to guess what was the matter. I knew by Mme Beaudry that Mme Déliquaire was not sleeping better. An uncomfortable foreboding filled my mind about her, and I was not quite impressed by the confidence the specialist had apparently showed in the unimportant ulcer, but there was in M. Déliquaire's behaviour towards me at this moment an antagonism I had never seen before, and which could hardly have any bearing on his wife's illness. Nervously I awaited his first words. They came hoarsely, very mixed up, because he was probably nervous.

'I was just passing and I thought I would tell you,' he said, 'I went to see the notary after lunch. This is the time of year I tot up my accounts. What I spend from one winter to the other I put in a book so that it 's there when I need to take stock of my situation. To my way of thinking the notary is a man who has both our interests at heart. I said I would be glad for him to tell me just how much grass there is on this orchard. His clerk brought in the plan and we figured it out as close as could be, taking into consideration the buildings and the kitchen garden and everything which is not pasture land, and I said to him: "Do you think, speaking fair, that the orchard, good as it is, is worth all the butter and milk I give her every week?" He said: "How much do you give Mme Henrey?" and I said: "For forty thousand francs, I 'll swear." He said: "The grass is good. Many is the time I 've been there and seen it myself, but twenty-five thousand francs is the right amount." So now you can go and ask him yourself. I tell you, he 's a fair man and has both our interests at heart. At any rate, this is certain, I don't want your orchard any more.'

'How very strange!' I said slowly, trying to read into his mind. 'I never even fixed the rate. You suggested it yourself two years ago. It was your plan entirely. I know the price of milk has gone up. It 's about the only thing that has. On the other hand, from what I hear, there 's no longer a black market in butter. In the village I can buy all I please at the controlled price. Look! There 's a packet on the table! In the evening, when I go to the post office with my mail, I no longer have to stand in a queue behind the farmers' wives sending parcels of butter illicitly to Paris. There 's enough to go round now. That 's the reason for the slump. But why didn't you come and tell me that you were not happy about the arrangement? Of course I 'll take back the grass if you do not want it. As for the year that is just finished, would you like me to make up the difference?'

'No,' he answered. 'That 's not the point.'

'I didn't realize,' I said. 'The whole thing is so stupid. You are fighting the person who is the keenest in the world to help you. Do you think I don't know what you must be feeling, with your wife being ill and prices dropping?'

'I 'm not saying I won't take the orchard again, but I 'll have it at my price.'

'Let 's not decide anything now,' I said. 'We can talk about it again another day. There 's no hurry.'

'I 'm giving you the grass back, fair and square.'

'But of course. Perhaps you are wise to lighten up. Would you like to give me The Point back too? It 's not much use to you without any water, and Ernest Poulain does so much want it for his horses.'

'I 'll not give The Point back. You 've got no right. It 's in the contract. You won't get it back, do you hear? I 'd go to law.'

'I only thought it might help you. Of course, I am perfectly aware that you are the legal tenant. Now, what must I do? Shall I ask Bobby to settle with Mme Déliquaire for the milk and butter at the end of each week? Or would you rather we went somewhere else?'

'I don't know,' he answered. 'Why should you go anywhere else? There was never any question of that.'

'I was merely trying to do the right thing.'

'I reckon you can pay at the end of each week.'

'And you will tell me how much you are charged for the machine to sow the manure? Of course, I shall also pay you for your time.'

'Who said so? You 'll do nothing of the kind. Besides, it doesn't mean because of the orchard that I shan't lend you the horse and cart when you need it. Didn't you send me a *stère* of elm the other day as a present?'

'Let 's not talk about that. I remember you telling me, the day after M. Cauvin came, that there were no friendships in business.'

He went to the door. The logs crackled in the fire, emitting fierce heat. The tea poured out in one cup only, undrunk, was deep gold, a tea leaf floating towards the brim. Upstairs the plumber's boy was lustily singing a java. Plaster, brought on boots, was all over my floor. I should have offered Déliquaire a cup of tea, and even now, had it not been for a fear that he would refuse angrily, I would have done so. His ill humour was not gone. My humility, breaking his unfriendly words, had put him still more on edge. He would have felt better if I had given him, by flaring up, a chance to insult me. Not having yet completely rid his system of what ailed him, fresh bitterness was on his lips.

'Landowners will see,' he said, tugging at the door, which always grated against the tiles, 'that if prices drop they 'll have to buckle under. I 'll feed the butter to the pigs before I give it away.'

'Tell Mme Déliquaire I shall be coming to see her,' I said, trying to look composed, but quite miserable that suspicion should have embittered our relations.

He put on his clogs which he had left on the stone step. I watched him cross the garden, unlatch the white gate, set off with long steps, his bent back making him look older than he was, down the orchard in the direction of the stream.

I do not think that even yet I realized the black foreboding that had seized our farmers. I did not know, for instance, that heifers and bull calves had dropped so steeply that there was virtually no market. The ordinary people had no pity for the farmers, having watched them during the Occupation and afterwards, gorging themselves with banknotes, eating fatly whilst the towns and cities starved. The Déliquaires and the Poulains were extravagant more by nature than by vice. What profits they had not squandered were in farm equipment and livestock. Heavy taxation and capital levies, which should have come after the Liberation, when the money was really there, waiting to be taken, had come suddenly now, when the cash had been spent, on the eve of the slump. With illness hitting the Déliquaires simultaneously with this financial gloom, all the earth seemed to be opening under their feet. They were sick with unnamed fear.

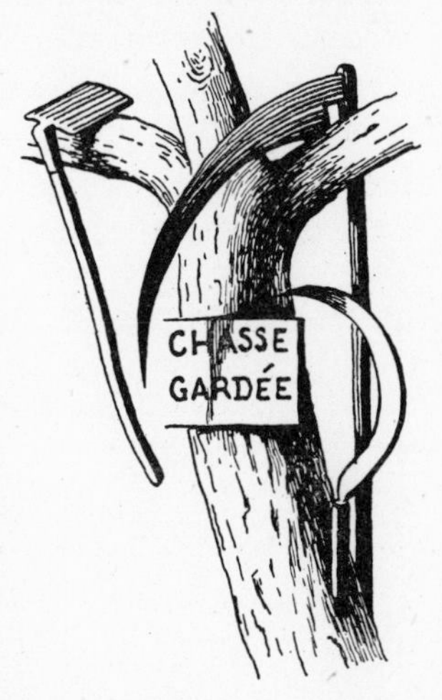

I was myself considerably put out by having a house cold, full of draughts, and covered with plaster. In my bedroom I would turn the taps, forgetting there was neither cold nor hot water. My radiators were exasperating. I did not know how to dress to keep warm. I brought my typewriter down to the table in the low room, hoping to write a little, but the plumber's boy burst in at every moment, singing through an opening in his mouth adjacent to the tightly lipped cigarette. I stopped him during one of these journeys, asking his name.

'Jacky.'

'Jacky what?'

'Jacky Lefort.'

'You wouldn't be a son of the night club Lefort?'

'Yes, I am.'

'Do you play in the orchestra?'

'Yes.'

'That 's funny. I must have danced to your music.'

Having, on this occasion, his hands free, he removed the cigarette from between his lips and smiled with teeth still white, not yet spoilt by cider. His father, who had worked for Baudon as a mason or a bricklayer, kept a *buvette* and dancing place in the workmen's quarter on the other side of the main road to Caen, and Mme Bayard, who before the war had been my charwoman and my most gossipy friend, living just behind this night club, and being an early goer to bed, used to complain bitterly of the noise made by Lefort's customers on their dispersal in the small hours of the morning. I had once danced there with a veterinary surgeon from North Africa, very small of stature, to whom I said: 'Isn't it awkward being so short when you have to look after big animals like bulls?' 'No,' he answered (it was during a tango), 'I like big animals best. There is like a chord of sympathy between us.'

'Who taught you music?' I asked the boy.

'Nobody. I don't know any.'

'But to play the accordion?'

'You don't learn to play the accordion. It just comes, or doesn't come.'

'You play by ear?'

'I don't know by what I play. I just play. My father plays. Four of us play together.'

Tired by this conversation he replaced his cigarette, quite dead, in his mouth and returned upstairs, sending clouds of dirt on to my hair through the gaps in the floor-boards. I thought that presently I would suggest to Bobby that we might go to bed early and listen to something on the English radio.

The next day, rain having started, Matthieu's lorry which the plumber and Jacky had brought right down the orchard stuck in sudden mud, and somebody was sent to find Déliquaire to come with the horses. The postman, dripping under his cape, put his head through the window with the morning mail. There were the usual women's magazines which I loved, the *Evening Standard* which I read for the Londoner's Diary and Eileen Ascroft's fashion articles, Elizabeth Bowen's new book *The Heat of the Day*, and a bulky registered envelope containing the letters forwarded from my flat in Piccadilly. One was from Julia Cairns of Weldon's (Bobby called her 'Aunt Zoolie') offering to propose me for the Society of Women Journalists, which I eagerly accepted, having for some time been in friendly correspondence with its gifted literary adviser, Miss Brenda Spender. I looked up from my seat by the fire to see Mme Beaudry with an old sack round her wide waist.

'How is Mme Déliquaire to-day?' I asked. 'Did you go round this morning?'

'I should think I did go round.'

'I thought about her a lot. I wondered if she would have a good night.'

'Some night she had, and with the plaster they 've made her swallow to line her stomach. It was Roger who gave it her last evening, pouring it into her throat, just as if the poor woman had been a cow. Not a wink did she sleep, and with the screech owls all about the house. "Mme Beaudry," she said to me, "I thought of getting up and coming to see you at about three in the morning."'

'Poor woman.'

'She couldn't sleep. Her heart seemed to stop, then beat too furiously. She said: "Mme Beaudry, when I heard Déliquaire snoring, as if he hadn't a care in the world, not bothering if I were to die, I gave him a good thump in the ribs. 'What 's the matter?' he shouts, waking up. 'Can't you hear me turning and tossing like a lost soul?' I answer. 'No,' says he. 'The more shame on you,' says I. 'For all you care, I could die like a dog.' 'What do you want me to do?' he asks, rubbing his eyes. 'Nothing,' I shout out. 'Go to sleep again.'"'

'Men are all like that,' I said. 'They just sleep.'

'She would have made something hot to drink, if there had been a fire, but there weren't even any dry sticks, and besides, there was no water.'

'No, of course, they are short of water. Now with the rain, perhaps, it will be different.'

'Now perhaps, but it wasn't in the night.'

'They have to go down to the stream each time.'

'It wasn't any good yesterday going down to the stream.'

'What was the matter with the stream?'

'Mme Kettel, who lives in that pretty half-timbered house, a bit like yours but smaller, on the land M. Déliquaire rents from M. Sandret on the road to Saint-Vaast, decided yesterday to do half a year's washing in the stream which flows past the bottom of her house. That being so, M. Déliquaire going last evening with the donkey and the pails to fetch home some water, found it full of yellow soap.'

'What a woman Mme Kettel is! They are waiting for her to die to turn her house into stables, but she 'll outlive them yet.'

'She 's a woman who does her washing all in a lump two or three times a year.'

'Why shouldn't the Déliquaires have taken the donkey down to our stream? Is it so much more awkward?'

'The water was fouled, so they said, on account of too many cows being in the higher-up orchards. Coincidence, you might say. Mme Anger's cows were in the meadow just beyond your wood, M. Victor Duprez's cows were on the slopes opposite your bracken, and the Poulains had theirs across the hedge here. All those animals fouling the water the same day! It *is* a coincidence, wouldn't you say?'

'Yes, it is strange.'

'If she could have made herself something hot she might have gone to sleep again.'

'Naturally,' I said. 'If only she could spend a morning from time to time in bed.'

'A morning in bed! Sunday is their silver wedding. They are planning a big family lunch. Mme Déliquaire asked me this morning to do the washing-up but I said: "Not in front of the guests. I have my pride, Ma'am Déliquaire. To wash up in front of people who are less important than I would hurt my dignity. If I do the washing-up," I said, "it will be after they 've left the house." I would slink in, so to speak, to oblige Mme Déliquaire when they 've gone off to the pictures or to dance at Bennerville. Beaudry and I would not go to the lunch even if we were invited. I 'd only have to serve and carry, and what for?—a bit of chicken, a slice of lamb, a sugared cake? That 's what they are going to eat. Mme Déliquaire asked me to help her kill the chickens and pluck them. I 'll do that to oblige, but I 'll have them know Beaudry and I own our house and our bit of land. Do they own their house? Do they own their land? And M. François, the foundling? Does he own anything? And M. Roger with his young wife who, at last, is going to have a baby, and never a place to have it in!'

'What?' I cried. 'Jeannine is going to have a baby? I thought several times she was looking that way!'

'Three or four months gone, I believe.'

She laughed.

'They were always saying they wouldn't be so silly. She reckoned she was sharper than the other girls.'

'We all say that,' I said.

'It 's easy to say,' said Mme Beaudry.

'Can't they afford to go on living in the flat? Perhaps Mme Déliquaire could fix them up with a bed in the farm.'

'What bed? And where? Not in the same room with M. and Mme Déliquaire and the dog, I suppose! And not in the same bed as M. François, or with Jacques and the new farm hand, Jean!'

'Do the two boys sleep in the same bed?'

'They do indeed, and with Jean wetting the sheets, it 's a pretty to-do for Jacques.'

'Jean wets the sheets?'

'Does he wet the sheets! Poor Mme Déliquaire, she never dared tell him. She said: "It 's too awkward, Mme Beaudry, he being my nephew. I was thinking you could do it better."'

'Did you?'

'I did, Ma'am Henrey. I said to him: "You ought to take care. You drink too much before going to bed." And the cigarette stubs, not nicely put away in an ashtray as Beaudry puts his, but all over the floor. "And," I said, "it 's not my place to clean up after a lad like you."'

'What did he say?'

'You know what it is, Ma'am Henrey. Those lads are foul-mouthed. I wouldn't repeat what he said. If I had a lad of fifteen who smoked thirty cigarettes a day I 'd whip him.'

'I 'm with you,' I answered, 'so would I.'

'We say that,' she went on, 'but they get so strong. A woman has a job to keep a lad in order. As for M. Déliquaire he wouldn't care to say anything to a nephew of his wife's. Besides, he has to go careful, like the rest. Young people don't accept criticism. They 'd lose no time in slamming the door in one's face. The worse they are brought up the politer you have to be. The less they do the less you dare say. And there 's another thing. Who will run the farm now Jacques is walking out on them?'

'What do you mean—walking out on them?'

'Didn't you know he was leaving, perhaps to-day, perhaps to-morrow? Jacques is a good boy, but he 's discontented. The land no longer appeals to them, Ma'am Henrey, no, not though it gives them a healthier life and better food than ever they would have in the towns. They want the cash to twiddle in their thumbs. Motor-cars, motor-trucks, mechanics—that 's what gets them. And the cinema in the evening. I don't say that if M. Déliquaire owned his orchards things might not be different. Though, more likely, the sons would only stay till the parents were dead so that they could sell the land and divide the money. As things are what would Jacques be staying for? I wouldn't be surprised but that he was a bit jealous of his brother; all the fuss they made of Roger at the time of his wedding, the animals they killed, the money they squandered, and now, seeing him and Jeannine lolling about the house all day. Of course Roger was always the favourite with Ma'am Déliquaire.'

'I didn't know.'

'She didn't bring them up when they were babies. The granny, Mme François that would be, brought them up, while M. Déliquaire and his wife were in service. When they took the farm it was different. Jacques, being the younger, had to go on with his schooling, but Roger stayed with mother, milking the cows, always in her skirts. It was natural she took him more to heart.'

'You mean Jacques's family has got on his nerves?'

'He has signed up for three years in the army, in some mechanized arm, where he 'll learn about trucks and tanks. He reckons that is the cheapest way of being trained, and as they pay him quite a tidy sum for volunteering he says he 'll put it in the bank to start a business of his own when he comes out of the army.'

'The world 's a funny place, Mme Beaudry. Here I am, terrified they 'll take my son, and Jacques rushes into uniform. Why aren't men tired of playing soldiers?'

'M. Déliquaire has a lot of land to look after with his wife ill and his two sons leaving him in the lurch.'

'What are you suggesting? That he won't be able to manage?'

I began to understand more clearly Déliquaire's frame of mind, his inexplicable desire to surrender his richest grazing land. I thought: 'Why didn't he come and explain? I would have so liked to help him. Doesn't he know that a woman loves to help?'

From the commotion outside I surmised that the Déliquaires had arrived with the horses. Mme Beaudry went off to finish her scrubbing and I went as far as the window to inspect.

Jacky, at the wheel of the van, was making the engine turn very fast to help the horses, who on the steep incline were slithering in the mud. The rain was coming down in torrents. Déliquaire, wearing a thick coat I had bought him in Charing Cross Road for Christmas, was giving orders to Jacques who held Miquette by the bridle. I was glad, in a way, to see that in spite of their troubles, the Déliquaires pursued their good-neighbour policy, and putting on a raincoat and a hood, I went out to speak to them.

The truck was soon extricated. Déliquaire held out his big hand and said:

'I 'd have come before, ma'am, but we were spreading manure in one of the orchards.'

'I think it was very nice of you to come at all. You are lucky to have this rain for your manure. I do hope it goes on till to-morrow.'

'I shall be here at eight.'

'Do you think the rain will go on? I understand for the first time how farmers must feel when they invoke the weather for their crops. It would be terrible to have the wind blow away so much money!'

'You mustn't worry so, ma'am. The weather is set for rain.'

'I 'm not so sure. The wireless just now foretold bitter cold.'

'To-morrow I shall be here. On Sunday we give back the machine.'

'Good night, Déliquaire.'

Darkness had fallen impenetrably. The workmen had gone. The fire in the low room was very hot. I had drawn the blinds, and with Baba, the white and chocolate cat happily clawing the thick homespun of my skirt, my mind was once more centred on my reading.

My son, according to his custom at this hour, was playing in the cottage with his grandmother. The village watchmaker had come on his bicycle earlier in the week to carry off the mechanical part of our grandfather clock, and as he had also taken Matilda's only watch I had been obliged to lend her mine. Once or twice I had glanced towards the empty face in the corner of the room, thinking it was time for my son to return. Then I heard him racing across the boiler-room in his Wellingtons, and I was about to shout out to him, vexed that he was bringing mud into the house, when he was breathlessly upon me, exclaiming:

'Émile, the Poulains' servant, is here. Vevette and Annick are cruelly burnt. It 's very serious. You are to telephone immediately for the doctor.'

'Burnt? In what way? Did he tell you?'

'He doesn't know. He was in the yard. He heard screams, terrible screams. Mme Poulain rushed out of the house and sent him off for help. I think he went to the Michelins' first, but their telephone was out of order.'

'Oh, I do hope ours isn't out of order too!' I cried. 'It nearly always is when we need it, and Rettol has been cutting down the trees. A branch could easily have fallen across the line.'

I listened anxiously for the dialling tone.

'It 's working!' I exclaimed when the noise came up, almost deafening me. 'Thank God!'

I first called the Poulains' family doctor but he was out, and the maid said he might be ten minutes, he might be an hour. I thought of telephoning immediately to Dr. Lehérissey who had attended me during my confinement, but knowing the peasant dislike of spending money, I was afraid of getting into trouble if both doctors arrived more or less simultaneously, for the maid would presumably deliver my message as soon as her master returned from his visit. Trying not to panic, I told Bobby to persuade Émile to run back to the farm and bring me back the necessary permission to call Dr. Lehérissey. I thought it would also save time to tell the doctor what sort of a burn it was.

After ten minutes, Émile not coming back, I telephoned again to the Poulains' doctor. The maid said:

'Oh, you 're Mme Henrey? The doctor is not back yet but

Ernest Poulain has called, and as it 's urgent he has gone to fetch Dr. Lehérissey.'

I was surprised by the speed with which Ernest had got down to the village. He could have taken his light van. Even so it suggested that Émile must have lost a good deal of time in asking me to telephone; he had probably been held up at Mme Michelin's house. I was quite alarmed by now and, going to the cottage, discussed the situation with Matilda, who was ironing the sheets. Émile still not coming back, I put on a raincoat and rubber boots, and ran out into the night.

As soon as rain falls these undulating orchards ooze with water, which seems to gush out of the black earth as if subterranean springs were in ebullition. One stumbles and slithers in the mud. The grass itself appears in danger of being washed away. On moonless nights crevasses take shape across one's path, apple-trees extend their uncovered roots and low crooked branches to trip one and scratch one's face. Hedges loom with ditches full of entangled prickly undergrowth, especially the wild rose, to tear one's legs, stockinged or bare. When the wind howls, the loneliness adds an element of fear to the scene, and in narrow lanes, covered overhead by immensely tall trees, joining high their dripping boughs, not yet green but eerie like skeletons, one is sometimes afraid as I was that night, my mind already full of tragedy.

When Ernest or his servant Émile came across to my farm, knowing every gap and being lithe as cats, they squeezed through the hedge above my kitchen garden, but for me that was not possible. I was obliged to take the long route by the white gate to which is attached the letter-box that no longer has a back, winter gales having wrenched it off the hinges. Here is the lane, just wide enough for the Poulains' hay-cart, whose wheels have dug deep tracks against banks covered by moss and white violets. Here, that summer day I have already described, I first saw Henriette, the serving-maid, looking like a wild girl astride the white horse. Night birds screeched, wood creaked in the hedgerows, the rain beat against my face, wetting even my hair under my peaked pink bonnet. Treacherous flints and useless unbroken stones tripped me up. I wished I had brought a lantern. I had been afraid once before at this spot, that impenetrable midnight coming home from supper with Victor Duprez, when he had told us so curiously that because we had bought the estate from him years before he now hated us. I had imagined stupidly that, once over his threshold, no longer protected by the laws of hospitality, he would creep to the top of my Point and shoot us. This triangular orchard again rose above me, unseen, but felt. Here were the trees that Rettol was to cut down, the elms, the wild cherry, and the ash in which birds would already be making high nests, squirrels appearing. By peering forward I could already see lights in the Poulains' brick house.

Against a background of whistling wind and driving rain, I suddenly heard from the gate leading to The Point, convulsive sobbing that brought my footsteps to an immediate stop, filling me with such terror that for a moment no limb would obey a command to move. Overcoming this fear, I called out to give myself added courage, searching the bushes with anxious eyes. The sound of my renewed advance seemed to act on the sufferer, who now wailed hysterically, and as it was a woman I ran forward with compassion, thinking that perhaps these cries came from childbirth. I soon made out a huddled form, the face buried in the hands, the elbows resting against the gate of The Point. I took the shoulders gently, trying to turn the sufferer round, but not seeing anything but vague outlines, I was beaten back a moment later by hands flying out, repelling my efforts to alleviate.

The lights of the nearby farmhouse and my hurry to be with the Poulains beckoned me. I need not stay and be scratched by this fury who, for all I knew, might have an accomplice hiding in the undergrowth, when Émile could so easily investigate with his lantern. I never for a moment connected this hysterical sobbing with the accident across the way. I fled down the flinty slope, the wind still howling, the rain soaking me.

There was a car in the yard which I took to be Ernest's. Not a dog barked as I entered the narrow stone corridor, pushing open the door leading to the low room.

On a bench, at the end of the long table under the window, sat Yvonne Poulain with Annick on her lap—Annick yelling, one arm all red with a blister above the wrist, but otherwise apparently unhurt. The fire was down, not cheerful, two or three small pieces of wood trying to burn, but not succeeding. André, in clogs, was mopping water or some upset food on the black range. The red tiles on the floor, very worn, very uneven, but of an effective baked colour, sandy and rough in texture, were all wet, and books and sheets of paper, some out of copy-books, were strewn everywhere, soaked like the floor, with here and there, very pitifully, little girls' clothing—a jumper, a tiny skirt of poor quality, wet like the other things on the floor, and the buttons torn off, as if the garments had been removed hastily by panicky fingers.

With her back to a tall Normandy cupboard, the sort old curiosity shop people search for in out-of-the-way farms, very darkly polished with silver fittings, stood a tall woman with a jug in her hand. She was Mme Vauclin, come to fetch the milk at the time of the accident, now remaining to see what she could do, the milk jug never having left her grasp. Looking round, not yet accustomed to the glaring light, the desolation of this usually well-ordered room, the suspicion of not yet understood tragedy, I said:

'In the lane, against the barrier leading to The Point, there 's a woman sobbing. Ought not somebody to go?'

'Oh,' said Yvonne, throwing a strange glance at Mme Vauclin, 'that will be Henriette!'

'Henriette!' I exclaimed. 'Why Henriette?'

'I dealt rough with her,' said Yvonne, allowing bitterness still to pierce a certain shame in avowal; 'but wouldn't you have done the same?'

'I 'll go and fetch her,' said Mme Vauclin, putting her jug on the table. 'I 'll tell her she can come back, that she need not fear anything.'

'Oh, yes, she need not be afraid any longer, but if she doesn't want to come back, let her stay where she is.'

'I 'll bring her back,' said Mme Vauclin.

'What happened?' I asked, turning on Mme Yvonne. 'Poor Annick. She isn't crying now. She 's brave. Let me look at the arm, Annick!'

'Bobo,' she said, holding tighter to her mother with the other arm.

'What happened?' I repeated. These little injuries were not

those which gave a keyed-up atmosphere to the farmhouse. Where was Yvette? Why was Yvonne not with her, wherever she was? Yvonne was calm, as a person is calm after a too great emotion. Her eyes were moist and unseeing. Her voice was low and pitiful, tired, as if strained by too much emotion, too much shouting, anger perhaps.

'The doctor has arrived. He 's upstairs with the granny looking after Yvette. Oh, Mme Henrey, it 's terrible. The two children, Yvette and Annick, were playing on the floor at the foot of the stove. Henriette upset a cauldron of boiling soup. She 's such a fool. She keeps too many things on the stove. They clutter the place up. But really, I don't know what happened. I don't suppose anybody will ever know exactly what happened. I was here, where I am now, but with my back turned, feeding little Marie-Madeleine. There were shrieks, shrieks, Mme Henrey; the soup fell all over them.'

Tears began to roll down her cheeks, but not convulsively. One had the impression she was trying to reassure herself.

'Of course the cauldron might have hit them. Think, Ma'am Henrey, the weight! Henriette caught hold of it, managed to save it from slipping over. She 's probably scalded.'

Mme Vauclin came in, dripping.

'The girl won't come,' she said. 'She says she 'll never come back. She 'll kill herself.'

'Let her stay where she is,' said Yvonne. 'She 's mad.'

'She 'll catch pneumonia on a night like this,' said Mme Vauclin.

'Let me come with you,' I said. 'Perhaps, together, we might do something.'

Émile was holding Henriette by the elbows, and she had placed an ankle through the ironwork of the gate to prevent him from dragging her across the courtyard. She sobbed louder when we came up to her.

'Henriette,' I pleaded, 'Mme Yvonne won't scold you any more. Accidents happen. Mme Yvonne even says you prevented the iron pot from falling.'

'Come on,' said Mme Vauclin, shaking her milk jug. 'It 's all upset. Give me some more milk. Come on. Let 's go to the buttery. There 's nobody in the buttery.'

This appeal to her services calmed Henriette, who allowed us, the man having slipped off into the night, to lead her into the buttery, where she poured some more milk into Mme Vauclin's jug. I lost sight of Mme Vauclin after this. Doubtless she had supper to make for her own family. I was left with Henriette, who immediately ran round the corner of the house and through the garden. I ran after her, stumbling a good deal, this terrain being unknown to me, and eventually found her leaning over a low wall, not unlike an area wall, but I could merely distinguish a black cavity.

I clutched at her back, noticing the broadness of her shoulders, the strength of her stocky limbs. She shook me off, and all further pleading being unsuccessful I returned into the house, where I was met by André shouting:

'Where 's the maid?'

'She 's upset, André. She won't come in.'

He gave a whoop of boyish unfeelingness, and ran out into the rain. Yvonne was sitting where I had left her, Annick in her arms. They were both very quiet. I went to the stairs to listen.

'Is she crying?' asked Yvonne.

'Yes,' I said, 'but she 's bound to if the doctor is dressing her wounds.'

'I can't go up,' said Yvonne. 'I can't bear it.'

'I could nurse Annick if you liked. You could try. It might be better.'

'No,' she said, 'no.'

Ernest came suddenly through the passage into the low room, his arms filled with bandages and gauze in packages. He put them down on the table, looking round searchingly. He peered at me twice, his face very red, his ears sharp and detached. Suddenly he emerged from his own painful thoughts, realized my presence, and jerked out his arm to shake hands. Then, turning to Yvonne:

'I better take the things up.'

'You better,' she said.

I went to sit beside Yvonne. Annick babbled a little. Her arm only hurt when she rubbed it against her mother's dress. Her eyes peered round me at something beyond. André had come into the room and was busy wiping the stove clean. He was as serious-looking as just now he had been cruel and stupid. After a while he peered into the black pot and exclaimed:

'There 's some left.'

He tipped it in our direction, so that we could see the two or three potatoes emerging from the liquid. Then, with an effort, he lifted it and was half-way across the room, when Yvonne called out:

'What are you going to do with it?'

'Throw it away.'

'Throw away the soup? What 's come over you? We 'll have to eat, won't we? Your father will need his supper. The others also will need theirs.'

'Oh?'

He put it back, his nailed shoes harshly hitting the red floor.

Émile came in silently with a net basket full of faggots, which he placed in the drawer under the hearth—a drawer like the one in our cottage—and then, seeing all the paper lying sodden on the floor, he picked it up and put it with the faggots to dry, saying:

'It 'll be dry in the morning. We 'll have to light a fire.'

His movements were slow and awkward, and with his long drooping moustaches he looked like a Celtic warrior. People said he never washed; his sheets, when the laundry woman had them, were as black as the grate.

Ernest came down and, looking at me, said:

'Aren't you going up? The doctor is just finishing.'

'Oh, yes, please.'

The room was large; there was a double cherry-wood bed with a crucifix over it; Mme Castel was holding Yvette in her arms. Dr. Lehérissey was putting on the last bandages. A tall woman, imposing, whom I learnt later was Mme Petit, loomed over the group, whose varying expressions were lit by a lamp without a shade. The doctor, my excellent friend, whose features these last years had much aged, held out a finger for me to shake. I thought he was surprised to see me. All my attention, of course, was immediately centred on Yvette, who was now placed tenderly in the wide bed, the lamp being wedged between the pillows.

My heart throbbed with pity. Yvette was all bandages except for her face and her hands, but though her hands were unhurt, her face was seriously burnt. Cheeks, forehead, chin, nose, ears, all that was visible were daubed pink with mercurochrome; two wisps of gauze met over her hair. She was already patient, resolved to be good. Her eyes were dry. She was propped up, holding her little hands delicately in front of her like a doll whose limbs are governed by elastic. Her face had lost the freshness of childhood, and she looked like a little old woman in a lace bonnet. Yet she was too small for that! She reminded me of the children one sees in certain seventeenth-century paintings, dwarf-like humans, dressed in lace, bodies too large, feet too small, features wrinkled. Her eyes, inspecting us in turn with intensity, questioned pitifully.

Yvonne had silently come in, standing by the door, apparently overpowered by the authority of Mme Castel, who was announcing things, giving orders.

'We 'll need a fire. Of course, I shall stay with her all night; there 's no fear that I shall sleep. At my age one doesn't sleep any more. Oh, doctor, will her poor little face be marked?'

The doctor was not willing to commit himself. I sensed he thought Yvette's condition graver than the family believed.

'She mustn't scratch,' he said. 'That 's important.'

'I shall never have my eyes off her,' said Mme Castel.

Dr. Lehérissey took a pair of scissors from his case and cut off a fistful of hair over each ear. I gave a little cry, seeing the scissors shear off so roughly the pretty locks. They fell lightly on the worn carpet and heavy boots trod on them. Ernest was awkwardly fingering the sides of his trousers.

'Papa!' cried Yvette. 'Papa!'

He made a forward movement, as if wishing to clasp her in his arms, then drew back, mute.

It was now Annick's turn to have her arm bandaged, and seeing the doctor advance towards her, she turned, panic-stricken, and clasped her mother's neck. She cried a good deal while he did her dressing, but more from fright than because it hurt her.

'Was anybody else injured?' asked the doctor.

'Nobody else but the maid,' said Mme Castel. 'I think the soup must have splashed over her. It could hardly have been otherwise.'

'Where is the maid?'

'She won't come in,' explained Mme Yvonne. 'She threatens to spend the night in the orchards.'

'Go and get her,' said Mme Castel, addressing her son-in-law.

'It will not be much good,' answered Ernest. 'The sound of my voice will drive her away.'

'I can't dress her wounds if she 's not here,' said the doctor.

Ernest went down, and a few minutes later returned to say there was no trace of Henriette. The doctor had fastened his bag and was ready to go.

'I don't think Henriette was burned,' I said at last. 'I was with her in the buttery when she gave some milk to Mme Vauclin. I should have seen scalds on her arms.'

'That 's true,' said the doctor.

We all went slowly down the stairs, except Mme Castel, who stayed with Yvette. I waited for a few moments, then creeping through the wet night, slipping and stumbling, made my way back to the farm.

The next morning the sun rising in a clear sky picked out Déliquaire, Roger, and Jacques wending their way down my orchard in a procession—Déliquaire alone in front, almost patriarchal; Roger leading Miquette, harnessed to the machine; Jacques, standing up, whip in hand, in the farm-cart drawn by the white mare. Gales, sharp frosts, possibly snow, had been forecast on the English radio, and I was jealous that Déliquaire had spread his manure the previous day in the rain, whereas he was coming to sow mine when strong winds and night frosts might combine to make the whole thing a waste of money. Rettol and Bouveau were felling the trees on The Point. Jackie, with a different plumber, had come to work on my radiators. A few minutes later Nicol, the builder, arrived with his two sons and two workmen to make some little paths of cement in the poultry yard, so that Matilda, who was always grumbling about the mud, could walk agreeably between her cottage and the stables.

Nicol, who was from a sunny part of France and who spoke with a strong Burgundy accent, advanced very cordially to meet me, whispering that I should doubtless be glad to hear that, a widower, he was about to marry a most engaging widow. I said I was delighted about the widow, that I wished him happiness, but why was he coming to-day when the weather was about to turn very cold?

'Why should it be cold?' he asked.

'The wireless says so.'

'My dear madame, I have no time to listen to the radio, and why should I fear the cold?'

'Because a month ago, when I implored you to start work, you kept on putting me off for fear of the weather. You said something about frost not being good for cement.'

'It won't be as cold as that.'

'But there is a chance of frost. For the last six weeks the weather has been glorious, just like spring. It seems funny choosing to-day. Especially turning up on a Saturday morning. I suppose you will fill the poultry yard over the week-end with your abominable material? Why could you not start before?'

'We start when we can, madame.'

'Not when it 's convenient to me, but when it 's convenient to you.'

I was vexed, not so much with Nicol but with the plumbers, who were making my existence miserable. I was longing to write. My nerves were at their worst.

And all the time the sky was becoming a deeper blue, while a cold sharp wind was blowing from the north, bringing across the grass the salty tang of the sea.

XIV

On waking next morning I looked out of my window to see the whole countryside covered in deep snow, the first of the winter, a shining dress beautifying valley and hill and distant woods, changing the aspect of this well-loved view, looking east, from the wide bay of Le Havre to the pepper-pot towers and elongated windows of the Louis XIII château.

'Oh, Bobby!' I cried. 'Here is your dream—deep snow!'

He was up immediately. Nothing else would have enticed him so effectively from his bed. The snow lay virginally white on the orchards, not a human footstep having sullied it on this Sunday morning when the farm was as lonely as if it had been beyond the habitations of man.

Two plumbers and Jacky, the boy, had worked till late the previous night to finish my room, and I had myself spent two hours rubbing the plaster from the furniture and sweeping the floor. Unfortunately, when the furnace was relit and the hot water circulating, I found that only half my radiator heated, presumably because of an air-lock that I was not capable of putting right. I had, therefore, to look forward to having the workmen back on Monday morning.

Meanwhile though the room was chill and the buttress damp with new plaster, I was glad, immediately after breakfast, to begin work again. At least I had the satisfaction of imagining the manure snugly under the snow, unable to fly away on the wings of the north wind. This Sunday was, on the whole, uneventful. Matilda and Bobby went to see the Poulains, and their report was satisfactory. The tiresome mess which the Nicols had left was entirely hidden under snow, which turned planks and tarpaulins into ski-slopes and toboggan-runs for the chickens, and when the poultry, tired of this novelty, went off into the orchard I did not fear, also thanks to the snow, that they would poison themselves with the artificial manure.

On Monday morning Giles Matthieu arrived. Something for

the radiator had to be made specially in the shop, with the result that until evening we were again without water and heat. I wrote a card to Mme Bayard, my pre-war charwoman, asking her to come and polish my floors and make my room habitable again. I then went to fetch the milk from Mme Déliquaire, where I gathered that the silver wedding lunch had proved a very sad affair, both husband and wife being too ill to enjoy the good things. Déliquaire, who was weak in the kidneys, had gone to bed immediately after coffee, leaving Mme Déliquaire who had not slept all night, and Jeannine who was beginning to feel dizzy and sick, being in the third month, to look after the guests, who comprised the père François, M. and Mme Trémois, and the nephew from Etretat. Jacques's imminent departure made them all feel as if calamities were falling too thickly upon them. He was due to leave on Friday. After breakfast on the Sunday morning I had sent Bobby to Mme Déliquaire with a Shetland shawl I had bought for myself in London just before Christmas but, already having several, decided to give her in case she might have more sleepless nights. She now asked me how I had known that it was their wedding anniversary, and I think she felt that this present was of bad augury, that it suggested she would soon have to take to her bed because of the increasing pain in her stomach. The atmosphere was so heavy in every way that I hurried back to the cottage, where I gave the milk to Matilda before going to see Yvonne Poulain.

I found Yvette much less well than I had hoped. Indeed her sunken eyes, her facial burns even more repellant now the mercurochrome had lost its vivid camouflage, her listlessness, alarmed me. Many visitors had come over the week-end and were immediately taken up to the bedroom, where Mme Castel received them, either in bed next to Yvette, for she was becoming quite exhausted with watchfulness, or fussing about, recounting over and over again how the accident happened.

I had been invited up with Mme Woolf, a relation of Mme Michelin, a very good woman who lived with her numerous family in a smaller house adjoining the big one in those tree-covered grounds exactly opposite the Poulain farm. We sat on the edge of the big bed, talking about the slump in farm produce. What hit the farmers worst was the drop in the price of pigs, but

Mme Woolf, like myself, was merely concerned with the amount of money she could obtain in the village for her eggs. She said:

'It wouldn't be so bad if other things went down in comparison, but with so many children at school, in private schools where one has to pay, I really do not know how we shall manage.'

'Yes, indeed,' said Mme Castel, 'we have all become so accustomed to turn noughts into nines when we make out a bill!'

Mme Woolf and I smiled, struck simultaneously by this naïve avowal, but Mme Castel was already exclusively occupied with Yvette, who had asked for the chamber. Yvonne was with us. There were times when I suspected she was jealous of the way her mother sought to monopolize Yvette's affection. Once she let out the tell-tale exclamation: 'But I am her mother!' The more I considered our tiny patient, the more I was convinced that she was not doing well. Her little mind was taxed by grown-up conversation and a sense of her own ugliness. Unwisely she had been shown a reflection of her features in a mirror, and straightway she had sobbed. My own eyes were not dry when I heard the story. I said I thought it was time we went, and on my return home I told Matilda that I was grievously anxious.

In my sleep I quite distinctly heard the words: 'Ma'am Henrey!' The name was mine. I held my breath a moment. It struck me as strange that I was dreaming and yet not dreaming, there being no pictorial accompaniment to the clearly enunciated name. I turned over in the bed, seeking a change of position, a cooler place. I heard my son's heavy breathing in his room. The grey stone pillars of the fire-place, the half-timbering of the dividing corridor came to me through drowsy eyes. I realized quickly that I had not been dreaming. All my nerves were taut now. I sat up. This time the voice was not only clear but recognizable. 'Ma'am Henrey!' It was Ernest.

I leapt out of bed, opened the casement window and shouted 'I'm coming,' put on a dressing-gown and slippers, and ran down the stairs. It was half-past one. The fire in the low room was burning even more brightly than when, two hours earlier, I had gone to bed. In the garden Ernest was swinging his oil lantern.

'The child?' I queried breathlessly.

'Yes,' he answered, coming in. 'She's got a terrible temperature.'

The telephone had not finished making its first sustained ringing drawl, before Dr. Lehérissey's voice, thickened by sleep, answered: 'What is it?' 'Ernest Poulain is with me,' I said.

'Yvette has a high fever.' I gave him the reading. 'Very well,' he answered. 'I'll come straight up.'

In the room above a bed creaked. My son was turning in his sleep. I said:

'I was afraid of this. You did not notice. You had been with her all day. But I, seeing her suddenly, was more susceptible to the change. If there is anything I can do . . .'

He let slip an exclamation of annoyance, as if my offer had touched frayed nerves. Then he took his lantern and went off through the night. For half an hour I sat staring into the fire. The rain beat against the window panes. I made some tea. It was late when I went up again to bed.

As it was clearly expected of me in future to pay for my milk and butter, I thought it would be wise to settle my first week with Mme Déliquaire. I had come to no decision about my home orchard. I wished to know whether Déliquaire's visit had been prompted merely by a desire to furnish me with less dairy produce for the same amount of grass, or by a panic at the sudden turn of events, making him anxious, almost immediately, to make his farm smaller.

He had become grim and taciturn, often sitting in the evening at the end of the table in the low room of his farmhouse, his head sunk between his arms, a newspaper unread before him. He was angry, not so much angry with me, or with any other person in particular, but angry that fate, against which he could not act, had within a few days, inexplicably, turned so much fury against him. Nobody dared ask him how he intended to run the farm with his wife ill and his two sons gone. I thought of that line of faggots bordering the stream where Jacques had stood so picturesquely, with his cows and horses and the donkey, in the sunshine a week ago, and I wondered who would finish the work he had begun. Such queries must be answered before I offered my grass to another farmer.

Mme Déliquaire that afternoon thanked me in a much more kindly way for the shawl I had given her, having perhaps had the time to examine it; but she said that it would not be for wearing in bed but to put on when she went visiting. Her husband had gone to a funeral, that of Marion, the tiler, an artisan of the old school who had died of cancer, and in mentioning this I fancied the word stuck in her mouth. The notice, with edges of deep black, which the family had sent round to announce the death, lay on the deal table, and Mme Déliquaire taking it roughly and turning it face down said:

'This will do to reckon up our accounts.'

She totted up what I owed her for a week's milk and butter, without revealing what she felt personally about the new arrangement. It came to a good deal in terms of English money. Butter on the farm continued to be dearer than in the shops.

I said, more to fathom this mystery than because I minded much:

'At present there 's lots of butter in the village.'

'I know,' she answered.

'At the government controlled price.'

'Yes,' she said, 'and even lower.'

'Lower?'

'Quite a bit lower.'

'How is that?'

'Many farmers who did most of their business on the black market, sending their butter by post to private people in Paris, for example, did not declare all their cows to the government. Suppose, for instance, they had twenty cows, they said they had only eight or nine. But now that in Paris there 's butter in the shops, those farmers would be glad to sell to the government. They don't dare, for fear the inspectors would ask why they suddenly had a surplus. So, unless they feed it to the pigs, they must get rid of it to anybody at any price.'

This still did not explain to me why Mme Déliquaire was asking more for her butter than the controlled price. Perhaps her private purchasers in Paris were continuing to be faithful. I said:

'It 's all very confusing.'

Mme Déliquaire pushed the bill along the table and said:

'Have a look if that 's right.'

'Marion was a devil for his cider,' I whispered, turning the sheet of paper. 'At the time I was having my cottage built they mostly were. Gravé, the builder, was a dreadful drunkard. But what a fine workman! Young Clément, Duclos's grandson, when he came to prune the rose-trees said to me: "I can't make it out, Mme Henrey, I 'm a good, sober fellow, as reasonable as can be, but I take off my hat to artisans like Marion, who did a prettier job of work when they were drunk than we seem able to do when sober. Do you suppose, Mme Henrey, that reasonableness has its drawbacks?"'

'They did drink heavier,' reflected Mme Déliquaire, 'and they certainly did do some pretty work. But the one 's not necessarily the consequence of the other. To my way of thinking, they just put more soul into everything. There 's an old lady has a big farm beyond the château, near eighty now, who when the railway was being built, used to hide gourds of apple-jack under her skirts to sell to the platelayers, like women in old days who followed the armies, and the farther the track went the longer was her walk, but she did not mind because it was making her a fortune. And that reminds me, have you seen the gardeners working round that pretty villa on the road down to the sea? The man who has bought it made his money sixty years back, picking pieces of coal up behind the first goods trains on that same track. He followed them, as you might say, with a donkey, and I don't say that when he came across a wagon in a goods yard he didn't help himself if there happened to be nobody looking. In the summer, when the trippers came, he would sell them coal at a rare price.'

I counted out the money I owed her, and said:

'You won't let Jacques leave without coming to say good-bye?'

'Bless you,' she answered. 'You 'll be the first, and then, I dare say, he 'll go to every farm between here and Saint-Vaast. It 's the custom when they leave home.'

Whenever I had a moment I would go to the Poulains for news of Yvette. Yvonne, who at one time had feared the shock would prevent her from continuing to breast feed Marie-Madeleine, had recovered her milk. I made it a point not to go upstairs. In the low room I could generally be sure of finding Mme Petit, tall and white-haired, ironing at one end of the table, while a tiny old lady, spectacled, whose name I did not know, mended and darned.

Rettol and young Bouveau, bringing down two tall trees at the top of my orchard, had made a gap in the hedge by which I could save several minutes when going to the Poulains' farm. They would put down their axes and ask me for news of the little girl. Bouveau said it was a sad pity Mme Castel had not known how to chase away the fire. I allowed this expression to pass the first time, though it had struck me as a little strange. When, however, he repeated it, I asked him what he meant.

He cleared the hair from his forehead with the back of his strong hairy arm, and his youthful features, beautiful as those of a Greek god, manifested astonishment that I should seek enlightenment on what obviously, in his family, was the accepted method of dealing with burns. Being, however, more lithe with his muscles than articulate in words, he merely repeated, swinging his axe:

'Chase away the fire!'

'You mean the burn?'

'He means the burn,' said Rettol, wondering how to make me understand, 'but chase away the fire is the expression used.'

'How is it done?' I queried.

'The actual words are a secret,' said Bouveau, 'but my mother-in-law——'

'That 's my wife,' put in Rettol.

'—learnt them from her mother, who had them from her grandmother.'

'A sort of witchcraft?'

'I don't know what you would call it, ma'am, but when my baby son was burnt my mother-in-law chased away the fire.'

'The child was younger than the Poulains' little girl,' said Rettol.

'Ten months,' said Bouveau.

'How long ago did this happen?' I asked.

'My son is a year and a half,' said Bouveau.

'Oh! Quite recently? But what did she do? You haven't told me what she did.'

Bouveau stuck his axe in the cut-down trunk, rubbed his palms together, and making gestures explained:

'They pass their hands over the burnt skin like this and mutter some secret words. They also make the sign of the cross.'

'That 's right,' said Rettol.

'And do you believe this?' I asked, quite stupefied that, Rettol apart, this young man, so modern, so strong, not yet twenty, should in this atomic age speak so believingly of witchcraft. 'Do you really believe this?'

'But of course I believe it. Everybody believes in it. Look, Ma'am Henrey, it was breakfast. I was sitting with the bowl of boiling coffee in my lap, like this.' He sat down on the log and pretended to be holding a bowl of coffee on his lap. 'The baby comes up thus and knocks the coffee over his arm. Well, the mother-in-law chased the fire away, and there was nothing left but a little redness on the arm, and a blister where her hand had not quite passed.'

'The coffee might not have been hot enough?'

'It was boiling, for the simple reason I had not yet started to drink it.'

'That 's right,' said Rettol. 'It was boiling.'

Not feeling it was my duty to enlighten these delightfully medieval woodcutters, I passed on my way. In the courtyard

the Nicols were mixing their cement. I had a hen sitting on ten eggs, and I would dearly have loved to see the backs of these workmen.

After Matilda had closed herself in the cottage for the night, and while Bobby and I were having supper in the low room by the fire, Yvonne Poulain knocked at the door. She had a shawl round her head and shoulders, and in this garb, looking so small and timid, might have come out of the pages of one of Mrs. Gaskell's novels describing our industrial midlands a century ago. She held André by the hand, and said:

'There, I 'm disturbing you again, Ma'am Henrey, but I 'd like the doctor to know what Yvette's temperature is before he has his supper. She doesn't look a bit well to-night. I 'm sorely worried.'

I telephoned to Dr. Lehérissey, who said he was coming up immediately. Mme Yvonne was sitting demurely on the edge of a chair. Her eyes, in spite of her worrying, had been taking everything in, for this was her first visit to my house, at any rate in the evening, and after a while she said:

'I never knew it was so nice with you.'

'It is nice,' I agreed, 'but that is mostly due to the fire-place.'

'Well, I didn't mean that only, though the fire-place is nice,' she went on. 'I meant that it 's so cosy with the blinds drawn and you both looking so happy, with the chairs and the cushions and the books and things. I didn't realize it until now, but we don't seem to be able to shut ourselves up and be cosy in our place. There 's always people coming and going, though it 's only Émile with faggots or pig food.'

Her femininity was warmed by the softer lights, my sewing basket, a picture or two, little nothings of what appeared to her a more leisurely existence. The farmer's wife was suddenly aware that I was essentially a woman of the town. She was quite lost in a brief reverie, before saying:

'Well, I must hurry back. Thank you, Ma'am Henrey, for telephoning.'

The next afternoon, instead of going round to make my own inquiries, I sent Matilda, who took Mme Beaudry with her. I was anxious to be with Mme Bayard who, for the second day, was polishing my floors and the staircase.

Mme Bayard's son, whom I had known a boy, was, I have already said, training to be a schoolmaster, for she and her husband had decided, that this profession, once so ill paid, now offered surprising advantages and, what appeared to them who had worked so hard and precariously, almost complete security. He would have a house, his heating and lighting, a fine salary, limitless social benefits, and an excellent pension. He would be a young god in an increasingly socialistic paradise. All he had to do was successfully to pass his examinations. After that the state would supply his needs for ever and ever.

Bayard was employed by Barbe, the painter, who twice since the war had done my house inside and out. In all the village there was not a more honest couple than the Bayards, but Mme Bayard, who, on occasions when she came to clean the bedrooms, leaning on her broom, passed, for my great delight, the entire population in review, their qualities and shortcomings, their history to three or four generations back, had a feeling that life had not treated her and the good Bayard with the generosity that their unusual honesty merited. Bayard had been a prisoner of war in Germany whilst many people, farmers and shopkeepers, had enriched themselves; she had never had any truck with the Germans, whilst others who were less scrupulous were now highly considered; she had quite lately put her savings into a government loan which had gone down forty per cent in value. She and Bayard had been right to squeeze a little so that their son should live comfortably at the expense of the community.

She was much more fun to gossip with than Mme Beaudry, being as deep rooted in our rich black soil as the oldest of our elms. Her mother, a snuff-taking matriarch, speaking old Norman thickly, had been postwoman in the First World War, and rare stories she also had to tell. Mother and daughter expertly made mattresses with Caen wool. Our beds had not their equal.

Mme Bayard had her own system of doing the housework. She liked to do one room only at a time, spending about four hours making everything shine and smell deliciously of polish. When she had finished you would not have found a speck of dust, the tiniest cobweb. She was one of these women who, superbly retaining the meticulousness of old times, made strangers cry out: 'The French still have a way with them!'

At about six o'clock we were talking at the top of the stairs. Mme Bayard was saying to me:

'Now, Mme Henrey, listen carefully. Here is your parquet shining like a mirror, so slippery you must watch not to slip and break a leg. For a day or two it will be the tiniest bit damp and I wouldn't like you to let the dust settle on the surface, so here I have arranged everything—the O'Cedar mop with a flannel underneath, so that from time to time you can come and swing it gently across the floor.'

She began to show me what to do, rhythmically moving her hips and her ample bosom, unctuously passing her plump hands above this mirror of beautiful work, as a priest might pass his hands over a person or thing blessing it.

I said: 'Yes, Mme Bayard,' with no intention of doing anything, preferring to wait for her to come another time, for I had far too much housework as it was. She said, urged to begin a new subject of talk:

'I went to Caen yesterday. It 's amazing how the town is springing up again. One goes one day, a house is being built, reaching the first floor; one goes a week later, the house is finished and another begun.' She made a few movements with the mop, and went on: 'The old red light quarter, where one was frightened to go because of all the women standing half naked, or in their chemises, in front of the brothels, where really only the men dared go, well, it was all razed to the ground during the battle, and now where the brothels stood—I could tell you the names of one or two in the village who used to frequent them—where those brothels stood is a public garden. Flowers bloom on the vice of yesterday!'

'It does sound beautiful!' I said.

At this moment Matilda appeared at the garden door. We both stopped, looking at her, wondering what news she would bring us about Yvette.

'We were not allowed to go up into the bedroom,' said Matilda in a tense voice. 'She 's so much worse. Ernest's sister, Madeleine Montague, went up because she 's a member of the family. We were there when she came down, biting her lips not to sob. She said: "I can't bear it any more. It 's terrible to see her pinched nose and her poor little face that looks as if it was cut out of a church candle. All night she was delirious, looking first at one hand, saying: 'This is daddy,' and then at the other hand, saying: 'This is mummy.'"'

'Madeleine Montague is very sensitive,' I said. 'She is like me, like all Madeleines, quickly moved to tears.'

'Mme Yvonne is just as upset,' continued Matilda, throwing off her wrap and advancing as far as the keg of apple-jack at the foot of the stairs. 'She says Yvette is feverish one moment, shivering the next, and continually trying to cover herself up with her bedsheet, and that her little hands are for ever making the movement of an animal trying to bury itself in the ground.' Matilda, making pitiful little movements with her rheumatic hands, went on: 'Covering up her tiny body in its shroud.'

'That child is going to die,' said Mme Bayard, putting down the O'Cedar mop. 'They all do that when they are going to die. It 's an infallible sign. Mme Lefevre's old mother, where I used to polish the floors, the morning she was so feeble, asking me to come back in the afternoon, she did it. I had to slip out to make Bayard his lunch. In the afternoon they were tolling the bell.'

'It 's happened twice to my knowledge,' said Matilda, whose veracity I could not doubt. 'With my sister's husband in England, and when I was a very young woman, learning dress-making at Blois. A little girl of three we all loved and spoilt, who had diphtheria before the days they could vaccinate for it. The little angel started to make those movements with her hands, trying to pull the sheets over her, and the grandmother, on the doorstep, said to us: "She 's trying to bury herself. She 'll die." We thought her cruel and hard, the old granny. However, the little girl died. Perhaps she was not so cruel. She knew from the signs.'

'You 're as bad as Rettol with his witchcraft,' I said to Matilda, but Mme Bayard said conclusively:

'No, everybody would tell you that.'

There was a knock at the kitchen door and the sound of feet being wiped on the door-mat.

'It 's Jacques,' came the deep voice, 'come to say good-bye.'

He had left his bicycle outside. His cheeks were rosy like fresh apples.

'I 'm going!' he said, standing quite still, wondering what to do next.

'My poor Jacques,' I exclaimed, 'we shall all so miss you!'

'I 'm off to-morrow at five a.m.,' he continued, beaming. 'The early bus to Caen.'

'I wish you all sorts of good luck,' I said, starting to weep. Matilda was crying also. She had always had a soft corner for Jacques. 'If,' I said, 'you do not find a young and pretty woman to be your "godmother," perhaps I could be?'

'I 'd like it to be you,' he said.

'Then you must come and be kissed!' I exclaimed.

I kissed him on both cheeks, and Matilda did the same.

We were all very affected. We hoped he would have enough to eat in the barracks at Caen, that he would have a safe journey to Paris, that they would not send him off to some too-hot climate, that he would be happy and come back quickly to see us. We all talked at the same time, crying copiously. Even Mme Bayard was very moved. Jacques said:

'I must be going. I 've so many people to say good-bye to, I 've no idea how I shall get round to all of them before I have to go in the morning.'

'Oh, you 'll be late home to-night,' said Mme Bayard.

'Jacques,' I said, 'don't go accepting too much hospitality. Beware of the little drop of this and that.'

'I 'll take care all right,' he said.

'Good-bye, good-bye, Jacques! Write to us.'

'I 'll write, ma'am.'

We watched him take his bicycle and push it up the grassy slope of the damp orchard.

XV

ANDRÉ, I am happy to say, did not receive fifteen francs to carry the holy water at his sister Yvette's funeral. The old wives' tale about death following the pulling up of her sheets was proved a lie by Dr. Lehérissey's prompt administration of penicillin, which once again miraculously saved a human life.

While Yvette was making rapid progress, Déliquaire went down to the stream every morning and continued, alone, to make his faggots so expertly that it was a pleasure to watch him. Though cold winds alternated with sunshine, the signs of spring multiplied, and soon the pear-trees broke into bud.

Going down every evening, as usual, to the village, I heard often repeated a rumour which I at first dismissed as inaccurate but later I began to take more seriously. The story was that Victor Duprez, our charming mayor, was planning to sell his magnificent farm on the other side of The Point.

Our land was so intermingled that I was quite alarmed at the idea of a future unknown neighbour. As long as I had known our village, first Victor Duprez's black-bearded patriarchal father, then himself, such a bundle of picturesque contradictions, had imprinted their violent characters on farms and orchards as if they had been, which in a way they were, the seigneurs or squires.

My house was originally bought by the patriarch for a younger son who died. Victor had used my home orchard for keeping ponies, and against the back wall, when I bought the house, there were some roughly built stables which I had immediately taken down. I think Victor had become very attached to the place. Often when he spoke of it tears rose in his eyes, but one never thought it strange when he cried, especially on a subject as dear to him as the soil. Certainly if he could hate, he could love; if he could swear and work himself up into a towering rage, he could bewitch one with smiles and soft words. Had it not been for his father, Victor would never have sold me my farm, but his father's policy was to sell, always to sell. He used to say that for a land agent it was wrong to fall in love with a property. 'The next one is always better than the last,' was his maxim.

When the father died, Victor determined to avenge the sale by finding the next best thing at hand. A certain M. Allard, a Parisian gentleman, owned a pretty modern house with a fine but small farm across the lane from my own. Victor bought this property, and it was as if the place had been touched by a magic wand, so much prettier did it quickly become.

I must add here that when I bought my farm there were only two or three orchards other than the one in which the house stood, and indeed the estate was so small that it could not have been in any way self-supporting. A few months later, a certain Mme Paul having died, her children, in order to divide her fortune equally, sold her orchards, very beautiful, very picturesque, and all of them a hedge away from my own. The patriarch immediately came to see me, with the orchards, so to speak, in his pocket. They were very cheap, but I was not very rich and I could only afford to buy half of them. The others remained unsold until, the patriarch having died, Victor bought M. Allard's farm. He then increased the size of his estate by adding to it what remained of the Mme Paul orchards. We thus became opposing owners of identical sized farms, our orchards overlapping like joined fingers.

Victor Duprez had an agent and a farmer to run the estate, which was much better kept than mine, more carefully planted, drained, hedged, and manured. He was very much the gentleman farmer, experienced since childhood, having money to spend. He lived richly, entertaining his clients in the Allard house, serving vegetables and fruit from the walled garden, dairy produce and meat from the farm. When there was fish it would come straight from Trouville. Imagine what a modest woman I must have seemed, alone in my servantless house, bogged up in the rainy season in my orchard! I was not even—and this was a matter of sorrow to me—able to return the hospitality of his table.

When I was only lately back in Normandy, after the war, I was offered an orchard belonging to M. Gravé, the builder, who was deaf M. Gravé's brother, an orchard nearly as fine as my home orchard, uncommonly green, which Victor Duprez and I had always wanted to own. I was on the point of buying it when I had a pang of conscience, having heard that Victor Duprez considered that he always had some sort of right to buy this piece of land. I dined that evening with him and unwisely, I expect, for I am too soft-hearted to be good in business, told him that M. Gravé had approached me, whereupon he blew off my head and I yielded.

This orchard was exactly opposite the place down by the stream where I had met Jacques making the faggots; its lusciousness was due to M. Gravé having during more than thirty years emptied the human manure of the village (the owners of villas and the shopkeepers paid him to take it away) upon the grassy slopes. At Christmas the pasture was as emerald as in summer.

Maître Vincent, after I had taken my mail to the post office on the Monday night, asked me into his study, where he told me officially that the mayor was willing to sell. He mentioned the figure of £15,000 on which, by French law, there would be one-third duties to be paid by the purchaser. M. Duprez was not agreeable to any division of his property. I could not, for instance, merely buy any orchards that I particularly fancied.

This confirmation of rumour by the notary strangely saddened me. I could not believe that Victor Duprez was not selling his home without a heavy heart. Even though it was a matter of following his father's maxim, he had lavished too much real love upon the estate not to be crying secretly now. Why was he doing it?

'Perhaps,' I said to Maître Vincent, 'M. Victor Duprez will change his mind. I think he will not sell, after all.'

'It is not in a notary's power to delve so deeply in a man's mind,' answered Maître Vincent. 'I do not know what he will decide to-morrow. Perhaps, as you say, he will not sell. This evening, however, I am empowered to offer you the estate.'

'I cannot afford it, especially if the big house must be included. I do not think I could afford the rest, or even part of the rest. I merely regret M. Gravé's orchard. I think one is sometimes punished for being considerate and kind.'

'There are no friends in business, according to the saying, madame.'

'Somebody else was telling me the same thing a few days ago.'

Maître Vincent smiled with compassion.

'I hope you are enjoying your winter?' he asked. 'I hope we shall soon see your little boy's film.'

He rose, and opened the door very courteously.

The news greatly unsettled me. I could not calm myself. I was unable to write. The first rumour of the sale, coming so quickly after Mme Déliquaire's illness, M. Déliquaire not wanting my home orchard, Jacques's going into the army, Yvette's horrible accident, the sudden dip in farm prices, brought a curious feeling of tragedy. Matilda was also moved, though she had the satisfaction of inspecting at all hours of the day her three hens sitting on a dozen eggs each, all potentially future members of the farmyard.

At this moment of uncertainty and unhappiness on three sides of my orchards—the Déliquaires to the east, the Poulains to the north, and Victor Duprez to the west—M. Vannier, the butcher, told me he had decided not to give me any sheep to put in the small enclosure near my house. We had talked about this plan for a long time. There were to be three sheep, with two lambs each. In September he could have sold the lambs for as much as his total initial expenditure. In other words, the sheep would have remained in his possession as net profit.

Fear that prices would drop, even more than now, had made him nervous. He had only just started in business and could not take a risk. Hearing from him that the whole scheme merely required £50, I suddenly wondered if it would not be fun to do it myself. My risk would be less than his—I had no grass to pay.

This thought had scarce taken shape in my mind when I wondered also if I should not employ the rest of my orchard to fatten three young bulls. I asked M. Vannier what they cost at this season. He paused in the act of cutting my joint, to mark with a stub of pencil the possible profit for me in buying the three animals now and selling them in September. He said, unless things went wrong, I should make twenty pounds on each animal.

I felt so elated with these dreams that I told him that if he discovered the animals and came to inspect them from time to time, I would give him some interest in the undertaking. We finally decided that I should own the sheep, the lambs, and two of the young bulls. The third bull would be his. He would buy it with his own money, but I would charge him nothing for the grazing which, if his suppositions proved correct, was worth twenty pounds, his profit when he resold the animal, suitably fattened, in September.

I came home that evening as if I had discovered a land bright with gold. Matilda was enthusiastic. She thought the lambs would love her like Mary's little lamb, and she said that everybody in the village blamed me for not making more money out of the richest orchard in the neighbourhood. They said I must be a very stupid woman to give it to Déliquaire for so little money, and that, in my place, they would certainly know how to make it pay.

'I thought you might be afraid of the young bulls,' I said.

'Why should I?' she asked. 'They are castrated. Everybody knows they become fat and gentle. When you are both gone I shall like to hear them at night, rubbing themselves against the side of the house. I often wished Déliquaire would not take his cows away so quickly to other pastures. They are so friendly.'

'I also fear that Déliquaire will be angry.'

'What business has M. Déliquaire to be angry when it was he who gave up the orchard?'

'We shall probably do something wrong, and he will laugh at us.'

'What wrong can we do? They just eat grass. There's nothing in the world one need do to them. They never come in at night. They can't have babies like cows. Who has ever heard of a young bull falling ill?'

'The best thing,' I said, 'would be to ask Maître Vincent to advise us.'

The next evening, therefore, I went to see Maître Vincent, who was probably disappointed that I had not come to buy Victor

Duprez's property. When I told him about my plan he said I was wrong.

'You know,' he explained reprovingly, 'city women should not play at being farmers. You would make a great deal more money selling the grass to your farmer, and getting on with your knitting.'

'M. Déliquaire came to see me in a huff. Apparently he had consulted you. He thought the orchard was not worth the milk and butter his wife had been giving me.'

'He panicked a little. I am certain that at heart he would like to go on with the orchard. Even if you gave it him for a lower figure, you would still be better off than trying to turn farmer yourself. That sort of thing has never paid. You certainly know all sorts of things that M. Déliquaire does not. The secrets of the town are yours. You are an authoress. Concede to your farmers a superior knowledge of the land.'

'People laugh at me for having such a magnificent orchard and making so little money out of it.'

'You draw dividends in other ways, in a pretty place for your mother to live, in health for your son, in beauty and quiet where you can pursue your gentle occupations. A wise woman knows her limitations.'

'I think it would be fun to have sheep and cattle belonging to me.'

'You will be doing what M. Victor Duprez does, but that sort of farming calls for a bailiff. You will run into complications.'

'How can I know about things if I don't occasionally take a risk?'

'I would prefer to keep danger at arm's length. It often comes uninvited.'

'I am equally afraid of being over-cautious. One quickly becomes so dull. What do I risk with just a few animals?'

'You risk losing them, madame. You might then lose something else, an orchard, perhaps, or a hayfield, and then more orchards, until you might be obliged to sell your whole estate.'

'I know from experience, Maître Vincent, that what you say is invariably true, but I am not a woman easily influenced. I have to think a problem out for myself. I have a hunch that by going ahead I could make money.'

'Then nothing I can add will make any difference. Would you

like to ask M. Vannier to come and see me? When he has bought the animals I could check the price and pay him.'

'Yes, I would like that. I should feel safer.'

I was very obstinate. I went round to see Vannier, telling him I had authorized Maître Vincent to advance him the money, but as a concession to the notary's view, I said I would only have one sheep and two lambs. For the rest, our arrangement would remain unaltered. He would buy three young bulls, one for himself and two for me. He said:

'I think you are right about the sheep. They are very bad for

the pasturage. They do the grass as much harm as young bulls do it good.'

'Why did you not tell me this,' I exclaimed, 'when we originally planned to have sheep?'

'It was not my business to tell you,' he answered. 'I am surprised the notary did not warn you.'

'He merely said he was against having sheep,' I answered. 'He also said that you should be careful to choose gentle bulls. "It 's not that bulls are dangerous," he said, "but they are less easy to manage than cows."'

'Oh, they are not bad,' said M. Vannier.

'I am afraid because of Bobby. He is so fearless. He never seems to realize that he could be kicked.'

I bought three rump steaks for supper and climbed slowly back to the farm. My mind was only just beginning to grapple with this question in a lucid manner. Until now it was as if my

faculties had been partly paralysed. Obvious facts, facts I had always known, suddenly sprang up before my eyes, and left me trembling at the extent of my stupidity. Vannier had spoken of keeping the bulls on the orchard till mid September, but by then my orchard, so magnificently planted, would be strewn with tons of apples, and cattle, greedy for apples, only needed to eat a few to die in a single night. The apples choked them, the fruit not passing from one stomach to the other. Normally, as soon as the fruit began to fall, our farmers put their cattle elsewhere, on more barren fields. And even in early August, before the apples fell, the fruit, ripening on the trees, tempted the beasts, who at this period of the year were put in chains to prevent them from raising their heads to tree level. Often they slipped their chains, losing them in the long grass. I would first have to buy chains, which expenditure would minimize my profit, and then, if the cattle slipped them, be obliged immediately to put them on again. Alas! I was certainly not capable of fitting chains to a bull! Only a man could do that.

Hitherto, whenever I had the slightest trouble, Bobby would run to the Déliquaires, who would come immediately and put things right. They were uncommonly obliging in this way. They gathered my apples, sold a number of tons, and with the rest made cider so excellently that this year all those who had tasted it said that it was the very finest for ten miles round.

The angelus was ringing as I reached my lane. Rettol and Bouveau, who had been cutting down some trees, had just smashed a telephone pole. My wires hung loosely over the grass. Few things made me so utterly miserable as to be without the telephone, for imagine my predicament if Bobby had fallen ill in the night! I had also asked Rettol to clean up the hedge bordering the lane, and this he had done so well that nothing remained in it. I could have cried with vexation.

He said: 'I 'll put down some stakes and two rows of barbed wire.'

'Oh, no!' I exclaimed. 'Would you have the place look like a concentration camp? It shall be done properly with lengths of hazel fastened to oak pillars.'

'Oh, madame,' he answered, 'have you thought of the price?'

What Rettol referred to was the amount of labour, of hard work with saw and axe. Two young oaks, of which I had many, would supply the stakes; the hazel to be nailed transversally grew abundantly in both my woods. These would be for nothing.

He said: 'We shall need one day to fell the oaks and fashion them; another to cut the hazel rods and bring them, together with the oak, in a cart from the wood; a third to drive in the stakes and nail the rods. Three of us working all the time, madame. We cannot ask less than ten thousand francs.'

How helpless I felt in situations like these! Déliquaire and Ernest Poulain would think me very extravagant when barbed wire alone, against tree-trunks, some branches thrown untidily against the gaps till the wild rose had time to grow, would have amply sufficed. I kept on coming against an inborn desire to have things looking nice. The notary blamed me particularly, and was always saying in a meticulous voice:

'The less you do to the land, madame, the more money it will bring you in. Never build, never improve, never make a change.

When you come to sell, all you have thought so important will count for nothing.'

Maître Vincent thought in terms of buying and selling. He knew that these days families did not keep land for long. Land was bought and sold as men are born and die. The great thing was not lose too much at the end of one's tenure. He thought, astutely, that if Victor Duprez was really obliged to sell his farm, the immense improvements he had made would hardly be taken into account by the purchaser. Clever men, wise, sombre-faced landowners, refused even to mend the roof of a farmer's house when the rain beat through. The chimney could smoke! The door could fall from its hinges! The barns could tumble down! They would argue, prevaricate, promise something some other time, smile, and if smiling was no good, snarl, bite, but never unloose their purse strings. I had given my first farmer, Goguet, out of pity, a cow to help him grow rich. As soon as I had gone, during the war, he pillaged my house. How clearly did the notary warn me at the time, so distant now, of the giving to Goguet of that cow.

'Townsfolk and farmers do not mix,' he had said. 'You are tempted to re-create a little Trianon. Like Marie Antoinette, you want to play at being a country woman. You will rue this day, madame. I tell you, it cannot work.'

The ten thousand francs that Rettol asked me for my hedge was certainly more than the work, however heavy, justified, but I lacked that experience and authority which would have allowed me to know, and tell him in certain words, exactly what I would pay, no more. He smiled blandly, enjoying my flushed stupidity, satisfied, in advance, that as he was dealing with a woman and not a man, I would meekly obey, and I, remembering that I had more or less given a free hand to Vannier to buy bulls and sheep, and that as they would be mine I must not allow them to run away, was obliged to nod and merely add:

'Please let the work be finished quickly.'

Back in my house I felt utterly miserable, discovering at every moment new reasons why I must not go through with this experiment, but alarmed lest Vannier had already gone to the notary to fetch the money. I would have telephoned but the line was wrecked. I began at that moment to be bitterly vexed with

Rettol, for by his awkwardness he could cost me two hundred thousand francs and more. I had no sort of pity for him who, at his own expense, would have to pay the post office engineers twelve pounds or more for a new pole and a day's work fixing up the wires. I said: 'What is twelve pounds, compared with two hundred pounds?' And as my imagination flew with swift wings, I considered that in addition to this monetary loss, the bulls would wreck my apple-trees, tear them up perhaps, break into my garden, destroy the peaches and the pears, kick Matilda, kill my son. 'I must have been mad!' I exclaimed.

There was also the stream at the bottom of my orchard across which Déliquaire's cows, when they came to feed here, crossed at will, both sides of the water being theirs to roam. But when he and I were competitors I would have to prevent my animals from going over to him. Rettol, or another, would be obliged to put up stakes and dig a pool and that, if I did it properly with a foot-bridge of hazel, would cost me nearly as much as my hedge, and so I kept on recalling the notary's severe phrase: 'You would make more money by renting your orchard to Déliquaire.'

Immediately after breakfast I flew down to the village, going directly to Maître Vincent to ask if Vannier had yet been to collect the money.

'Not yet,' answered the clerk, who gave me back the authority I had signed.

A great wave of relief rushed to my head. It was market day. Vannier was at his stall in the market-place. I broke the news to him.

'Just as you please,' he said, 'but in a few more hours I would have bought the animals.'

I felt suddenly quite faint.

I no longer minded paying Rettol for the hedge, believing, as indeed was the case, that I had just made a vast saving, perhaps even prevented a tragedy. The sun was shining when I returned to the farm. I was becoming used to seeing the hedge so bare, and the post office engineers were busy repairing the line. Bobby was with them. He had translated the words printed on an encased coil of wire, MADE IN U.S.A., and I caught the query:

'How do you know? Are you the son of the house? English?

You don't say! I was in London during the war. I drove De Gaulle for a while. Do you remember him?'

I suddenly saw Déliquaire coming down the lane, angry and flustered.

'Somebody has opened a gate by the Bourgogne!' he exclaimed. 'The donkey has escaped——'

'Don't worry, M. Déliquaire,' said Bobby. 'It came in here. Roger is leading it back on the halter.'

'Plague on these people who open gates!' said Déliquaire, looking relieved.

I left him critically inspecting my fence, conjecturing, I suppose, about my rumoured bulls, not guessing that I was meekly disposed to have him back at a reduced rent. This decision was fortified by having just seen Déliquaire so put out by the escape of his donkey. I wondered what would have happened to my sheep and my cattle if somebody had left my gate open. If Bobby and I had been there we might, of course, have run after them, but had we been in London, or filming in some other part of the world, Matilda might not even have noticed their absence till they were miles away.

I had a tiff with Rettol, which merely served to make us better friends. I had ordered a ton of coal and some barley from Fournier, who, knowing how damp my orchard was, would take no risk of having his lorry bogged up. He therefore gave orders for his horse and cart to precede the lorry to my farm. When the truck, having hauled the merchandise up the steep hill, reached my gate, the sacks would be transferred to the waiting cart, which would safely negotiate the swampy earth.

The two vehicles arrived during the warmth of the afternoon. Rettol, his son-in-law Bouveau, and the son of a neighbouring farmer were finishing my fence, which now looked extremely fine. The woodcutters went over to shake hands with the truck driver, who proved to be Rioux who had come to fetch me at Lisieux before Christmas, and the carter, a little old man with white hair who looked exactly as one pictures the cabbies of half a century ago. This wizened individual threw his reins over the big white horse and climbed down for a comfortable chat.

The Rettols had, at my request, cut down a very dry pollard which I badly needed for the fire in the low room, and they asked the carter to bring it down with the barley and the coal, which of course he gladly did. The sight of Fournier's white horse in my orchard, however, invariably put my nerves on edge, for this was the same horse which, suitably caparisoned, functioned at every village funeral, and whenever I saw it my mind was filled with hatefulness for theatrical trappings—a horse dressed in a medieval coat of black and white; plumes, tall candles, roguish choristers simpering and laughing behind red-eyed mourners, and a hearse driver whose only thought was to get rid of the coffin and quench his thirst at the first cabaret.

I would have doubtless repressed my ill humour had not all these men come outside my window whilst I was writing. Rettol's voice, then brazenly rising, proposed that all should follow him to my cider press where a cool cask was waiting to be tapped. The five men, abreast, sang their way indecorously over the grass, under the trees in bud, flouting my authority.

Though I had made it clear to Rettol that he could have the key to the cellar when he was thirsty, I was not prepared to see him invite others with airs of being master on my land. When, therefore, Rioux and the carter had gone, and the woodcutters were again busy swinging their axes, I called Rettol for a private talk, giving him the fullness of my mind.

He accepted my anger with dignity, offering no trivial excuse but taking nobly the just blame. I told him that in future my cellars would be closed to him except when I gave myself the pleasure to invite him personally. I was glad not to see him depart from his usual politeness. During the next few days, when the roll of bread and the dry sausage came out of haversacks, the woodcutters would go to the farm from which they borrowed what implements they needed, and there I think they were more at their ease, laughing and talking without disturbing me.

On the first day of spring, which was a Monday, I went to see them after breakfast. They were talking about a cow in the farm I have just spoken about which, instead of being taken to the bull, had been injected by an expert from Paris who had been passing that way. This system, which was quite new with us, might soon allow our farmers to experiment with new breeds. I had always wanted to cross our Normandy cows with Herefords. Rettol then said:

'They 'll be tolling the bell this midday, madame.'

'Who for?'

'Émile Duclos, the gardener, who died at five this morning.'

Though I had been expecting it, the news shocked me profoundly. The funeral was to be at ten-thirty on Thursday.

The morning broke in a haze of heat. Everything in the garden, in the orchards, along the hedgerows, was bursting out as if to receive our good friend into the tender glories of spring. Here was summer heat. Here were the birds singing with more lusty throats. The flies, the wasps, the bees, a myriad gossamer-winged insects, came out of winter hiding, filling the sweet-scented air with buzzing sounds. By one of those exigent requirements which sometimes clash with a mood, a mind's sadness, I had to be photographed with Bobby for *Woman's Own*, which had just bought the serial rights of my new novel *Philippa*. The pictures had to leave for London by the night mail, and for the first time in the year I was to wear a flimsy summer dress and he a clean silk blouse. I washed his hair quickly, dressed myself with fingers clumsy with gardening and the handling of logs and faggots, and while the distant church bell began to toll for the arrival of the body into the church, I smilingly posed both in and out of the old farmhouse.

My thoughts were entirely at the funeral, fearing increasingly that I should be irretrievably late. In the autumn when Duclos's wife, that sweet woman, had died, the service had been curtailed because the family knew that he was himself too ill to stand undue strain both to body and mind, and they had said to themselves that his funeral, which must follow rapidly, could be sufficiently elaborate to do for both of them. The church to-day would be packed, the service elaborate and long. The important thing for the guests was to show themselves afterwards in the vestry, shaking hands sadly with the near mourners. That I must do or for ever bear the silent reproaches of the Besnards and their son, and perhaps worse, the bitter reasoning of my conscience.

The photographer had taken eight or nine pictures in different parts of the farm, the sun remaining extremely hot, for which at least I was grateful, Bobby's hair being still damp, I being in a light dress for the first time. We had no animals to enliven these scenes, the cows being, as usual, on the strip of pasture between the small wood and the stream, the ducks having gone off to the far stretches of the water, and the turkeys and hens enjoying their morning walk to distant orchards. This was not the first time I had watched M. Fournet-Postel, the photographer, at work. He made the pictures for my book *The Return to the Farm*, notably a gruesome photograph of the knife with which old Hommet, the sorcerer, cut his throat, when on the point of being apprehended by the police for his part in denouncing his son-in-law, my then farmer Goguet, to the Germans for keeping a shot-gun hidden in my cider press. The Fournet-Postels were good church people, the wife playing the organ, and being, in addition, the village piano teacher. Their pretty daughter divided her time between the piano and the dark room. His womenfolk were, he said, at the funeral, and it was he who kept on assuring me that we had plenty of time to take just one more picture. He said also:

'You are very lucky to have me at all. On Monday I am going to the photographic congress in Paris, and shall be away for at least three weeks.'

I asked him if he was going to exhibit, but he said, no, not this time, only to buy the various cameras and films and plates which he hoped to sell to holiday-makers during the summer holidays. For a last picture he had put it into his head to catch the magnificent *berlou*, which had just appeared with his blue and red neck and his fan outstretched. At that moment the bell down in the village started to toll. I left him with his camera poised and ran up to my room to change into a coat and skirt, put on a hat and gloves, and snatch up a handbag. We then ran to the top of the orchard where the car was waiting, he stumbling over the rough grass with his heavy equipment, I tripping and turning ankles on high heels. The driver took us rapidly down. The bell tolled more distinctly. The first mourners were climbing back up the hill. In sight of the church, the parvis appeared empty. Tears of remorse and anger rolled down my cheeks, but of quick decision I exclaimed:

'There 's the procession turning by the market-place to go to the cemetery. Drop me just behind. I shall go with them.'

Telling the driver to take M. Fournet-Postel to his shop and to fetch me at the cemetery in an hour's time, I slammed the door and hurried to take my place in the slow-moving cortège. People were standing in front of shops and houses. I was immensely relieved, rather glad in a way to pay my respects intimately with the close members of the family rather than with the crowds at church.

Soon we had left the village and were pursuing the wide climbing road towards the isolated railway station and cemetery, facing each other across the track, high, high above the marsh-land and the bay with sapphire sea, distantly marked with great liners sailing in and out of Le Havre.

Along the white road, with the rhythmical sound of the horse's hooves and the slow steps of the black-clothed mourners. The hot sun made everything shine and sparkle—the tricolour flag unfurled, the brass pieces on the ornate tawdry hearse with its dusty black feathers, but on all sides covered with red and white roses, which filled the dusty road with their magnificent perfume, scenting the hot day as if one were in a garden.

Clop . . . clop . . . clop . . . clop . . . went the hooves of M. Fournier's white horse, the grizzled, white-haired carter who had delivered my coal and drunk in my cider press dozing in the hot sun. Clop . . . clop . . . clop . . . clop. On either side of the hearse softly trod the strong men who at the cemetery would lift the coffin, strong men, none stronger than one with curly pieces of hair encircling his baldness—the woodcutter Rettol; another, tall, rather gawky in a Sunday set of strange-fitting clothes—his son-in-law Bouveau.

Clop . . . clop . . . clop . . . clop. Here, on the outskirts of the marshland, was Mlle Lefranc's small villa, where the elder Bouveau, with bullets in his thighs, leaving a long trail of blood, dragged himself after the battle in the doll's house where he had hidden the British parachutists. On the other side of the road was the mean row of houses in one of which lived the Goguette, widow of my first farmer, reduced to penury after being rich, obliged as part of her rent to milk the owner's cow night and morning.

Clop . . . clop . . . clop . . . clop. Magnificent plane-trees with boughs trained to form six-armed candlesticks, not yet in leaf but proclaiming amazingly the art of the expert gardener. How sweet smelt the roses from Nice and Monte Carlo where to-day, why yes, to-day, there is carnival! It is mid Lent. He died on the first day of spring. He is being buried on carnival day. Something in this thought made me less sad. One is more certain of resurrection on a feast day.

Eight little choristers in dirty laced surplices almost danced in front of the caparisoned white horse. The priest, young, spectacled, and bored, knew not how to keep them in order. André Poulain, was not amongst the choristers. His father Ernest had told me, the night before, that he was taking his young son to a neighbouring village in the motor-car. Yvette was now sufficiently recovered to play in the sunny garden, but Marie-Madeleine was coughing so much that Mme Yvonne thought of sending for Dr. Lehérissey. The other children had probably been neglected during Yvette's critical illness.

A man with a cap was walking with back bent, to the left of the hearse, and he looked, from the rear, so much like the dead man that I imagined for a moment I was dreaming, for these are the sort of tricks dreams play. I supposed that the man with the cap was a brother. Then I searched for M. Besnard and Clément, in black behind them. There were others I had not seen before. But obviously only the family was going to the graveside. They would be touched that I had come with them.

The new cement pylons of the railway station shone in the sun, and so did the steel rails and the goods wagons on the siding. Instead of turning left, which would have led us to the booking hall, we passed under a bridge and emerged at the gates of the cemetery, the doors opened at the sight of us, the gravediggers taking off their caps, standing at attention, waiting for a sign from the young priest. The graves seemed to climb into the sky, so steep was the terrain, grave above grave, cross above cross, marble doors above beflowered family vaults.

The white horse stopped. Rettol and Bouveau reverently took the coffin from the hearse. These two powerfully built men, the old one and the young one, had a fine meekness in their rugged expressions which denoted what was best in their characters. Thus they had carried the electrician Des Houle to his grave. The broken pole had lain, as we passed, along the side of the road. The tricolour flag was carried by Riquet Roginsky, whose wife Nénette had hanged herself by a bull halter from a beam in her cider press during the German onrush in that tragic summer when France fell. I had walked to this cemetery for her also whilst the hours passed, bringing nearer the doom of the country, the dire necessity for me to flee. The sun was hot, as it was hot now. German aeroplanes swooped over menacingly. My heart thumped at the memory. Panic seized me a second time. In the goods yard of the railway station were rows of sleeping cars put there for safety by a government of frightened men. Now the sun fell burning on the steel rails.

The coffin had been placed at the mouth of the family vault. We broke our lined formation to walk slowly towards it. The white horse looked round as if counting us as we passed. The white-haired driver came lazily down from his high seat. M. Besnard suddenly saw me and made a quick surprised movement of thanks.

Now each of us in turn threw holy water over the coffin. The family lined up for us to shake hands with them. M. Besnard and Clément thanked me pitifully. I kissed Mme Besnard on both cheeks through the black crêpe. Many climbed up paths, their shoes crunching on the gravel, inspecting the names on graves. British bombs had dropped here at the time of the Normandy landing, bombs intended for the railway station, but which instead of tearing up the steel tracks merely opened graves, Nénette's grave, for instance, whose stone was rent. Even in death, after suicide, she had found no peace. Higher, higher, names of all the people in the village. I wondered about ourselves. I hoped not, on the whole. A grave of earth only as yet, but covered with flowers—the electrician Des Houle. Now, suddenly, a hole so deep I shuddered and let out a cry of surprise and fear. Right down at the bottom was Émile Duclos in his beautiful shining coffin. Rettol and Bouveau were walking away. They said:

'This is thirsty work!'

Back at the gates the white-haired carter hitched himself up into the driving seat of the hearse and, cracking his whip, sent the coal-horse off at a brisk gallop, galloping down, down, along the white powdery road, the hearse so light now, that it clattered and vibrated. Bumpety, bang! Bumpety bang! Along it went. Bouveau and Rettol, briskly walking along the road, made a quick jump to one side, not to be caught by the wheels. They turned to the perched-up driver and waved to him, laughing gaily because of the sunshine. I, looking round the group of black-dressed family mourners, said timidly:

'I have a car if anybody would care to come back with me.'

'Oh, madame, thank you so much for coming,' said M. Besnard, 'and perhaps if you could take these two ladies . . .'

XVI

The sunshine, which had warmed M. Duclos on his last journey, was hidden during the next few days by rolling banks of white mist, through which courting birds sang deliriously. A curious stillness hung over the farms. One would have said that after so many happenings a calm had descended upon the plateau. Rettol and Bouveau, the fence terminated, went off elsewhere. Jacques wrote from his barracks. We missed his happy presence. The cart no longer crossed our orchard with him standing up in it, cracking his whip over the white horse. Déliquaire and his wife shared, with their nephew Jean, the work on the farm; Mme Déliquaire saying she felt somewhat better, though at times overcome by giddiness.

While I was gardening one afternoon Yvonne Poulain came to the hedge with Yvette in her arms, an Yvette with hair cropped short like a boy's, her face almost healed, but cheeks white and no smile on her lips. The slightest thing caused her to make a backward movement of alarm, tightening her hold round her mother's neck. Bobby's toy panda, leaning against a peach-tree, filled her eyes with tears of fright. This was her first airing since the accident. Dr. Lehérissey had spoken severely, saying it was not sufficient for children to be in the country but that they must be brought out of warmed rooms to breathe fresh air. Mme Castel, excellent grandmother, had an old-fashioned failing for layers of woollen garments and stuffiness.

Our kitchen gardens faced each other across a clipped hazel hedge and a long line of peach-trees, giving us baskets of fruit in autumn. The peach-trees, looking like Japanese prints, were in riotous, delicate bloom, but as M. Beaudry was still too tired to work for us, we had decided to do as much as possible ourselves.

For several hours each day I dug the ground with a heavy fork, Bobby pulled out the weeds, Matilda made holes and put in the sprouting potatoes. Occasionally Mme Beaudry, finding some excuse to come into the kitchen garden, would let fall some derogatory remark or mention that she and her husband had, the previous Sunday, turned over and planted twenty-seven rows. She claimed I was left footed because I thrust the fork into the earth with my left foot. I asked her if it mattered. She said that everything mattered; that it was stupid not to do each thing in the way it should be done. Though I disliked the habit she had of barking at one, I complied like a guilty schoolgirl, immediately training myself to use the other foot. Three of our hens, each with large families, scratched as we dug, and we had not the heart

to send them away, the fluffy yellow chicks running here and there, real Easter cards, tripping over weeds, panicky when losing sight of the mother hen. Baba, the chocolate and white cat, who still preferred the heat of a fire or a bed to food, followed me here with affectionate attachment. The pekinese lay stretched out amongst the violets. Miquette, the grey cat, who would soon be a mother again, and now in the sentimental, purring stage, lay on her back in the strawberry bed. These afternoons, exhausting, kept us all in the open air.

Towards tea-time the white mists would roll away; then suddenly spring would appear to have registered a step forward. Cowslips had grown thicker, covering new stretches of meadow, violets choked the hedgerows, the white and violet kinds, both smelling sweet, the tall pear-trees in the orchard, looked at closely, revealed myriads of pink blooms still tightly folded between velvety green outer coverings. Round my house, plum- and greengage-trees were in wedding-dress white; so were the pear-trees against sheltered walls. The cherry-trees were hiding their blossoms in clenched hands, waiting for another few days to release them riotously.

This winter, being the first I had spent altogether in the country, had imprinted a vivid picture in my mind. Mistress of a thirty-acre kingdom, lady of the manor in the old-fashioned sense of the word, poor and rich at the same time, I had the impression of having been given a tenure of life outside my own span. I felt as if, reading rural, provincial descriptions of the past, I had been allowed to smell the smells, breathe the air, take in with keen eyes the colour which surrounded dead generations, come back to life only through the printed word, except for me the privileged one.

One morning, about a fortnight before Easter, I made an exception and went down to the village, and it struck me that the shops, the streets, the market-place, were very animated, though purely in a family manner, not, I mean, by the addition of strangers. The butcher, the baker, the mayor's uniformed porter, the village policeman, the white-haired carrier who, having no coffin to drive to the cemetery, was now delivering casks of beer, the doctor, Ernest Poulain in his gig, beaming with delight, his rosy cheeks rosier than ever, his two little girls being out of danger, the pony prancing, the village blacksmith hammering a red-hot shoe on the anvil, enormous, his arms sinewy, his great neck as red as the horse-shoe he was fashioning, Giles Matthieu in plus-fours, the admiral down from his Louis XIII château talking lumber with M. Fournier, Mme Baudon behind her counter commenting in her shrill voice on each passer-by, between adding up bills and inquiring after the health of her customers. . . . The notary's daughter-in-law and her young sister, timid, wide-eyed, her hair done up old-fashionedly in plaits, were watering the notary's garden, having planted round the sprouting chestnut-tree borders of bright flowers. Through the open door of the notary's office, leather-bound volumes, dusty, romantically recording the buying and selling of orchards, half-timbered houses, and cider presses since Napoleonic times, the dates marked with ageing ink on the spines, slept against cobwebbed walls, whilst a typewriter clicked and a farmer in clogs, seated on a bench, waited his turn to go into the inner room for a consultation.

Denise Vaneufville, the chemist's daughter, having recently married the notary's eldest son Jean, and now in the process of bearing him a child, had become the new and important element in this large house from which five years earlier the women and youngest son had disappeared so tragically. Maître Vincent had

come to the village from the department of the Creuze in 1911, as clerk to the then notary, whose daughter he married and to whose practice he quickly succeeded. I imagine him as having been an exceptionally good-looking young officer in the war of 1914, and his bravery at Verdun, in the cruel trench warfare of the time, was of the same quality as the brilliant intellect he later brought to bear on the smallest details of this exacting profession. Always his courtesy was profuse, though his words, invariably uttered with a smile, had a legal ring about them which suggested that they, and no others, fitted the situation, making it inescapable, like the last judgment. More than Victor Duprez, born amongst them, tapping them on the shoulder, drinking deep with them, more probably than the excellent village priest in a thoroughly churchgoing community, the notary knew the innermost secrets of every crafty, scheming peasant, every clogged, sharp-knuckled landowner, every widow living her last years alone in a picturesque house in the middle of an orchard, milking her one cow and feeding her hens. The life annuity in return for the orchard, the house and garden after death, the little loan, the mortgage, the breaking-up of an estate to divide the inheritance equally, as the law requires, amongst children, the division of beasts, farm implements, gigs, hay-wagons—all such secrets were every day poured into the polite ears of the notary, acquainting him to the last penny, with the hopes, fears, and financial stability of the villagers and country folk who each Sunday filled the church whose bell rang for the weddings and tolled for each death. The history of my house and of all those who had lived in it, quarrelled within its stone and half-timbered walls, been born where I gave birth to my son, died there or committed suicide in the oak-beamed cider press down by the clear stream, each piece of litigation between neighbours—all these things, in spidery writing, on parchments bearing the stamps of the consulate, the empire, the restoration, the reign of Louis Philippe, and so on and so on until the present republic, were to be found in those leather-bound volumes to enlighten Maître Vincent, who though not by birth of this soil had by now become assimilated to it. To such an extent was he an integral part of this sea-girt tip of the rich Pays d'Auge that wherever apple crops, hay crops, land, farm contracts, leases, sales, expectations, were discussed, his name was bound to arise. People liked to tell you in whispers that he had little parcels of land everywhere, which he had purchased for next to nothing at the precise moment that it had been wise and profitable to buy. Whenever a farmer, owing to his moral laxity or drunkenness, was obliged to sell his land, one would be certain to hear it said that who but Maître Vincent was rich enough, and enough in the know, to hold the mortgage. One heard these things. I cannot tell to what extent rumour was accurately informed. I think it certain he had a flair for judging a man's character and his foibles, and a quickness for noting what must be done and not done to the soil to make it, through good years and bad, yield forth its fruits and prove in the end a good investment. Patience in listening, long thought before acting, a cool, even temper, and a life entirely devoted to his work, his family, and the strictest economy had placed him, from a worldly point of view, in an unassailable situation. If from time to time before the war, when talking to him, I had observed a slight, perhaps imagined, disillusionment from a too thorough knowledge of human nature, a too great experience with the closeness, cupidity, and suspiciousness of the Norman peasant, Flaubertian in spite of the age, I looked upon him, surrounded by his family, as a supremely happy man, confident in himself, his fortune, and his future. His wife had come to pay me a visit of courtesy after the birth of my son, when I was first downstairs in the big room, feeling proud but weak. I remember her hat, which was pink, her blue eyes, and the aloof dignity of her person. She had knitted a dress for my baby, and I took her upstairs to show her the half-timbered, stone-fire-placed bedrooms. She said:

'The only time I have a good rest is when I have a baby—then, at least, I have a fortnight in bed.'

She had three sons and a daughter—Jean, the eldest, Marie-Claire, Jacky, and Yves. When the allies invaded Normandy the girl was eighteen and the youngest boy, Yves, about twelve. Jean was fighting with the *maquis* in the Creuze, Jacky was with the notary in our village, but Marie-Claire and Yves were with their mother in a house which the notary owned at Caen. The girl went to classes and the boy attended one of the schools for which the ancient city was famous.

Nicol, the builder, who had lately constructed the cement pavement between Matilda's cottage and the stables, was in the habit at this period of the war, of bringing Mme Vincent and her two children backwards and forwards at week-ends. He was building something at Caen and had a *laissez-passer* signed by the Germans. After the battle had begun, however, his lorry was turned back. Communications were cut. Eventually, when the dust of battle had cleared, Maître Vincent, penetrating into the stricken city with a beating heart, found that not a stone of his house remained. Then feverishly he searched amongst the dead and wounded. He even went out into the fields and roads distractedly questioning refugees, imagining that perhaps his wife and two children had joined the poor creatures fleeing before the armies. Weeks and months passed. Hope came and went.

Could they not have been taken to Germany as hostages and come back to him one day—the woman, the girl, and the boy pushing open the door of his office, his home? But though he waited and hoped, they never appeared on the threshold.

A long time afterwards, when I was back in the village, a service was held in the church, the saddest, most strangely pathetic service our people had ever been called upon to attend. A catafalque was raised, in front of which massed flowers were banked—blue cornflowers, white carnations, and deep red roses. Flags hung everywhere. A funeral mass was intoned for the mother and her two children whose bodies had never been found, whose departure from this world could still only be presumed. The aged priest made a touching oration, saying that the blue stood for the boy's youthful vigour, the white for the girl's purity, the red for the mother's fortitude. All the mourners, and I think the entire village was present, now passed before the parents and the two families in the vestry, for aged Maître Gontand, who had been notary before Maître Vincent, was there with his wife. Maître Vincent's blue eyes were washed colourless by months of tears; those of Mme Gontand were so dry that one could only, in looking at them, think of two pebbles dried by a scorching pain. Maître Vincent's tears were flowing so fast that they fell piteously on the blackness of his jacket. Jacky, at that time as slim and delicately made as a girl, hid himself behind his brother Jean, whose lines, sharpened by the *maquis*, were more manly.

The immense overflowing sorrow of our notary had the effect for many months of turning him into a recluse. He continued to attend scrupulously to his work, but one was faced with the portrait of a man for whom success and the wealth he had slowly amassed were but of little avail. As his fields and properties rose in value, so his feelings were benumbed by the blackness of despair. Some time later Jean came to spend a short time in London with us. He was already in love with Denise Vaneufville. Plays and ballets, drives to Hampton Court and Windsor, were seen by him as through a distorting mirror, his mind turning exclusively on the young woman who, now gardening with her young sister, turned to say to me:

'We would be so happy, Jean and I, and my father-in-law, if

you could come with Bobby to lunch on Sunday. Midday, if that would suit you.'

I reflected I had not yet seen the notary in the intimacy of his home. The presence of Denise in his house, his expectancy of soon becoming a grandfather, was beginning outwardly, at any rate, to mellow his grief. I much looked forward to this lunch.

We went to the baker's first, where I bought a four-pound loaf of bread, our great number of Easter chicks devouring all the food we could procure for them. I bought also two smaller crisp loaves for ourselves, the bakers closing on Mondays. With these I led the way to the front part of the notary's house, which had been decorated in bright colours in honour of Jean's marriage to Denise Vaneufville.

A little maid opened the door, relieved me of the bread, and leading the way through the dining-room, with the table set for lunch, showed us into a small boudoir, or smoking-room, with some strangely assorted chairs, a round table, and several book-cases filled mostly with illustrated books of the pre-1914 sort, voyages through Switzerland, Alsace, Lorraine, and other picturesque corners of Europe. A heavy door opened and Maître Vincent, looking very small, greeted us with the wistful smile which made his personality so endearing. I said:

'I have been looking at your books. There is one showing the Alsatian girls in their butterfly bonnets. I spent a holiday there once. It rained all the time and I did not see many bonnets.'

'Of course, when I went there,' he answered, 'it was in rather special circumstances. A great many of the girls wore their bonnets, yes, and their lace pinafores too, and they kissed us. They all kissed us, and gave us fruit and wine and cakes. I was very young, and we had marched in to liberate them from the Germans, to bring Alsace back to France.'

His face had lighted up, and he was half crying, half laughing.

'That was the end of the war we won,' he said. 'A very different war from the last one.'

'I always think you must have been a very good-looking young officer, and quite popular with the girls.'

'I suppose I wasn't bad-looking,' he said.

The young couple came in, Jean a little wider in the shoulders since I had last seen him, Denise not far from her confinement, but very happy, and running every few moments between the boudoir and the dining-room, where she had whispered discussions with the new maid about some detail regarding the state of the food and the choice of the wines. It was very touching to see how the house, already being moulded by the feminine presence of Jean's wife, seemed to be waiting for the creation of a new family. Three branches of the tree had been wrenched away by the storm, but this spring the sap would flow powerfully into new wood. Maître Vincent looked on with a smiling docility as if thinking of this, and his voice, much lower than that of the young people, seemed purposely to have given up the ring of authority. One knew, of course, that it was latent for their good. We spoke during lunch about land—one always spoke about land with the notary—and he said to me:

'Have you ever been up to the Mont Canisi, where the English had their naval guns in the First World War and where the Germans had a fort during the second one?'

'No,' I answered. 'All I know about it is that Mme Bayard who rubs my parquets lives in a hut which our Tommies left behind in 1918. Her husband must have taken it to pieces and brought it to the village in a handcart.'

He said: 'It 's curious that you have never been to the top of the hill. One has such a good view across the Channel.'

I mentioned a moment ago that we had been discussing land. I had asked him if it was true that he had bought up much of the low ground where Roger Déliquaire did his duck shooting, and that he was making a good profit on it. He nodded affirmatively.

'One must buy land cheap and wait,' he answered. 'Buy when nobody wants it, sell when others are buying.'

We agreed that in time our village would probably join up with Deauville just as Brighton is joining up with Rottingdean or Rottingdean with Newhaven. That was how he began asking me about the Mont Canisi, which is as near Deauville as it is to us.

He said quietly: 'I 've just been buying a little land there for Jean. I think you should do the same.'

'What?' cried Jean. 'This is the first I 've heard of it!'

His father lifted his glass, with a sly look as if he were not averse to my knowing that he could still indulge himself in refusing to consider his eldest son as quite grown up. Would there be any fun left to a rich widower were he not occasionally allowed to scheme affectionately on behalf of those he loves, those who have less experience of the tricky world than a clever notary? Jean, who himself had a nice understanding of the value of money, went on with playful anger:

'It 's always land with you, father. One never has a chance to handle one's money!'

He winked, pretending that if he had his own way he would throw his cap over the windmill, travel in style to distant places, but as he rose to help Denise with the liqueurs, his arm quickly stole round her waist, and we knew he had compelling reasons for staying at home.

The house, which after the tragedy had appeared lugubriously large, was now quite differently disposed. The first floor had been turned into a bright apartment for the married couple; above this, Jacky, courting but still unmarried, had a bachelor flat. We visited the apartments in turn and then went to Denise's drawing-room for a formal call and to taste her home-made cherry brandy in glasses given her as a wedding present. Maître Vincent's pleasure on a Sunday afternoon was to walk out with his family. I invited them to tea on the farm and we climbed the hill slowly because of Denise.

The young women of the village had gone into the lanes to pick great quantities of cowslips and violets and the blossom of the wild cherry that rose above the hedges. The beauties of spring appeared to me in a new way, for I had momentarily placed myself beyond reach of the jealousies and suspicions of the peasants who formed my chief society. Déliquaire had been waging a cold war against me during the last few weeks. I was continually vexed by minute problems which grew to absurd importance and prevented me from admiring the lipstick-painted daisies at my feet. I had wondered, till I was tired of wondering, why Déliquaire seemed suddenly to bear a grudge, though experience should have told me that the chief reason was doubtless that I had spent four months at a stretch on my farm and that he was bored with my presence. This quarrel he had picked over the grass in my orchard was simply due to a feeling that I was taking advantage of him by staying too long. 'If she had gone away after Christmas,' he must have thought, 'I could have sold their share of milk and butter.' He thought perhaps I was watching him. 'Why is she here this year?'

The spring grass was pushing up tender and green after the rain. My orchard was very beautiful. This time a year ago cows were already on it. Soon I should be obliged to make a decision as to whom it should go.

When I met Déliquaire cutting faggots down by the stream, I had said to him:

'I will not dispose of the pasture for three weeks. If you want it come and tell me. I shall do nothing behind your back.'

Of course I was wrong to say that. He would think I was unable to do without him. Maître Vincent echoed:

'Never go to them. Make them come to you.'

'The clover is coming along nicely. How much did it cost you?' asked Jean. 'Twenty thousand francs? And how much does he offer you for the pasturage this year? Twenty-five thousand francs?'

He laughed.

'It makes the orchard look nice, this clover,' I said.

'Nice specially for the cows. The cows that graze here will giver richer milk. For you, except æsthetically, it will make no difference. On the contrary, in three years' time the ground will have slipped back.'

'If I gave the pasturage to somebody else, to the Poulains, for instance, Déliquaire would have a stroke, I think.'

'I expect he would be furious, but if you go to him he 'll tell you he doesn't want it.'

'The Poulains would give me more for it. They would put the cows here at night after milking them electrically.'

'More for it? Five pounds more in a year! And for five pounds you would make an enemy of Déliquaire, a crafty, revengeful enemy! In London,' said Jean, 'you would spend that in one afternoon to have your hair washed and set.'

'Here it all seems so much more important. One doesn't like to be got the better of. One gets stupidly worked up. They won't yield. I won't yield. I suppose there are fewer things to think about.'

'You just have to get to know them.'

'Like you, I suppose.'

'Like me? I own two orchards just outside the village. I went to the farmer whose land skirts my two orchards and offered them to him. He said: "No, I don't think so. The grass is sour and the apple-trees are old. What made you offer them to me?" "Well, if it 's like that," I answered, "you shall wait till you have cut the hay and gathered in the fruit before giving me a just price, a price based strictly on the yield. In that way you needn't insult my land now. You can save your breath. We shall see plainly what the orchards are worth."' Jean paused. 'I should never have gone to his house. In the end I so lost my temper that I let the grass grow wild and the apples rot on the trees.'

'You? Maître Vincent's son?'

'Well, I didn't quite do that,' he said, 'but I kept the land. I decided to sell the hay to any stray customer who might walk into my father's office. Somebody or other is always after a bit more hay in late summer.'

'Why can't one deal with them in a sensible way?'

'It 's self-defence,' he said; 'they think you 're trying to get the better of them all the time. They are not really cunning. If I had gone to my farmer and offered him a packet of worthless shares, he would probably have bought them all from me at any price I liked to ask.'

'The truth is,' said Maître Vincent, 'that we are a little near the sea. Things have been spoilt by Deauville and the other resorts. You would find things more as they used to be twenty miles inland, the other side of Saint-Vaast. Or nearer to Lisieux. Now, if you want a really sound investment, I have two orchards near Lisieux which six months ago would have been snapped up in twenty-four hours, but now, money being rarer, are still on the market. No buildings, just grass and apple-trees. The cost works out at a hundred and thirty pounds an acre.'

'Oh, no!' I exclaimed, laughing. 'To rent them for a song to some farmer who will tell me the grass is sour and the apple-trees too old? I see no fun in that. I want to see the buttercups come up in the spring and smell the hay on my land. I want, for a few months at least each year, to live on it.'

We ate bread and butter in the low room by the fire, and I offered my guests a pot of honey which a reader had sent me from Australia. Bobby had just electrified his model village under the cherry-tree in the garden and he dragged Jean out to inspect it. An hour passed lazily. We escorted them back to the top of the orchard.

'Who plants your young apple-trees?' asked the notary.

'M. Besnard. Why?'

'There shouldn't be stones round the base. In the old days, do you know how a Norman farmer planted a young tree? First of all he dug a big hole, which for one whole winter lay open for the ground to freeze. Then he would collect earth from the country lanes, and in the spring he would fill the holes with this rich, manured soil. The third year he would put in his trees.'

'I wish you wouldn't tell me these things. I shall believe my young apple-trees are doomed from the start. They cost me a lot of money. How do you like my fence, the oak and the hazel balustrades?'

'It will be better when the undergrowth has come up and hidden it.'

I winced, not daring to tell him how much it had cost.

'Listen to Ernest Poulain's lambs,' I said. 'They are the prettiest things in the world. What a pity they damage the grass. It would be such fun to have some.'

'I don't think they do any harm to the grass.'

'But everybody told me the contrary. Even Vannier, the butcher, said so.'

'They crop it close, but this field of M. Poulain's is as green as a billiard table. They certainly don't appear to have done it any harm.'

'That is what Ernest Poulain claims, but I didn't believe him.'

'Well, you should have some sheep yourself and see.'

'But you told me not to.'

He laughed.

'That 's true,' he said. 'I advised you not to play at being a farmer. I am sure you would be wiser to admire the cowslips and the violets and let Déliquaire farm the land. Why load yourself with more worries than you need? Enjoy the country, my dear madam. You 're so lucky to have this fairyland to live in!'

On the Tuesday before Easter Mme Beaudry came to rinse the washing, and I could see immediately she was going to regale me with one of her stories. Towards the close of the previous week she had gone to M. Vaneufville, the chemist, to collect a cough mixture she had ordered, and while he was doing it up in paper Dr. Lehérissey walked in.

'What are you doing here?' asked the doctor, tapping Mme Beaudry amicably on the shoulder, for he had known her since first she had come from Brittany.

'I 'm coughing, doctor,' she said in her deep, barking voice. 'I ordered a syrup.'

'Well, what do you know about that! You cough and you prescribe your own remedy! Why don't you come to see me? This syrup may not be at all the thing you need. What do you suppose doctors are for?'

'Well, doctor, what must I do? Take the syrup or leave it?'

'You can't leave it,' said the chemist, handing it to her over the counter. 'I made it up specially for you.'

'You 'd better take it,' agreed the doctor. 'After all, I don't suppose it will kill you, but all the same I think you ought to come and see me. Come on Monday, fairly early in the morning, so that you don't have to wait.'

On the day of the visit it was pouring, and as Mme Beaudry sat in the doctor's waiting-room water dripped from her gamp. As she was a tidy woman she was ashamed to see her umbrella make puddles on the floor. When she was shown in the consulting-room, Dr. Lehérissey asked her to take her clothes off and lie down on the couch.

'Heavens!' he exclaimed. 'But, my poor Anastasia, aren't you ashamed of letting yourself grow so fat! Look at this!'—catching hold of a fistful of obesity—'how dare you eat so much!'

He laughed. She laughed. But when he felt her pulse he added more seriously:

'Now, Anastasia, we must take this thing up resolutely. I shall write you a prescription.'

She was sitting on the edge of a chair in her chemise, her stockings falling over her ankles. As he wrote he kept up a monologue, telling her what she would have to do. But Mme Beaudry was not listening. Her eyes were fixed on her corset, and her mind was in great agitation, wondering how she would put it on again. 'Because, Mme Henrey,' she said to me, plunging her strong arms into the washpail, 'it was my new corset, my Sunday corset as you might say, the one I wore for the first time at Roger's wedding exactly a year ago to-day. I kept it for weddings and going to the hospital. I must tell you, Mme Henrey, it is one of those corsets with several thicknesses. One has to do up one part first, and then another on top of it, if you get my meaning. It 's supposed to make one slimmer, only I couldn't wear it for every day. It would hurt too much. Besides, I can't bend in it. Did you notice the way I sat during Roger's wedding lunch?'

Dr. Lehérissey, hearing a noise, looked up from his desk where he had been writing the prescription, and taking off his spectacles, for he could not see with them at any distance, considered his patient:

'Sapristi!' he cried. 'How on earth are you going to get into that fortress?'

'That,' answered Mme Beaudry, looking up and panting a little, 'is exactly what I am wondering myself!'

'I tell you what,' said Dr. Lehérissey, 'I 'll come and help you. In my young days I was quite an expert. . . .'

He tugged and pulled. Indeed they both pulled and tugged together. An important hook broke and the corset was somewhat askew when, finally, Mme Beaudry left the consulting-room, grasping her umbrella in one hand and her prescription in the other.

'I felt as if my clothes were falling off me,' she explained, still rinsing the sheets. 'One side of me higher than the other and my stockings liable to come down at the slightest bump. I thought of the long climb up the road to Saint-Vaast. Then I saw M. Déliquaire coming along on his bicycle.'

The sight of M. Déliquaire on a bicycle was indeed an unaccustomed one, for he never lost a chance of climbing into his car, but lately, especially since he had given up delivering the milk for the co-operative, his petrol allowance was smaller, and he had to be careful. 'I 've enemies at the town hall,' he would hint darkly.

'Fancy seeing you on a bicycle!' exclaimed Mme Beaudry. 'Now if only you were in your car you could have taken me home.'

'But I shall have my car in an hour,' said the farmer. 'I shall be bringing Mme Déliquaire down to her doctor. Just amuse yourself for an hour, and we 'll all go back together.'

'It was still raining a little,' Mme Beaudry said to me, 'and I wasn't feeling very happy because of my corset, but I went as far as the town hall to read the notices and marriage banns. M. Déliquaire had to push his bicycle all the way back to the farm, but just before lunch he arrived with Mme Déliquaire, and while she was with the doctor I waited in the car.'

After Mme Beaudry had told me this story I walked to the farm to fetch the milk, and I said to Mme Déliquaire:

'I hear you brought Mme Beaudry up from the village.'

Mme Déliquaire drew herself up and asked with feeling:

'Did she tell you about the bump on my forehead, Ma'am Henrey?'

Her finger went to the red patch I had not at first noticed, but she probably thought it was more visible than it really was.

'No,' I answered. 'How did it happen?'

'Of course, she noticed it as soon as she saw me,' smiled Mme Déliquaire. 'It happened just after M. Déliquaire and I had left the farm gates. About a hundred yards down the road to Saint-Vaast, whom should we see but Mlle Martin who had been married that same morning, and so out popped my head to see the dress she was wearing, but at that very moment M. Déliquaire swerved not to run the party over, and I bumped my forehead something terrible!'

'And what was she wearing?' I asked.

'That 's the point,' said Mme Déliquaire. 'I never had a chance to see!'

XVII

THE weather in Easter week turned suddenly so hot that the bees droned from flower to flower in the garden as in high summer. The earth in our orchards, thirsty for rain, was cracking between the blades of grass, and only the richest pasture land like old Gravé's and our own retained a luscious green.

Déliquaire had put his cows on the orchard on the opposite bank of the stream, the one through which we used to pass to go to his farm. The new grass was not coming out, and from my bedroom window in the mornings I used to watch him putting forkfuls of hay at the base of his apple-trees so that his cows should not go hungry. But when Bouboule and her companions came down to the water's edge and looked upon the cool rich grass on the other side, they would use every artifice to upset the barrier of horizontal hazel sticks and splash contentedly over into our orchard.

Then a cry would go up: 'The cows are in the orchard!' I would be obliged to release Bobby from his lessons and send him running to the Déliquaires, and ten minutes later the boy Jean would arrive, with a stick, followed by his master.

After this had happened several times I went down angrily to meet them and remonstrate. I would say:

'Why can't you batten down the poles of your barrier, M. Déliquaire? Twelve cows at a time will make short work of my grass. My young apple-trees have not yet corsets to protect them. Besides, my garden doors are open. One day, when my back is turned, your animals will be at the vine and the peach-trees.'

Having, on the most recent occasion, given him the full vigour of my mind, I noticed with some pleasure that he hung his head in silence. This victory made me more generous. His cows were so accustomed to consider my orchard their own, that it was not surprising they were unaware of our new arrangement. Softening my voice, I therefore said at the end of my peroration:

'It 's not that you haven't a fine herd of cows, Déliquaire. I 've seldom seen such fat, happy animals.'

He looked at me sideways to make sure I was not pulling his leg, and his features, in turn, relaxed.

'Aye,' he said. 'They are fine beasts.'

That same day, after lunch, while I was writing my letters to catch the evening mail, Déliquaire arrived full of mysterious importance, asking if I could see him on business. The sun was at its hottest. The members of the farmyard with the turkey, fan out, magnificent, to guard them, were seeking the cool under an immense pear-tree so hidden to the sky by white blossom that it looked for all the world as if it had been sprinkled with sugar icing. Shadows, cast by trees, fell slantwise on the undulating carpet of green. The cherry-trees had burst out in a night and now looked like brides. Banks of wallflowers filled the air with their strong perfume. Some rose-trees already had buds. In the distance a farm wagon was creaking.

I sent down word that Déliquaire should wait a moment, whilst these things rushed into my brain. I was rather pleased to make him feel that, momentarily, I was the stronger. The singing of the birds, the noisy drone of a myriad winged insects, surprised me curiously. I could not quite get it into my head that I had seen the long winter through into blossom time. It was too hot to burn logs in the great hearth, at any rate till supper-time. That in itself was strange. This was the first day I had not lit the fire, for beauty's sake, in the morning.

When I came down into the big room, I saw him through the window waiting in the garden. Cuckoos echoed from hedge to hedge monotonously. The swallows were back on the high-tension wires.

'Come in, M. Déliquaire!' I cried.

'I'm disturbing you,' he said. 'You're writing letters.'

'That does not matter. I'm always writing something.'

There was a long pause. I thought it better to make a start, and said:

'I see that butter is unrationed from Saturday. The government has taken the subsidy off. It is to cost a hundred francs less in the shops.'

'Oh, you know,' he said deprecatingly. 'All that doesn't make much difference.'

'I suppose it doesn't,' I said, 'except to those of us who have to buy it.'

'Things aren't what they were for us,' he said meaningly.

'The slump didn't last very long,' I countered. 'The price of pigs is rising, they say.'

'Yes, but heifers don't sell for what they did.'

'And Ernest Poulain tells me that lambs are selling for a tremendous price.'

'I haven't any sheep, never have had. They are no good for the grass.'

'I wish I knew,' I answered.

Another long pause. He was feeling miserable about broaching the subject first. I came to the help of his pride, and said generously:

'Would it be about the grass?'

'Yes, but only at the price I mentioned,' he said all in one breath, with a faint touch of aggressiveness.

'Please don't jump down my throat,' I said, smiling. 'If I have not already disposed of the grazing, it was because I wanted you to make up your mind first. I wanted you to be the privileged one. I still have a very soft corner in my heart for you, in spite of your sortie the other day.'

'It wasn't a sortie.'

'I had the impression it was almost a declaration of war. It made me feel unhappy for days afterwards. But now, seriously, you want the pasture of the orchard but you have fixed twenty-five pounds as your limit. At least three butchers in the village are desperate for grass. They would cheerfully pay fifty pounds. Do you know that?'

'I know the names of two who would like the grazing to fatten their animals, and I wouldn't be surprised if they were willing to pay you a lot of money, but have you thought of the damage the animals would do to your apple-trees?'

'Yes, I have,' I answered truthfully, 'but when Ernest Poulain used to have The Point, he gave me a pint of milk and a pound of butter every week for it, and The Point is very small and there is no water on it.'

'The Poulains put horses on it.'

'Yes, of course, that is the reason it was so useful to them.'

'Horses are ruinous for grass like yours. The proof is that when I took The Point off you, I had to put down artificial manure. Have you seen the pretty lawn it has made this year?'

'I have. It is indeed a picture.'

'And you know what it costs to put down artificial manure?'

'I think I should be in a position to appreciate the expense. I have just paid twenty pounds to do this orchard, for which you generously offer me twenty-five pounds. Don't you think I should be a very silly woman to accept?'

'It may be good for me, but it 's just as good for the apple-trees, and I reckon you 'll be having a bumper crop in this orchard. Your trees are in beautiful fettle. There are none like them.'

'I put down the manure for the grass, not for the trees.'

He made a little gesture with the palms of his hands, as if to say this was really not his fault.

'It needs a large measure of affection,' I said, 'to give you the grass for twenty-five pounds when so many appear anxious to pay me considerably more.'

This argument, against which indeed there was no answer, broke down his ebbing resistance, for he said, rather lamentably:

'I 've had a cruel winter, with Jacques going off into the army and my wife being ill. I don't even know how I shall find enough money to pay for all the land I rent at the feast of St. Michael. Oh, don't misunderstand me! I shall pay the money, to be sure, even if I die in the attempt. But I 'm saying it will be hard.'

'I wished you had talked to me like this the other day. I should not have been long to melt. You were in such a blustering mood.'

He looked at the tiles on the floor, feeling, I suppose, that at last he was getting somewhere.

'If I gave you the pasture for twenty-five pounds,' I suggested, 'would you pay me the balance in work? That would not jeopardize your bank account, would it?'

He raised his eyes interestedly.

'My apples will need to be gathered. How much did I pay you for that last year?'

He started to think eagerly, but painfully, like a machine in which the wheels grind and sing. He said:

'It 's generally sixty francs a sack, and there must have been one hundred and ten sacks. But of course it does not follow that this year there will be the same. I think, for instance, there might prove to be nearer two hundred sacks. And then I generally lend you the sacks. And there 's the carting of the apples—those you sell and those you keep for cider. Last year you must have paid me near eight thousand francs for my labour.'

'Well, supposing this year you did it for nothing?'

With a speed I had not expected he answered:

'Yes, I 'll do that, and gladly, madame.'

We both rose to shake hands on the deal. I should, according to custom, have offered him something to drink, so that we could clink the glasses, but I had nothing to drink in the house—and it was too early for tea. As he was going I said:

'You would prefer, I expect, to give me the rent of this grass weekly, in produce, instead of having to pay out quite a large sum of money in the autumn. You would notice it much less. What do you think?'

'Yes,' he agreed, 'I would like that better.'

'Then I'll buy a copy-book,' I said. 'Mme Déliquaire will jot down what she gives the child morning and night.'

We parted at the garden gate. I felt tremendously relieved that this silly business was settled in such a sensible way. Déliquare also looked happier as he walked down towards the water with Mireille jumping against his corduroy trousers. The orchard was full of blinding colours, green and gold, pink and white. The tireless cuckoo filled the air, and spring, without surrendering its wild flowers and its blossoms, seemed to have stolen all the glories of July.

XVIII

SO MANY people came to our village for Easter that there was quite a carnival spirit, and the sands looked gay with coloured tents and parasols. Mme Baudon sat on her high chair, behind her desk in the grocery store, pleased that her counters were so agreeably stocked with butter which, now that it was free from government control, was arriving in large quantities. Beautiful chocolate eggs, tied up with real silk

ribbon of delicate pinks, and stuffed with pralines, chocolate bells, and nests with yellow chicks, not to mention cakes spread with the cream our farmers brought down in their chaises, these things made us pause admiringly in front of Mme Sorel's the pastry-cook. M. Vannier was busy putting frills round his lamb cutlets and trimming tender shoulders. Cars drew up for those inside to buy picture postcards of Norman scenes, and ices made with the cream of our cows.

As soon as the holidays were over to everybody's satisfaction, the farmers again had the village to themselves, and we in the middle of our quiet orchards returned to our usual way of living. But Easter had made as big a change to our surroundings as the transformation scene in an old-fashioned pantomime. Winter was gone, left so far behind that I sometimes caught myself wondering if I had not lived through it in a dream. The pear-trees, so old, so much taller than the tallest apple-trees, were clothed cone-like with white blossom, and then shed it in the wind. The apple-trees broke into little pink fingers, sweet and delicate as those of a baby, and then opened them riotously. The cherry blossom came and went. The lilac opened, wallflowers scented the red brick walls, and the grass turned such a green as no pen could describe.

Then one evening, just after five, the cows crossed the stream and came into the orchard, not surreptitiously as on earlier occasions, but advancing proudly, clanging their heavy chains, taking legal possession. We stood and looked at them as if we had never seen cows before. I felt my breast throb with emotion. They were hungry for this magnificent grass, but though they stopped every now and again, the herd continued as if anxious to discover how far this paradise would stretch. Bobby ran out, calling them by name, giving them affectionate taps. They began to graze, but still appeared to think that by going on they might find something even better. Their chains clanged musically, those chains which prevented them from lifting their heads to bite off the blossom from the trees. Inquiringly they came up to the house, attracted by our voices, anxious for human company, and several lifted their heads high enough to start eating the rose leaves and buds which I could never prevent from straying over the white barrier of my front garden. Two beautiful red buds which I had hoped to pick the next day, disappeared before I could save them. The herd swung slowly round to the thatched cottage, looking into Matilda's garden, rubbing their necks against the sides of the wall, not stopping till they reached the long walls of winter-cut logs which stretched like stockades against the bake-house and the kitchen garden. After dark, when we had drawn the chintz curtains in the low room, and were having supper by the fire, we could hear them tearing at the grass. They sensed our presence and would remain close to us all night. When I slept badly, counting the hours chimed doubly by the grand-father clock, I liked to listen to the animals below my windows. A milky, buttery smell came up on the wings of the night air. The next morning they were more at their ease, but still surprised at the wealth of tender grass round them. They were in repose at the hour I generally started to write, and on these occasions, as I looked fondly at them, they were faithful exactly to the coloured pictures which decorate our round boxes of Camembert cheese. Only the milkmaid with the tall lace bonnet was missing, but alas this custom has disappeared for a century and more. But our Norman cows are unlike any other cows, to me at least. The entire farmyard go to them when they are lying down, chewing the cud. The ducks waddle over their hooves. The hens peck insects from the corner of their eyes, those eyes soft and pathetic under ravishing lashes, as they look contentedly at the undulating carpet of grass darkened by clover, daubed here and there by a few cowslips or a tardy clump of violets.

Each evening at six Déliquaire, Mme Déliquaire, and the boy Jean, whom I was becoming quite fond of, arrived to milk. Déliquaire and the boy used a three-legged stool, but Mme Déliquaire sat back on her heels, her ample skirts stretched out gracefully on the grass, an appalling felt hat shading her pink cheeks from the evening sun. Her accent in the open air as she talked to the cows was purer Norman than in her cottage. She sang to them, telling them to keep quiet and not to keep on whisking their tails in her eye. Bobby and I each took a tumbler to sample the milk in the various pails, hot and frothy, which each day in this orchard became richer and creamier. Mme Déliquaire had now quite recovered from her indisposition and the doctor had given her permission to eat what she fancied. Her husband looked suddenly much younger, the alarums of winter having fled, turned to hope by this pleasant warmth made musical by the bees. Jacques sometimes came on leave from Fontainebleau, looking extremely handsome in his uniform, and if he happened to arrive on a Sunday his father would lend him the farm van, so that he could do the round of his friends in style. Being his *marraine*, I asked him what he would like. He blushed, and said that he had everything. I insisted. He answered:

'I think what I would like, ma'am, would be a little money. Life at Montgomery's headquarters is expensive—if one wants to cut any sort of a figure, I mean.'

This was the busy season for Matilda, whose hens were producing the most adorable families of chicks, which pursued us into the kitchen garden when we turned the soil or went off to explore the orchard, losing themselves in the still long grass. The garden was in need of a great deal of work, and Matilda had a magnificent time planting her various vegetables far from Mme Beaudry's critical tongue. Roger came occasionally to do the heaviest digging, but I was obliged to do almost everything else. I had put down in a note-book some scenes of my girlhood in Paris, and they suddenly struck me with their background of apaches and burning-eyed girls, fights and passionate love scenes as splashes of hot, human colour of some value to record. I decided to call this *The Little Madeleine* and to tell the whole of my girlhood courageously and in detail, through all our picturesque poverty and tribulations, till we left Montmartre and the bastion walls of Paris for a new life in Soho, and this book, which I would make long and exciting and vital, because true, I started immediately to write before even this one was finished, so intent was I on the idea. You may imagine that in these circumstances I limited my gardening to the hour between taking down the mail to the village and milking time.

In spite of our many chicks, more were on the way. I had designed a fine row of elevated rabbit hutches in oak with a roof, each compartment divided from the other by a sheet of asbestos, which one could easily slide out to make a double compartment. As we kept fewer rabbits than before, I turned my hutches into maternity wards for the spring rush, and just now all of them were filled. Our dear faithful *picote*, which exactly a year ago had produced that fine family of baby turkeys, had laid another set of eggs this spring. Just before Easter we had missed her at ten one morning, but as she was back by lunch we imagined she must have strayed from her male, who was attached to her in his double capacity of son and husband, that magnificent *berlou* we never had the heart to kill, purely on account of his beauty. The next day she disappeared again, and so on every morning, until Bobby was able successfully to stalk her to a hedge, far distant, where she had already laid six eggs. We took five and left her one. She returned to the hedge to lay another egg the next morning, and every evening we took one away till she had finished.

Matilda refused to bring up a complete family of turkeys, because of the complicated food they required when young. I therefore put my *picote* in the maternity hospital with five of her own eggs, six duck's eggs, and (after seven days) two hen's eggs. A hen called Brayoutte had the compartment on her right, a most friendly little woman born the previous spring, but for some reason or other cast out from the company of her brothers and sisters, with the result that she had taken to coming into the cottage at meal-times and feeding with us. At night the other hens pecked at her when she tried to perch, and so she always remained outside till the last moment, having late supper with the ducks. I put Brayoutte on ten duck's eggs, those laid by the female I had bought at Lisieux before Christmas, and in due course the first half-dozen broke their shells and looked hungrily out of the window, the sweetest things I had ever seen. We had a second hen sitting on duck's eggs, a lady called Beigeotte, the mother of a cock born on 6th December and named Noël. This

gentleman was an only child born on a ton of anthracite before we had even discovered that his mother was missing. We also had a rabbit, who was busy plucking out the softest part of her breast to build her nest with.

The lambs bleated in Ernest Poulain's orchard across the hedge, but there were fewer of them, many having been sold for Easter rejoicings. Ernest came to watch us digging, and sometimes Yvonne came in her garden. She gave me Yvette to keep one afternoon, her hair cut short like a boy's and still a little marked on the forehead, but lively. I took her on our front lawn and sent Bobby up to his bedroom to show her from the window, as in a peep show, his various teddy bears and strange dolls. At each new arrival Yvette cried out: 'Vevette wants. Vevette wants,' holding out her little hands, from which it was clear that she was a real little woman, cognisant of the eternal truth that it is the role of the man to give and of the woman to receive.

XIX

BABA, with his white legs and waistcoat, soft as ermine, the most affectionate of cats, had been missing for several days. I kept on looking for him on chairs where he liked to sleep, on the stool in front of the fire, on my eiderdown at bedtime. Our evenings were longer in the kitchen garden, shorter in the low room, where we grilled supper over the embers just before the nine o'clock news. Our reading aloud was cut down to forty minutes, to be in bed soon after ten. This was the time when Baba was normally our companion. We opened windows and called his name through the night, then came back disappointed, whispering: 'There 's no Baba!'

My *canette*, the duck whose life I had saved in January, had also disappeared. The miracle of her eyes had made of her an untouchable. She did what she liked, growing fatter and more loquacious at my expense. Having missed her for the first time on a Sunday we supposed she had gone off on a long expedition and been stolen by an unscrupulous passer-by, who perhaps had lamed her with a stone, then quickly jumped over a hedge and seized her.

Matilda one day reported having seen her at feeding time, but when she looked a second time the *canette* was gone and did not reappear. When, towards the end of the week, the *canette* made another swift apparition, I guessed she was sitting on a nest and began to search the orchard, anxious to save her from a fox.

I was very proud to think that somewhere, hidden from view, my *canette* was preparing to be a mother. Her companions were in a continual fuss, obviously in the secret, paying her frequent social calls, then returning home, loudly discussing the news.

Bobby and I searched the banks of the river, even in the most wooded part. Matilda gave us the first clue. There is a tiny square of swamp-land running down to the water. Stakes and barbed wire surround it for fear the cattle should stray into it, though, except in the rains, the ground, overgrown with reeds and wild thyme, is quite strong enough to walk on. In the middle of this, quite hidden till I stumbled on her, sat my *canette*, with a clump of sedge pulled over her to make a roof. I tried to coax her off to show me her eggs, but she was so angry that I gave up. Her bill was more painful against my naked hand than I had thought possible.

In the evening after supper, all the farmyard being locked up and I reading to Bobby in the low room, a tremendous noise reached us across the orchard. The *canette* was rolling up the hill through the long grass, letting out *quack-quacks* as if she were an engine under pressure. She looked quite different, the feathers on her head brushed the wrong way and a beady expression about the eyes. I gave her some bread soaked in milk, which she tossed all over the place in her anxiety to get it down quickly. I then opened the stable door to entice her in. She arrived, not with any intention of spending the night there, but to see that nobody had stolen her place, and when she saw all the baby ducks which had been born inder the *picote* and Brayoutte she marched through them with a horribly avenging air, as if saying: 'Don't suppose that because I 've been away for a week you can do as you please!'

I shut the door on her, and Bobby and I ran down to her nest.

Lifting the roof of sedge we found a nest of superb workmanship, all plaited like a basket, still warm, but with not a single egg. Though I had come with the intention of taking the eggs, I was annoyed to find them gone, and considerably mystified. I supposed they had either been stolen or raided by an animal, but as there were no broken shells this last supposition was not convincing.

In the morning, being released, she drank and rushed down to her nest, where in due course I again visited her. She seemed so perfectly happy that my curiosity overcame my fear, and braving her attacks, I slipped my hand under her down and quickly felt a number of eggs. Several times during the day I meant to go and bring her eggs back in a basket, but I simply had not the heart. That evening towards eleven, while going to bed, Bobby and I heard the fox barking in the orchard. We switched on the big lamps at the bottom of the garden, and I think we caught sight of him between the swamp and the cider press. I was angry with myself for not having driven my *canette* home.

In the morning she came back noisier than ever. I fed her and again ran to the nest. Once more the eggs were not visible, but this time, gently removing an exquisite blanket of down and herbs, I found them hidden below. I had not guessed that with her awkward bill she could do such delicate work. As I was kneeling down amongst the wild thyme which was her protection against being discovered by the fox by her scent, she arrived, escorted by her sisters, and brushing me aside, she uncovered her eggs and sat on them.

I wondered if she had been nervous in the night, nervous of the fox. I was certain she would end by being discovered and bled, but she looked so proud and happy under the sedge, surrounded by the wild thyme, listening to the water babbling in the stream, that I abandoned her to fate.

The next day I had to take Bobby to London. The weather was magnificently hot and we lunched as usual in the cottage, but rather earlier. Miquette, the old grey she-cat, was unusually affectionate, purring at all of us in turn, even at the pekinese against whose thick golden fur she brushed herself with arched back. Since Baba had disappeared Miquette would sometimes come to see us in the low room at night, but she was so ferociously jealous, even of her own son, that she would not come if Baba was there. They got on well enough together in the cottage, but when at supper-time Miquette saw Baba curled up on his stool by the fire and us reading, she smelt favouritism and refused to have anything to do with us. Her life was quite changed since he was lost. It was horrible to feel her delight. She was the only one now. She was far too old and clever to be caught in a snare. All her children, the grown-up ones, the ones that had not been drowned at birth, had been killed on night operations, either disappearing for ever or coming home to die, terribly mutilated, sometimes with gangrene. Did she, herself wandering at night, see these appalling accidents? Did she talk to them during their last hours?

Miquette was expecting her first kittens of the year. Her selfish affection was therefore doubled just now by the instincts of maternity. Bobby had arranged a comfortable box with cushions by the stove in the cottage, and even fitted it with electric light run off a torch. Normally Miquette would have been suspicious of a place known to us. She liked to have her kittens secretly, mostly in Ernest Poulain's barns, so that she could bring them back to us, in Indian file, tails up. But one felt that this time age was beginning to tell.

We were half-way through lunch. Miquette jumped up on my knees, purred even more loudly, gave a sharp cry and deposited her first kitten on my grey flannel skirt. The second followed a moment later. We put them in the box Bobby had prepared, and then a third arrived. But that was all. We decided to keep a tiger male with an orange nose, and called it Isidore. I ran up to change, and an hour later left with Bobby for town.

We only stayed in London for five days, during which we had a letter from Matilda saying that all was well, but that Baba had not come back. I had to take Bobby to a surgeon to arrange about an operation later in the summer. On the table in the waiting-room I found a copy of the American magazine *Life*, in which there were some pictures of Bobby he had not seen, and I tried to take his mind off the visit by showing them to him, but he wanted to conquer fear in his own way and said. 'No, leave me alone. I 'm making a little prayer.' It was now up to me to hide my emotion. The surgeon sent for us, and in less than a minute gave his opinion. The operation Bobby was to have was less serious than we thought. The next morning we returned to Normandy, arriving at the farm in the evening.

Baba had come back!

Very thin, his right paw horribly torn, his poor head scratched, and a haggard look of days and nights of thirst and pain, he was ours, but the adventure had made a grown cat out of him. He was like a lad who might suddenly have seen battle and returned furrowed.

He would run away from us and hide in the cool hay above the cider press, looking through the open door at what was happening in the orchard. He too could hear the water babbling in the stream and watch my *canette* being visited by her friends while sitting on her nest in the swamp. Twice a day I used to take food to Baba in his hay-loft and to the *canette* in the freshness of her sedge home. Then gradually Baba came back and would sit with us in the low room after the nine o'clock news.

Nobody had seen Miquette for several days, and Isidore began to look quite abandoned. At first it never struck us that anything serious could have happened to our wise mother cat, having taken her for so many years for granted, but after a week or so we commented more often on her absence, saying that she must be getting very old to leave her tiger baby. Then one morning, inspecting apple-trees along the hedge beyond my kitchen garden, I thought I heard a cat faintly mewing. Miquette was caught in a spiked iron snare, her right front paw so completely crushed high up that all the bone was broken.

I had a very old and frail gardener called the père Troussel, who was just then less than fifty yards away weeding the strawberry beds, and I shouted for him, knowing that he was a great expert with traps and gins and would open this murderous thing more quickly and efficiently than I. As he was lame he took a long time to catch hold of his polished walking-stick and hobble to my side. Miquette looked at me with deep eyes full of trust and gratitude. She was tiny as she crouched helplessly beside the rusty circular trap in which her hanging paw was imprisoned. When M. Troussel at last arrived he released her quickly enough. She ran off on three legs quicker than we could catch her all the way to the cottage for a drink of water, and though I would have liked to dab the wound with mercurochrome, I thought it wiser not to begin chasing her round the orchard. She slept for two or three hours on a blanket in the potato room, ate some lunch, and then went off painfully to the hay-loft over the cider press to die or recover alone.

Every evening Bobby and I used to climb the rickety exterior staircase to the hay-loft with food and milk. Generally Baba, whose wound was still very sore, would be lying a few yards from his mother, and both of them purred at our approach. Sometimes Bobby and I remained half an hour curled up in the sweet-smelling hay beneath the four-century-old rafters, gazing out through the open loft door at the sun-drenched orchard. Then we would gather up our dishes and go off to feed the brave *canette*, who had not yet been eaten by the fox.

As the cows were shortly due back in our home orchard, Bobby and I and the père Troussel decided to build a fence round the fence of our front rose garden, to prevent the roses that climbed over the inner one being eaten. We put down stakes every four yards, and two rows of hazel sticks transversally. We thus had a corridor or no-man's land, very narrow but effective, between the orchard and our garden, and on the whole I think it added to the picturesqueness of our encampment. The père Troussel was very slow and puffed wheezily, but he was of a generation of men who knew the right way to do each thing, and his knowledge was in inverse ratio to his strength. He had started seventy years earlier as apprentice to his father, a woodcutter, and, like Rettol, he believed in the strangest potions and cures, like bottling up an adder and a toad, and when they had killed each other, using their putrefied remains to take the poison out of snake bites.

My *canette* had four ducklings, but now that she was no longer on her nest she was not good at protecting her offspring. She had become suddenly timorous, and lost three. The remaining one kept very close to her, frightened by the young ducks hatched by the *picote* and Brayoutte, now several weeks old and aggressively strong.

We had five hens, all anxious to sit. Four of them were placed under pails, to 'refresh their bottoms,' as Mme Beaudry poetically said, the fifth, a magnificent mother, called Mme Golden Neck, was given twelve eggs and a bundle of hay above the rabbit hutches, so that she could make a nest in the open air.

I had made a note in my diary that the chicks should hatch on the 22nd July, which was the St. Madeleine, but on the 18th I noticed a mass of yellow fluff, and discovered that seven were out of their shells. Mme Golden Neck broke the eighth flying down from the nest, two were clear, and two remained which I hardly knew what to do with.

Golden Neck was proudly showing the world to her pretty seven children. Impatient, I broke one of the two eggs, revealing a perfectly formed chick which, however, did not live. I slipped the last egg under yet another hen that wanted to sit, and after a few days she presented us with the prettiest ball of yellow fluff. We put the broody hen under a pail and took the orphan into the cottage, where Matilda put it in a box.

The orphan quickly protested. Matilda or I would take it up in our cupped hands, and it would immediately show signs of contentment. I have never seen a chick take so naturally to a human habitation, and yet it was imperative that I should find some method of making her presence acceptable to Mme Golden Neck who, when I rashly arrived with the orphan, pecked me and nearly killed it.

Mme Déliquaire, whom I consulted, said:

'Wait till night has fallen, then go into the place where Mme Golden Neck sleeps, with a saucer of bread and milk in one hand and your orphan in the other. Whilst Mme Golden Neck is busy with the bread and milk, you can slip the orphan with the seven others. The next day she will never notice she has an extra child.'

Mme Déliquaire was now quite well again. She ate everything she wanted to, even duck, and was in such good spirits that she had persuaded her husband to drive her to Yvetot in the farm van to see her mother. When I arrived she was surrounded by parcels.

'Anybody would think,' exclaimed Déliquaire, lifting the bonnet of the car, 'that we were going off for a year!'

People had talked so much nonsense about her illness that she gave the impression of wanting to make up for lost time. Under a pear-tree Lucien, the farmhand, was sharpening the blade of a mowing machine on a grindstone which Michel Gilles was turning. Lucien had replaced the boy Jean who, having eaten more than he was worth, had been sent back to Yvetot. He was the same age as Déliquaire, in other words about forty-five, square shoulders, strong loins, knowing everything about farming, getting up at five in the morning, indefatigable but, for some reason, refusing to milk. He would carry great weights on his left shoulder, resting his right hand on his waist. All his movements were slow but picturesque, and when he spoke so patiently and gently one had the impression of a lion hiding its strength. He used to say that he had once been so drunk that he had been put in a strait jacket. The story went round, and I think some people were frightened of him, in the same way that they might be frightened of a barn owl hooting, or of passing a cemetery at night.

The day M. and Mme Déliquaire went to Yvetot with jars of butter and sides of bacon, Roger and Jeannine came up from the village to sleep at the farm, to guard it, but it all seemed so quiet after the village, where the cars and lorries sped along the main road between Deauville and Caen and where the church clock chimed every quarter of an hour, that they were stupidly afraid not only of the peace and quietness of the country but also, a tiny bit, of Lucien who, having retired at seven, was now snoring on his bed on the first floor. Jeannine was expecting her baby soon and was impressionable. She persuaded Roger that they would be better in his parents' double bed beyond the kitchen than in the attic, and before retiring she gently turned the key of the door leading to the staircase, so that at five in the morning, when poor Lucien tried to get out, he found himself closed in.

The good Lucien banged the door and shook the handle, but Roger and Jeannine continued to sleep soundly in M. and Mme Déliquaire's new double bed. When the sun had risen and Mme Beaudry arrived to do the coffee and milk the cows, she saw Lucien gesticulating from the attic window, praying for his release.

The Shetland shawl I had given Mme Déliquaire at the time of her illness gave her so much pleasure, that during my last visit to London I bought another to give to Denise Vincent for the baby she was expecting at any moment. I again found her with her little sister Françoise, under the chestnut-trees in the notary's garden, and putting the box in her hands, asking her to open it when I had gone, I ran into the office to have a word with her father-in-law, Maître Vincent, whose fine features were at last happy now that he was going to be a grandfather.

When, a few days later, I was passing the chemist's shop, M. Vaneufville came out to tell me that his daughter was at home and wished to thank me for the shawl. I found her modestly attired in a black dress, a little exhausted by the heat. She was off to have her baby in a nursing home at Deauville, and the shawl was already a treasured object in the layette.

Mme Beaudry was just inside the stable door plucking a fowl, and I was making cherry jam in the cottage. Baba and Miquette were now both hopping about on three paws. I had cut off Miquette's bad leg with a pair of scissors where it hung by a piece of skin just above the knee, and it had healed miraculously. From time to time I hurried out for a bit of gossip with Mme Beaudry, especially about the hay which was being cut in the Bourgogne. The hay was magnificent, and though the orchards were rather thirsty our apple-trees were laden with fruit, so luscious, so early, that several old trees which we had forgotten to prop up broke in two under the weight of apples.

Matilda, looking very upset, suddenly arrived, and not seeing me asked Mme Beaudry where I was.

'Here I am,' I answered.

'Oh!' she exclaimed. 'It 's terrible. Mme Gilles says that Denise Vincent has died in childbirth.'

I gave a yell at the awful unexpectedness of the news. Matilda went on.

'She had a baby girl, who is saved. Dr. Lehérissey had to use the forceps, just like he did with you. It was her heart. She lost too much blood.'

'Poor Jean!' I exclaimed. 'He loved her so desperately. If ever there was a love match this was one. And the notary! What has he done to have so much unhappiness! His wife, three of his children, and now his daughter-in-law!'

'He 's only just recovering from the last tragedy,' said Mme Beaudry, continuing to pluck her bird.

'I 've got some jam on the stove,' I said to Matilda. 'Do please see it doesn't catch or boil all over. I simply must telephone.'

I rushed into the low room and telephoned to the notary's office, hoping there might be some mistake, but it was true. Jean was both a widower and a father. His marriage had lasted only ten months. When, during the evening, Matilda and I heard the bell toll, we went about our work in tears.

The next day I called at the notary's house. The coffin, covered with flowers, lay in the boudoir between the notary's office and his dining-room, the small room, with the books about Alsace, in which we had drunk a glass of wine before lunch only a few weeks ago. Now the walls were hung with black, candles flickered, a monk and Denise's young maid-of-all-work knelt praying.

From here I went to the chemist's, running up immediately to the private apartment where Mme Vaneufville appeared dazed, her eyes bloodshot. I kissed her, and she said:

'How she suffered! You 'll never know how she suffered! The forceps, a haemorrhage, and then the heart stopped. Oh, Mme Henrey, did they tell you that Denise died in your beautiful white Shetland shawl? She was so cold. We tried everything, and at last gave her your shawl. She told us that was the only way she felt warm. She was conscious all the time. That was the worst of it. She knew exactly what was happening—like a person watching somebody else dying. Look! Here 's your shawl!' Mme Vaneufville crumpled it up in her hands and buried her face in it. Then she held it out, adding: 'It still smells of chloroform! Oh, but what pleasure it gave her!'

'How 's Jean—poor Jean?'

'He wouldn't sleep under the same roof as the coffin. He arrived here last night looking like a spectre, and threw himself on Françoise's bed. He 's still asleep, stunned. One wishes he could sleep for a long, long time. Maître Vincent is asleep too, over there, at his office. He was two nights without going to bed.'

A door opened and Mlle Lefranc, the midwife who brought Bobby into the world, came in with the baby, the poor, motherless baby, dark hair, full of life, a day old, looking at us with wide-eyed interest, dark eyes following our every movement, the only eyes in which there were no tears.

The funeral was to take place on Saturday.

I met Mme Déliquaire in the market, and as it was 22nd July, the St. Madeleine, I invited her to come and have a cup of strong black coffee at Mme Sorel's, the pastrycook's. Mme Sorel was also a Madeleine, so we would be three. Mme Déliquaire, like all of us in the village, was much affected by the tragedy, and was under the most dreadful apprehension for Jeannine, who was so nearly ready to have her baby. I did my best to comfort her, carefully hiding the fact that another young woman had just died in the same circumstances at Bennerville. From Mme Sorel's we went to Mme Trémois's, where we found Déliquaire. His van was in front of the church, and we all went up together. Lucien, who was under the oak-tree at the entrance to Déliquaire's farm, swung the gate open for us. Crossing the stream to my own farm, I met Michel Gilles, Bobby's young friend, bringing me a basket of cherries for the St. Madeleine, which he presented very sweetly.

On Saturday the heat was greater than ever.

I was breakfasting with Matilda when Ernest Poulain arrived. He said his mare had something wrong with her eyes and was bumping into everything. Would I telephone to the veterinary surgeon? We put a call through, but the veterinary surgeon said that on account of the funeral he could only come in the afternoon. I asked Ernest if he also was going. He said that because of the mare he could not but that Yvonne would be representing the family, and that she would be very pleased if I would go with her in the pony cart.

Half-way down the lane, the sea sparkling in front of us, the bell began to toll. Yvonne and I with town hats on, our eyes red, must have looked to the trippers like country bumpkins all dressed up. The parvis was full of pony carts, gigs, and cars. There was nothing to which we could tie Yvonne's pony, Izicar. We had to go up a side street and tie her to a telegraph pole, after which we went on foot to the notary's house, where the family was getting ready to follow the coffin to the church. In front of the post office on the opposite side of the street a young woman clerk said to us:

'For two days we 've all been crying inside. We 're in a dreadful state. The stamps stick to our moist fingers.'

As she spoke her tears flowed unrestrained. A crowd of holiday-makers, the women in shorts, showing indecently what was least becoming in their persons, were laughing at what was no more to them than a side-show. For the first time since the death of his wife I saw Jean, his eyes lowered on an open prayer book held in both hands. The notary, his father, was on his right, the monk in brown, barefooted, on his left.

All during the solemn service Jean's eyes, now drowned in tears, did not leave the coffin, and afterwards, whilst the procession was forming, catching sight of me, he threw his arms round my neck and wept like a poor, unhappy child—without a mother, without a sister, without a wife. All the women who had loved him and whom he had loved were dead.

We followed the wide powdery road along which I had walked in March, taking Émile Duclos, the gardener, to his grave. Yvonne Poulain was with me, and when at the cemetery we finally took leave of the mourners, she asked me to climb with her up the stony path to where her father, M. Castel, was buried. After making the sign of the cross, she bent down and arranged some very pretty red geraniums. Then we hurried away. Yvonne was anxious about her pony still tied to the telegraph pole down in the village. I was quite exhausted with fatigue, emotion, and sadness. We found Izicar unbridled, but patiently waiting. We set off in the pony cart, but half-way up the hill Yvonne, burning in the midday heat, handed me the reins and took off her stockings, her jacket, and finally her hat.

When Yvonne drove into the courtyard of her farm and saw her mother, Mme Castel, and all her children, she threw the reins to Émile, the handy man, jumped lightly down, and kissed her family, as if she had been afraid never to see them again. Then she said to Mme Castel:

'Mother, what lovely geraniums you 've put on father's grave.'

'I never put any geraniums on your father's grave!' exclaimed Mme Castel. 'I put some carnations, but they 're dead.'

André came forward and said:

'It was aunty who put them there, mother. She had some left over after she had decorated grandma's and grandpa's grave.'

Mme Castel looked at Yvonne and seemed touched.

I hurried home, kissed Matilda and my son, and hurried to the farmyard to see my orphan chick who was running about, happy as a ray of sunshine, though he had trouble in keeping up with his brothers and sisters. Every now and then he would cuddle up against Mme Golden Neck, expressing his delight at having found a mother.

On the day of the christening I went to see Mme Vaneufville. The family was drawn up in the sitting-room, watching Mlle Lefranc expertly dressing the baby. When she had finished she took the shawl from the cot and, placing the baby in it, handed her to the grandmother, who would carry her to the church. Françoise, with her dark plaits round her little head, was sitting prettily on a chair. Jean arrived, kissed me, gave a tender look at the baby, then went off into a dark corner, where for a moment I supposed he was crying. But no, he was putting a spool into his camera. All his affection for Denise was now heaped on the little girl, who was already her image. Maître Vincent came in, his features sad, but no longer in tears. He had been arranging some tiny gold effigies, family relics, that the baby was to wear at the christening.

I watched the little group going off to the church, instinctively walking close to the baby, the comfort and hope of two fine families.